Double Layer and Electrode Kinetics

BY PAUL DELAHAY

Advances in Electrochemistry and Electrochemical Engineering
  (John Wiley and Sons),
  PAUL DELAHAY AND CHARLES W. TOBIAS, Editors.
  Vol. 1, 1961; Vol. 2, 1962; Vol. 3, 1963.

Instrumental Analysis, 1957
  (The Macmillan Company)

New Instrumental Methods in Electrochemistry, 1954 (Interscience)

DOUBLE LAYER
AND
ELECTRODE KINETICS

PAUL DELAHAY

Coates Chemical Laboratory
Louisiana State University
Baton Rouge

INTERSCIENCE PUBLISHERS

A DIVISION OF JOHN WILEY & SONS, INC.,

NEW YORK · LONDON · SYDNEY

SECOND PRINTING, MARCH, 1966

Library of Congress Catalog Card Number: 65-16404
Printed in the United States of America

Preface

This monograph covers some fundamental aspects of the double layer and electrode kinetics to the exclusion of such specialized topics as electro-crystallization, anodic films, and semiconductor electrodes. These and other topics were omitted not for lack of significance but because they are not an essential part of the background that the serious student of electrode kinetics must master as a *starting point*. Electrode reactions are not reviewed systematically, although a number of them are discussed, or at least touched on, as applications of theory. Methodology and instrumentation are hardly mentioned, except when their discussion is relevant to theory.

Part One, dealing with the electrical double layer, can be considered independently of the remainder of the book. Some of the topics in Part Two can be studied by the hurried reader with only a rudimentary knowledge of Part One, but mastery of electrode kinetics requires adequate understanding of double layer phenomena. Detailed references are listed for specialized study of topics whose extensive coverage is not within the scope of this work.

The material of this book evolved from a series of lectures I have given periodically at Louisiana State University and as a Fulbright Professor, in 1962, at the University of Paris. The book was written in Baton Rouge, but some of the material needed in its preparation was gathered while I was in Paris. The time seemed propitious for the publication of this work since the key ideas on which present understanding rests have now evolved and been tested to such an extent as to warrant a synthesis and a critical survey. Yet enough unresolved problems remain to stimulate further work.

I am particularly thankful to some of my co-workers: Drs. D. Cole, R. de Levie, A. M. Giuliani, E. Solon, G. Torsi, and Messrs. V. S. Srinivasan, G. G. Susbielles, and B. Timmer. They made a number of valuable suggestions toward improvement of the manuscript and also helped me considerably with such practical tasks as verification of some of the equations and references and the collecting of diagrams.

I am most grateful for comments from Dr. R. Parsons, University of Bristol, who went thoroughly over the whole manuscript, and from Drs. J. R. Macdonald and C. A. Barlow, Texas Instruments, Dallas, who examined critically Part One. Dr. J. P. Hoare, Research Center, General Motors made valuable comments about Chapter 10. My co-workers Drs. H. Lauer, J. W. Murphy, and F. R. Smith also commented on some chapters. Professors A. N. Frumkin and B. B. Damaskin kindly communicated to me, before publication, the manuscript of a review on adsorption at electrodes. Their review was most helpful in the preparation of Chapter 5. Finally, I would like to thank Mr. C. J. Malré who typed the manuscript and transcribed the equations most competently.

I am very pleased to acknowledge my indebtness to the following persons and organizations: Dean A. R. Choppin and Professor H. B. Williams, Louisiana State University, for their enlightened understanding of my duties; Professor M. Quintin, University of Paris, for the kind hospitality in her laboratory; the Fulbright Commission for a professorship which made my stay in Paris possible; Louisiana State University for a sabbatical leave; the Office of Naval Research and the National Science Foundation for support of my research effort, which pertains to some areas covered in this book. Authorization by authors, editors, and publishers to reproduce diagrams is duly acknowledged.

Paul Delahay

February 1965
Baton Rouge, Louisiana

Contents

CHAPTER 1

Introduction

1-1 Evolution of Ideas on the Electrical Double Layer

This survey of double-layer phenomena is limited to interfaces composed of a metal in contact with an electrolyte solution or a molten salt. Emphasis is placed on mercury in contact with an aqueous electrolyte solution because present understanding has largely stemmed from investigations of this particular case. Other systems, however, are also treated (Chapter 6), and there are indications that future study of the double layer of liquid metals in contact with molten salts may open new vistas in the field. Evolution of ideas has been quite slow and the gap between theory and experimental confirmation has covered several decades both for the thermodynamic treatment and the simple model initially proposed by Gouy and Chapman. A few topics can be distinguished which are at the core of double-layer theory, namely, the thermodynamic approach, the Gouy-Chapman theory, and adsorption at metal-electrolyte interfaces. Concepts will not be treated in detail, and terms that may be unfamiliar to the reader will not be defined in these introductory remarks so as not to lengthen unduly this chapter.

The thermodynamics of double-layer phenomena which rests on the Gibbs adsorption isotherm is by no means a new subject, but adequate understanding has come only progressively. Gouy did the pioneering work during the first two decades of the century, and Frumkin extended his work in the 1920's. Further progress since 1941 was made chiefly by Grahame who clarified the thermodynamic analysis of an ideal polarized

1

electrode and showed that highly accurate thermodynamic data can be deduced from measurements of the double-layer capacity.

Models of the double layer go back to Helmholtz (1853) and Quincke (1861). The first detailed model is due independently to Gouy and Chapman (1913), who gave an analysis which starts with the same premises as the Debye-Hückel theory (1923). Agreement between calculated and experimental interfacial tensions was wholly unsatisfactory, for the necessity of considering the compact double layer had been overlooked. Stern modified the Gouy-Chapman model accordingly in 1924, but successful confrontation of the new model with experiment had still to await two advances: one in technique, the other in theory.

It was not realized in early measurements of the double-layer capacity with a mercury pool that solutions had to be thoroughly free of traces of easily adsorbed organic impurities. Purity requirements are less stringent in measurements with the capillary electrometer, previously used by Gouy and others, because of the slowness of adsorption with diffusion control in the fine bore of the electrometer capillary. If it had not been for this fortunate circumstance, early work on electrocapillary curves would have been marred by electrode contamination. Enough convection prevails at a mercury pool to speed up adsorption, and early capacity measurements were grossly in error. Grahame (1941–1949) perfected the technique and minimized contamination by introducing the use of the dropping mercury electrode in such measurements.

The other advance for successful verification of the double-layer model of Gouy, Chapman, and Stern was in the nature of an assumption about the compact double layer. An a priori calculation of the compact double-layer capacity is not possible with present knowledge, and some assumption has to be made about its value. Grahame assumed that the compact double-layer capacity is only dependent on the charge on the electrode and not on the electrolyte concentration. This hypothesis was the key to experimental verification of theory (1947, 1954), and provided data for further interpretation of the structure of the compact double layer by Macdonald (1954) and Barlow and Macdonald (1962).

The necessity of considering adsorption effects that cannot be interpreted in terms of simple electrostatic interactions of the type analyzed by Gouy and Chapman was briefly alluded to by Gouy (1910). Stern reintroduced the concept of specific adsorption and gave it a mathematical formulation based on the Langmuir isotherm (1924). Grahame (1947) suggested that specifically adsorbed ions approach the electrode more closely than ions free of specific adsorption. He advocated a model of the compact double layer with two planes of closest approach: the inner plane for specifically adsorbed ions and the outer plane for the other ions. The

Gouy-Chapman theory is applicable to the region beyond the outer plane, that is, the diffuse double layer. This allows calculation of the amount of specifically adsorbed ions [Grahame and Soderberg (1954)] and brings about the important problem of isotherm assignment.

Adsorption of ions and uncharged substances can be distinguished in the treatment of isotherms. Adsorption of uncharged substances was already treated by Frumkin in a pioneering work in 1926 by assuming that the Langmuir isotherm is valid at constant electrode potential provided particle-particle interaction is introduced much in the same way as in the equation of state for gases. Butler also treated adsorption (1929), but it was not until Parsons began in 1955 a series of fundamental investigations that the question of isotherm assignment was revived. Data of rather high accuracy are needed for unambiguous solution of this problem, and it appears at the present that the dependence of capacity-potential curves on the bulk activity of adsorbate provides the best criterion. Interpretation of such curves began with the work of Frumkin and Melik-Gaikazyan (1952), who showed that adsorption at a mercury electrode is diffusion-controlled. Lorenz (1958) gave a particularly elegant treatment of adsorption kinetics and reported adsorption exchange rates on mercury for a few substances. Conditions, however, were quite marginal and adsorption may have been completely diffusion-controlled. Isotherm assignment is not yet a fully settled question.

An important result that emerged from these studies pertains to the dependence of the standard free energy of adsorption on the electrode charge (or potential). Thus Parsons (1955–1963) found a linear dependence of this energy on the charge on the electrode for ionic specific adsorption and a quadratic dependence for uncharged substances. The last relationship was already arrived at, in terms of potential, from simple models by Frumkin (1926) and Butler (1929).

Ionic specific adsorption is complicated by the necessity of considering the discreteness of charge as was first shown by Esin and Shikov (1943). Much effort has been spent in further exploration of this effect by Ershler (1946), Grahame (1958), Parsons (1961–1963), and other workers. Calculation of the potential in the inner plane of closest approach is the most significant result that came out of this work. Results are still tentative, and further progress may require a different approach based on statistical mechanical theory rather than on "mechanical" models.

The considerable simplification of the Gouy-Chapman model of the double layer has been apparent for many years, and the success achieved by Grahame in confrontation of this model with experiment up to concentrations exceeding $0.1M$ is all the more remarkable. The

Gouy-Chapman theory does not involve the mathematical approximations of the original Debye-Hückel theory but it rests on similar simple premises. The need for a fresh approach had been felt for a number of years, but it is only recently (1960–1963) that the statistical mechanical approach, already applied to electrolytes, was transposed to the double layer. Two theories, having some common features, were worked out by Krylov and Levich (1963) and Buff and Stillinger (1963). They represent a significant advance in theory, but it is too early to assess their impact on future development of the field.

Most of the advances in the experimental investigation of the double layer were made possible by the availability of the mercury electrode which has almost ideal properties for such studies. Other metals, however, are of considerable interest, especially in kinetics, and a major effort has been made to understand their double-layer behavior. Present understanding, however, is essentially qualitative, and a number of problems still await solution. Interest is focused on the compact double layer because the diffuse double layer can be studied far more conveniently with the mercury electrode.

Investigation of the double layer with solid electrodes is hampered by experimental difficulties caused by electrode contamination, geometrical effects in capacity measurements, and, above all, by complications arising from the interference by electrode reactions and the formation of adsorbed films of hydrogen and oxygen (in aqueous solution). The interplay of these adsorbed films with specific adsorption is understood qualitatively, largely as a result of the work of the Frumkin school and that of Balashova (1956–1962) in particular. Interpretation of double-layer capacity measurements is also complicated by hydrogen and oxygen adsorption and by the frequency dispersion caused by electrode roughness. Radiotracer methods in which measurements are made *in situ* with control of potential were developed recently by workers in the Bockris group (1963). They appear quite promising, but scattering of data is still too high to allow unambiguous assignment of isotherms. It is fair to conclude that most of the work done thus far on the double layer with solid electrodes is significant *per se* but that its primary interest lies in the correlation with electrode kinetics.

Finally, the double layer for liquid metals in contact with molten salts should be mentioned. Experimental difficulties have been overcome, and some highly intriguing observations have been made by the Frumkin group. Correlation with models for molten salt structure should be of considerable interest, and the field may well be one of the most fruitful to explore in double-layer studies.

1-2 Evolution of Ideas in Electrode Kinetics

Electrode processes are heterogeneous processes with kinetics depending on an electrical variable characterizing conditions at the interface. The net reaction rate is proportional to the current, and the electrode potential is universally selected as the electrical variable. The current-potential dependence thus characterizes kinetics. Electrode kinetics has been studied since the turn of the century and the concept of overvoltage was introduced in 1899. Tafel advocated the plot of overvoltage against the logarithm of current density as early as 1905, but modern concepts came somewhat later. These were first introduced by Butler in 1924. Erdey-Gruz and Volmer (1930) used for the first time the transfer coefficient in the description of the current-potential curves in the particular case of hydrogen ion discharge. This coefficient is universally accepted to this day as an expedient to avoid detailed knowledge of the activation state in the interpretation of experimental kinetic data. The essential correlation between double-layer structure and electrode kinetics was recognized by Frumkin as early as 1933, and his original treatment still stands today.

The foregoing contributions embody the essential background of what one might call a formal description of electrode kinetics. Correlation with first principles has been attempted with some success by a number of authors. Gurney (1931) proposed tunnel electron transfer. His attempt was unsuccessful at the time, but his idea is now being revived (for example, Christov, 1958). The concept of transition (activation) state, which became a powerful tool in the interpretation of gas kinetics, was introduced by Horiuti and Polanyi (1935). The type of potential energy diagrams used by these authors provides a simple and descriptive representation of energy variations and a graphic interpretation of the transfer coefficient. Such diagrams, however, have serious limitations. Several theories of charge transfer have been advocated during the last decade (Marcus, Gerischer, Levich and co-workers). The problem is a difficult one, even for processes involving no major change in configuration, but it is at the core of electrode kinetics. This approach might provide theoretical background for correlation between electrode kinetics and molecular structure, and the highly interesting but often semi-empirical correlations of this type which have already been established may become more refined and acquire a deeper significance with further progress in theory.

Electrode kinetics until approximately 1947 was primarily limited to hydrogen ion discharge and, to a minor extent, to electrolytic oxygen evolution. A few other reactions had also been studied, and a wealth of information had been gathered in polarography, but without any real kinetic interpretation. Hydrogen and oxygen overvoltage phenomena were emphasized because of their considerable practical importance and the possibility of study without interference by mass transfer. It is remarkable that many of the fundamental ideas on electrode kinetics originated from these studies despite the discouraging complexity of these two processes (except for a few metals, for example, hydrogen ion discharge on mercury). Investigations of these reactions also drew attention to the compelling need for high purification of solutions in electrode kinetics. This need was fully recognized by Frumkin (1935) and was further emphasized by Bockris (1947). Solution purification by preelectrolysis and adsorption of impurities has now become standard practice. The question remains, however, whether presently achieved levels of purity are adequate for processes which are particularly sensitive to traces of impurities.

The limitation imposed by mass transfer was progressively removed by developments in methodology and instrumentation, and the study of inherently simpler processes than hydrogen or oxygen evolution became possible. Hydrogen overvoltage thus lost its unique place in electrode kinetics, and the field became broader. The hydrogen and oxygen electrodes are still of fundamental importance, and current interest in fuel cells has stimulated further study.

A number of techniques have been developed since 1947 for the study of increasingly faster reactions, and it would seem that the present need is more for application of existing methods than for further refinements and more sophisticated instrumentation. Less stress should perhaps be placed on instrumental aspects and application of novel techniques to well-known electrode processes, and more fundamental problems should be emphasized. Nevertheless, the developments in methodology and the solution of the often complicated mathematical problems posed by mass transfer played a very significant role in the evolution of electrode kinetics. The work of Dolin, Ershler, and Frumkin (1940) on the impedance of the hydrogen electrode was the precursor of future developments which began in 1947 with the application of faradaic impedance measurements to relatively fast electrode processes (Randles, Ershler). Other methods were worked out in a number of laboratories (Gerischer, Barker, and others). The kinetic interpretation of polarographic currents transformed classical polarography into a useful method for the study of electrode kinetics. However, this application of polarography is hampered by the necessity of adding a maximum suppressor in a number of cases.

The newer techniques generally involve control of mass transfer by diffusion, and this simplification of the mass transfer problem often allows full mathematical analysis of electrode response. Steady-state mass transfer is much more arduous to interpret, in general, because of the rather formidable mathematical aspects of hydrodynamic analysis. One particular electrode, however, namely, the rotating disk electrode, has been fully treated by Levich (1942) and has provided a convenient tool for the study of moderately fast electrode processes under well-defined conditions of steady-state mass transfer. Applications of the rotating disk electrode were progressively worked out, mostly by the Russian school of electrochemistry. A few other systems which lend themselves to rigorous hydrodynamic analysis have been investigated, but they do not seem to have any particular advantage over the rotating disk electrode. The electrochemical engineering aspects of such studies, however, may be important.

Elucidation of electrode process mechanisms rests primarily on the analysis of current-potential variations, and various methods are now available for deriving the maximum possible information from such variations. Determination of stoichiometric numbers (Horiuti, 1948) allows discrimination between various mechanisms, but may not suffice for unambiguous assignment of a particular mechanism. The determination of reaction order which was advocated and extensively applied by Gerischer and Vetter (1950) has proven most valuable. [Note also Petrocelli (1951) and Lewartowicz (1952).]

Another approach was followed by the Prague school under the initial impetus of Brdička and Wiesner (1943) for electrode processes with coupled chemical reactions. These workers, and Koutecký in particular, postulate a given mechanism and then derive the corresponding current-potential characteristic and/or limiting current. The idea goes back to Eucken (1908) and has been applied, in particular, to the perennial problem of metal complex discharge with preceding dissociation. Considerable success was achieved for rather simple processes such as reduction preceded by ion recombination, and the kinetics of a number of chemical reactions was investigated in this fashion. The development of relaxation and perturbation methods by Eigen and colleagues since 1954 has somewhat deprived this application of polarography of its uniqueness, but this contribution of the Prague group nevertheless remains in the forefront of modern electrochemistry. Application to rather complex processes is still possible, at the cost of mathematical difficulties, but the reverse process of analyzing experimental current-potential characteristics and deducing mechanisms is quite uncertain and often does not lead to an unambiguous answer. This remark applies to any method of analysis solely based on current-potential characteristics and it points toward the need for methods allowing detection and, if possible, quantitative determination of intermediates. Much remains to be done in this area and only a few techniques are available at the present.

One can, as Vetter and others did, study the change in kinetics caused by addition of the product which is suspected of being an intermediate. The influence of variations in conditions of mass transfer may also provide some clue about the formation of sufficiently stable intermediates. This attack of the problem is quite limited, and more refined and sensitive techniques are needed. Application of electron paramagnetic resonance (E.P.R.) to the identification and quantitative evaluation of radicals formed as intermediates in electrode processes [Geske and Maki (1959)] offers interesting possibilities, mostly in organic electrode processes. Most of the work in this area thus far has made use of electrode processes as a convenient technique for the preparation of radicals and their subsequent study by E.P.R. Radicals must be quite stable to diffuse a sufficient distance away from the electrode where they can be detected by E.P.R., and this condition imposes a severe limitation. The rotating disk-ring electrode (Frumkin, Levich, Nekrasov, and Ivanov, 1959) offers the possibility of studying intermediates which are generated on the disk and rapidly transferred to the electrically insulated surrounding ring electrode. The potentials of the disk and the ring are adjusted independently. Application thus far has been limited to development of the method for processes with well-known intermediates. A number of other techniques have been applied which involve rapid variations of potential or current following the generation of intermediates. Altogether, available methods are still wholly inadequate.

It was pointed out at the beginning of this survey that the correlation between electrode kinetics and double-layer structure was analyzed by Frumkin as early as 1933. This problem has been actively investigated by Frumkin and his school since then, but it is only since approximately 1958 that attention of other investigators has been attracted to this particularly important aspect of electrode kinetics. To be sure, there was some awareness of the correlation between double-layer structure and electrode kinetics, but it was often believed, quite erroneously, that the matter could be dismissed whenever a large excess of a so-called indifferent (supporting) electrolyte was present. Four basic cases can be considered according to whether there is specific adsorption of the supporting electrolyte and the reactant and/or product. Quantitative interpretation is not available for all four cases. Progress was relatively slow, even in the absence of specific adsorption, because of the lack of detailed knowledge and accurate data on the double layer.

Application was initially limited to hydrogen ion discharge on mercury, but the scope of such studies has been considerably widened since 1950. Gierst, in particular, has systematically re-examined a number of polarographic processes since 1958 from the double-layer aspect. Understanding of the role of specific adsorption for solid electrodes is less advanced than for mercury despite the wealth of observations largely gathered by the Frumkin school. Understanding is largely qualitative. Recent work on the distribution of potential in the compact double layer may pave the way for further progress.

The study of electrode processes in presence of an adsorbed organic substance is directly related to the effect of double-layer structure. Technological applications in metal plating and corrosion inhibition have been studied for many years, but fundamental understanding is far from satisfactory. Much information was obtained by polarography, but it was realized only recently (1956) that adsorption with diffusion control complicates matters at the dropping mercury electrode because of varying coverage during drop growth. The Prague group and particularly Koutecký, Koryta, and Weber made detailed calculations to take coverage variation into account.

Presence of the organic adsorbate has *at least* two effects, namely, the variation of actual current density with coverage and the change of potential in the outer plane. These two effects account for most of the variation of measured exchange currents in some cases, especially at low coverage, but for some other processes measured exchange currents are not accounted for by these two corrections. The catalytic influence of certain organic substances which accelerate hydrogen ion discharge is related to this general problem. Such catalytic processes have been known since the early days of polarography, but they are now being reexamined in detail (for example, Mairanovskii).

The work described thus far has dealt with the definition and measurement of parameters for electrode kinetics, the elucidation of reaction mechanisms, and the study of double-layer effects. Detailed analysis of mass transfer is only incidental to these three objectives although it is often essential because of mixed control by charge transfer and mass transfer. Correlation of kinetic parameters with molecular or atomic properties is a more ambitious and ultimately more fundamental problem. Such a correlation encompasses the effects of the nature of reactants, products, electrode, and medium. This problem is related to the theory of charge transfer already alluded to previously. Success has been limited as a whole, but some correlations have been established mostly in the polarography of organic compounds, the reduction of metal ion complexes, and, to a very limited extent, for the electrolytic evolution of hydrogen and oxygen on various metals. Correlation of electrode kinetics with surface properties, as in metal deposition on solid electrodes, has received a new impetus in recent years (Bockris, Fischer, Gerischer among others), and definite progress has been made. This aspect of electrode kinetics will not be dealt with here. Semiconductor electrodes will not be treated either.

1-3 Definitions, Nomenclature, and Notations

a. Potentials

Definitions will find their place in subsequent chapters, but it may be worthwhile to comment briefly on the term "potential" here. There is no need to discuss the usual thermodynamic "electrode potential" since Guggenheim's masterful treatment is available (1). This treatment is covered, together with the wearisome matter of sign convention, in the excellent monograph of Ives and Janz (2). Potentials will be expressed according to the recommendations (2) made by the International Union of Pure and Applied Chemistry at its Stockholm meeting (1953).

Rigorously defined electrode potentials suffice in the analysis of the electromotive force of electrochemical cells, but it is useful, expecially in the treatment of models, to introduce Lange's *inner, outer,* and *surface potentials* (1930). Essential points will be covered briefly, and the reader is referred to Overbeek (3) and, in particular, Parsons (4) for further details. The so-called absolute potential will only be mentioned since its introduction in electrochemistry has led to much erroneous interpretation. There is no need for this concept in the treatment of the topics covered in this book, as was forcefully argued by Ershler (5).

The *electrochemical potential* $\bar{\mu}$ of a particle i at a point A in the bulk of a phase α is defined as the work which must be done to bring particle i from a point where the potential is zero to point A. This potential is, in principle, a measurable quantity. We may divide phase α into (a) a homogeneous volume deprived of charge and double layer and (b) a shell with the charge and double layer. The electrochemical potential $\bar{\mu}$ can be divided according to this model into the work w_1 required for the transfer of particle i to point A in the homogeneous volume and the work w_2 required for transfer to point A inside the shell. The positions of point A in the homogeneous volume and inside the shell must, of course, be the same as in the real phase α. One has $\bar{\mu} = w_1 + w_2$. The work w_1 may be called the *chemical potential* μ of particle i in the phase α. It is not a measurable quantity since the decomposition of phase α into two components has no physical counterpart. The work w_2 can be expressed formally as $z_i F \phi$, where z_i is the ionic valence of particle i, F is the faraday (that is, the charge per mole of univalent ions), and ϕ is the *inner potential*. The inner potential is not a measurable quantity. The inner potential may now be divided into two components corresponding, respectively, to the charge on the empty shell and to the oriented dipoles in the double layer. Thus $\phi = \psi + \chi$ where ψ is the *outer potential* and χ the *surface potential*. The outer potential is a measurable quantity which can also be calculated from the theory of electrostatics. The surface potential is not a measurable quantity.

If one plots the potential ψ as a function of the distance from the surface of phase α, for example, for a sphere of 1 cm. diameter, it is found that ψ is essentially constant at distances of 10^{-3} to 10^{-5} cm. from the surface of phase α. The potential falls off at greater distances and approaches zero asymptotically, and it drops at smaller distances because of short-range interactions. The constancy of ψ between 10^{-3} and 10^{-5} cm. adds another definition to the one we gave above, namely: ψ is the work to be done to bring particle i from a point where $\psi = 0$ (infinity) to a distance within 10^{-5} to 10^{-3} cm. of the surface of phase α.

We now consider differences of potential between two phases α and β and define the *Galvani difference of potential* $\phi_\alpha - \phi_\beta$ and the *Volta difference of potential* $\psi_\alpha - \psi_\beta$. The latter is a measurable quantity and the former is not, except in the case of two phases α and β having the same composition. We then have

$$\bar{\mu}_\alpha - \bar{\mu}_\beta = (\mu_\alpha + z_i F \phi_\alpha) - (\mu_\beta + z_i F \phi_\beta)$$

or, since $\mu_\alpha = \mu_\beta$ because of identity of composition,

$$\bar{\mu}_\alpha - \bar{\mu}_\beta = z_i F(\phi_\alpha - \phi_\beta)$$

The difference of potential $\phi_\alpha - \phi_\beta$ is then measurable because it is proportional to the difference of electrochemical potentials. $\phi_\alpha - \phi_\beta$ is simply equal to the e.m.f. of the cell having two terminals α and β of identical composition.

b. Nomenclature and Notations

A pragmatic approach is adopted in matters of nomenclature and notations, for there is no point in bewildering the reader with terms and symbols that are not used by most prominent workers. Notations overloaded with subscripts and superscripts are cumbersome and make the simplest equation unnecessarily complicated. On the other hand, the elimination of most subscripts and superscripts by systematic use of letters of various alphabets leads to a confusing multiplicity of symbols. Occasionally, the same symbol may be used for two different quantities when there is no risk of confusion. Notations in this book are simplified as much as feasible. Even so, some of the symbols are more involved than we wished. Reference is made to Van Rysselberghe's most recent reports

(6) on the codification of electrochemical nomenclature by the International Committee on Electrochemical Thermodynamic and Kinetics for further discussion of nomenclature problems.

1-4 Literature

A few key references will be given here with brief comments. Only recent electrochemistry textbooks can be retained (7–10) and two of them (9, 10) give only an elementary introduction to the double layer and electrode kinetics. The second edition of Kortüm's book (7) is the most thorough of electrochemistry textbooks. There is no monograph on the electrical double layer, although excellent reviews are available. Two books on electrode kinetics are available (11, 12), and a fairly substantial introduction is given in Fischer's book (13) on metal deposition. The book of Frumkin, Bagotskii, Iofa, and Kabanov was the only one on electrode kinetics for a decade. It covered the field with sufficient detail, but not in an overwhelming way, and unfortunately it was not translated into a Western language. Vetter's monograph (12) is excellent for its comprehensive coverage and has its place in every electrochemist's library. The most important books in which mass transfer and methodology, for example, polarography, are the main topics are listed in Sec. 7-4.

Additional references include: two collections of authoritative, periodic reviews (14, 15), symposium papers (16–21), proceedings of meetings of the International Committee on Electrochemical Thermodynamics and Kinetics (22, 23), two compendia of electrochemical data (24, 25), and reviews on the double layer (3, 4, 26–30a) and electrode kinetics (27, 31–40).

REFERENCES

1. E. A. Guggenheim, *Thermodynamics*, 2nd ed., Interscience, New York, 1950, pp. 331–354.
2. D. J. G. Ives and G. J. Janz, *Reference Electrodes*, D. J. G. Ives and G. J. Janz, editors, Academic Press, New York, 1961, pp. 1–70.
3. J. T. G. Overbeek, *Colloid Science*, Vol. 1, H. R. Kruyt, editor, Elsevier, Amsterdam, 1952, pp. 115–193.
4. R. Parsons, *Modern Aspects of Electrochemistry*, Vol. 1, J. O'M. Bockris, editor, Butterworths, London, 1954, pp. 103–179.
5. B. V. Ershler, *Uspekhi Khim.*, **21**, 237 (1952); *Chem. Abstr.*, **48**, 471 (1954).
6. P. Van Rysselberghe, *Electrochim. Acta*, **5**, 28 (1961); **8**, 543 (1963).
7. G. Kortüm, *Lehrbuch der Elektrochemie*, 2nd edition, Verlag Chemie, Weinheim/Bergstrasse, 1957.
8. G. Kortüm and J. O'M. Bockris, *Textbook of Electrochemistry*, 2 Vols., Elsevier, Amsterdam, 1951.
9. E. C. Potter, *Electrochemistry*, MacMillan, New York, 1956.

10. G. Milazzo, *Electrochemistry*, English translation by P. J. Mill, Elsevier, Amsterdam, 1963.
11. A. N. Frumkin, V. S. Bagotskii, Z. A. Iofa, and B. N. Kabanov, *Kinetics of Electrode Processes*, Moscow University Press, Moscow, 1952.
12. K. J. Vetter, *Elektrochemische Kinetik*, Springer, Berlin, 1961.
13. H. Fischer, *Elektrolytische Abscheidung und Elektrokristallisation von Metalen*, Springer, Berlin, 1954.
14. ‹*Modern Aspects of Electrochemistry*, J. O'M. Bockris, editor, Butterworths, London, Vol. 1 (1954), Vol. 2 (1959), Vol. 3, in press.
15. *Advances in Electrochemistry and Electrochemical Engineering:* Electrochemistry volumes edited by P. Delahay: Vol. 1 (1961), Vol. 3 (1963), Vol. 5 in preparation; *Electrochemical Engineering* volumes edited by C. W. Tobias: Vol. 2 (1962), Vol. 4 in preparation.
16. *Discussion Faraday Soc.*, **1**, 1–338 (1947).
17. *J. Chim. phys.*, **49**, C3–C218 (1952).
18. *Z. Elektrochem.*, **59**, 591–822 (1955).
19. *Reports of the 4th Soviet Conference on Electrochemistry* (1956), English translation by Consultants Bureau, 3 Vols., New York, 1958.
20. *Can. J. Chem.* **37**, 120–323 (1959).
21. *Transactions of the Symposium on Electrode Processes*, E. Yeager, editor, Wiley, New York, 1961.
22. *International Committee on Electrochemical Thermodynamics and Kinetics*, 2nd meeting, Tamburini (1951), Milan; 3rd meeting (1952), Manfredi, Milan; 6th (1955), 7th (1957), 8th (1958) and 9th meeting (1959), Butterworths, London.
23. *Electrochim. Acta*, **8**, iii–lxii (1963) (abstracts only).
24. B. E. Conway, *Electrochemical Data*, Elsevier, Amsterdam, 1952.
25. R. Parsons, *Handbook of Electrochemical Data*, Butterworths, London, 1959.
26. D. C. Grahame, *Chem. Revs.*, **41**, 441–501 (1947).
27. J. N. Agar and J. E. B. Randles, *Ann. Reports Chem. Soc.*, **51**, 103–117 (1954).
28. A. N. Frumkin, *Z. Elektrochem.*, **59**, 807–818 (1955).
29. A. N. Frumkin, *J. Electrochem. Soc.*, **107**, 461–472 (1960).
30. R. Parsons, *Advances in Electrochemistry and Electrochemical Engineering*, Vol. 1, P. Delahay, editor, Interscience, New York, 1961, pp. 1–64.
30a. J. R. Macdonald and C. A. Barlow, *Proceedings of the First Australian Conference on Electrochemistry*, A. Friend and F. Gutmann, editors, Pergamon, Oxford, 1964, pp. 199–247. The authors list mistakes they noticed in a number of papers dealing with the double layer.
31. J. O'M. Bockris, *Modern Aspects of Electrochemistry*, Vol. 1, J. O'M. Bockris, editor, Butterworths, London, 1954, pp. 180–276.
32. J. O'M. Bockris, *Ann. Rev. Phys. Chem.*, **5**, 477–500 (1954).
33. D. C. Grahame, *ibid.*, **6**, 337–358 (1955).
34. P. Delahay, *ibid.*, **8**, 229–248 (1957).
35. H. R. Thirsk, *Ann. Reports Chem. Soc.*, **54**, 17–29 (1957).
36. M. Fleischmann and K. B. Oldham, *ibid.*, **55**, 67–79 (1958).
37. J. E. B. Randles, *ibid.*, **56**, 32–41 (1959).
38. H. Gerischer, *Ann. Rev. Phys. Chem.*, **12**, 227–254 (1961).
39. W. H. Reinmuth, *Advances in Analytical Chemistry and Instrumentation*, Vol. 1, C. N. Reilley, editor, Interscience, New York, 1960, pp. 241–292.
40. R. A. Marcus, *Ann. Rev. Phys. Chem.*, **15**, 155–196 (1964).

PART ONE

THE ELECTRICAL DOUBLE LAYER

CHAPTER 2

Thermodynamics of the Ideal Polarized Electrode

2-1 Application of the Gibbs Adsorption Isotherm

Thermodynamic analysis of electrode-electrolyte interfaces is considerably simplified in the absence of electrode reaction (oxidation or reduction). Grahame and Whitney (1) coined the expression "ideal polarized electrode" for electrodes fulfilling this condition. A number of electrodes can function as ideal polarized electrodes, and conditions are particularly favorable for mercury in aqueous solution because of the high overvoltage for hydrogen evolution. The range of potentials that can be covered with other metals is somewhat narrower than for mercury.

Considerable doubt existed for a number of years about the possibility of treating by thermodynamics a metal-electrolyte interface on the assumption that no electrode reaction occurs. Such misgivings unnecessarily complicated thermodynamic analysis, though the correct result was ultimately derived in a number of treatments. Grahame and Whitney (1) showed that the Gibbs adsorption isotherm can be applied to the ideal polarized electrode without any loss of rigor and with much simplification. The historical background (11 references) can be found in Grahame's review (2). Parsons and Devanathan (3) gave a very thorough analysis, and Parsons (4) considered a particular case of his more general treatment which shows very well the essential points. This analysis follows Parsons (4) except for a slightly simpler case than his (no $z - z'$ electrolyte). Further details, with which we need not concern ourselves here, can be found in other papers (5, 6). The reversible electrode was treated by

Grahame and Whitney (1) and Mohilner (7) in much the same way as the ideal polarized electrode. Relevant data on the mercurous ion-mercury electrode were recently reported by Koenig and co-workers (8).

We consider the cell

$$Cu' \mid Ag \mid AgCl \mid KCl, H_2O, L \mid Hg, M \mid Cu''$$

in which an amalgam of metal M is in contact with a solution of potassium chloride in a mixture of water and the completely miscible solvent L. The cell is completed by a silver-silver chloride electrode and is connected to a potentiometer by the copper wires Cu' and Cu''. The voltage being applied is such that the amalgam electrode behaves, for all practical purposes, as an ideal polarized electrode. We apply the Gibbs adsorption isotherm to the amalgam-electrolyte interface and write for a *constant pressure and temperature*

$$-d\gamma = \sum \Gamma_i \, d\bar{\mu}_i + \sum \Gamma_j \, d\mu_j \tag{1}$$

where γ is the interfacial tension at the amalgam-electrolyte interface; the Γ's are the surface excesses of the ionic species i and uncharged species j; and the $\bar{\mu}_i$'s and μ_j's are the corresponding electrochemical and chemical potentials. In the application of Eq. 1 to the above cell we select Hg^+, M^+, and the electron e as the components of the amalgam phase, and K^+, Cl^-, H_2O, and L as the solution components. Thus

$$\begin{aligned}
-d\gamma &= (\Gamma_{Hg^+} \, d\bar{\mu}_{Hg^+} + \Gamma_{M^+} \, d\bar{\mu}_{M^+} + \Gamma_e \, d\bar{\mu}_e) \\
&+ (\Gamma_{K^+} \, d\bar{\mu}_{K^+} + \Gamma_{Cl^+} \, d\bar{\mu}_{Cl^-}) \\
&+ (\Gamma_{H_2O} \, d\mu_{H_2O} + \Gamma_L \, d\mu_L)
\end{aligned} \tag{2}$$

where the three pair of parentheses correspond to the amalgam, the ionic components, and the uncharged components, respectively. Equation 2 is now transformed to eliminate single ion electrochemical potentials and to introduce the potential E of the amalgam electrode versus the reference electrode. This result is achieved by writing all necessary equilibrium equations and by introducing the Gibbs-Duhem equations. The equilibrium conditions for the amalgam and the amalgam-Cu'' junction are

$$\mu_M = \bar{\mu}_{M^+} + \bar{\mu}_e$$
$$\mu_{Hg} = \bar{\mu}_{Hg^+} + \bar{\mu}_e$$
$$\bar{\mu}_e = \bar{\mu}_e(Cu'')$$

By noting that the charge q on the metal per unit area is

$$q = F(\Gamma_{Hg^+} + \Gamma_{M^+} - \Gamma_e)$$

where F is the faraday, we obtain for the first groups of terms in Eq. 2.2

$$\Gamma_{Hg^+} d\bar{\mu}_{Hg^+} + \Gamma_{M^+} d\bar{\mu}_{M^+} + \Gamma_e d\bar{\mu}_e$$

$$= \Gamma_{Hg^+} d\mu_{Hg} + \Gamma_{M^+} d\mu_M - \frac{q}{F} d\bar{\mu}_e(\text{Cu}'') \quad (3)$$

In an analogous way we have for the solution and for the equilibrium at the Cu'–Ag–AgCl junctions

$$\mu_{KCl} = \bar{\mu}_{K^+} + \bar{\mu}_{Cl^-}$$

$$q = -F(\Gamma_{K^+} - \Gamma_{Cl^-})$$

$$d\bar{\mu}_{Cl^-} = d\bar{\mu}_e(\text{Cu}')$$

[Note that the charge on the solution side is equal to $-q$.] Hence, the second group of terms in Eq. 2 becomes

$$\Gamma_{K^+} d\bar{\mu}_{K^+} + \Gamma_{Cl^-} d\bar{\mu}_{Cl^-} = \Gamma_{K^+} d\mu_{KCl} + \frac{q}{F} d\bar{\mu}_e(\text{Cu}') \quad (4)$$

The terminals Cu' and Cu" have the same composition, and consequently

$$d\bar{\mu}_e(\text{Cu}') - d\bar{\mu}_e(\text{Cu}'') = -Fd(\phi^{Cu'} - \phi^{Cu''})$$

$$= F \, dE_- \quad (5)$$

where the ϕ's are the inner potential and E_- is the potential of the amalgam versus the reference electrode as read on the potentiometer. The subscript on E_- indicates that the electrode is reversible to an anion (chloride ion). Combination of Eqs 2 to 5 yields

$$-d\gamma = q \, dE_- + \Gamma_{Hg^+} d\mu_{Hg} + \Gamma_{M^+} d\mu_M$$

$$+ \Gamma_{K^+} d\mu_{KCl} + \Gamma_{H_2O} d\mu_{H_2O} + \Gamma_L d\mu_L \quad (6)$$

Two Gibbs-Duhem equations can be written for the amalgam and solution, respectively, and two of the chemical potentials in Eq. 6 can be eliminated. Thus

$$x_{Hg} d\mu_{Hg} + x_M d\mu_M = 0$$

$$x_{KCl} d\mu_{KCl} + x_{H_2O} d\mu_{H_2O} + x_L d\mu_L = 0$$

where the x's are the mole fractions. It does not matter which two chemical potentials we eliminate, but it is convenient to select μ_{Hg} and μ_{H_2O} since the corresponding substances are generally present in very large excess in dilute solutions and dilute amalgams. Hence

$$-d\gamma = q\, dE_- + \left(\Gamma_{M^+} - \frac{x_M}{x_{Hg}}\Gamma_{Hg^+}\right) d\mu_M$$

$$+ \left(\Gamma_{K^+} - \frac{x_{KCl}}{x_{H_2O}}\Gamma_{H_2O}\right) d\mu_{KCl}$$

$$+ \left(\Gamma_L - \frac{x_L}{x_{H_2O}}\Gamma_{H_2O}\right) d\mu_L \qquad (7)$$

Equation 7 is the fundamental relationship for thermodynamic analysis of the particular ideal polarized electrode treated here. It follows from this equation that only the *relative surface excesses*

$$\Gamma_{M^+(Hg)} = \Gamma_{M^+} - \frac{x_M}{x_{Hg}}\Gamma_{Hg^+}$$

$$\Gamma_{K^+(H_2O)} = \Gamma_{K^+} - \frac{x_{KCl}}{x_{H_2O}}\Gamma_{H_2O}$$

$$\Gamma_{L(H_2O)} = \Gamma_L - \frac{x_L}{x_{H_2O}}\Gamma_{H_2O} \qquad (8)$$

can be determined by thermodynamic arguments. Equation 7 takes the form

$$-d\gamma = q\, dE_- + \Gamma_{M^+(Hg)}\, d\mu_M + \Gamma_{K^+(H_2O)}\, d\mu_{KCl} + \Gamma_{L(H_2O)}\, d\mu_L \qquad (9)$$

in terms of the relative surface excesses. In the writing of Eq. 9 we shall simplify notations and omit in the subscripts the substance with respect to which the surface excess is relative. It is understood that the Γ's appearing in further equations are relative surface excesses.

Instead of introducing relative surface excesses, Grahame and Whitney (1, 2) select a reference surface corresponding to $\Gamma_{H_2O} = 0$. Nothing is gained by this *arbitrary* procedure for it must be realized that only relative surface excesses can be obtained from thermodynamic argument.

If the reference electrode in this derivation had been reversible to the cation instead of the anion, an equation identical to Eq. 9 would have been obtained except for the term in $\Gamma_{K^+(H_2O)}$ which could have been replaced by $\Gamma_{Cl^-(H_2O)}\, d\mu_{KCl}$. We can therefore write Eq. 9 in the condensed form

$$-d\gamma = q\, dE_\pm + \Gamma_\mp\, d\mu \qquad (10)$$

which holds for constant pressure, temperature, and composition of the electrode. There $E_\pm$ is the potential with respect to a reference electrode which is reversible either to the cation (E_+) or the anion (E_-), and $\Gamma_\mp$ is the anion (Γ_-) or cation (Γ_+) surface excess. Equations 9 and 10 hold for $z - z$ electrolytes, but they can be generalized (2–4) to $z - z'$ electrolytes (cf. Sec. 2-3).

2-2 The Electrocapillary Curve

It follows from Eq. 9 that the charge of the electrode per unit area is given, at constant temperature and pressure, by the *Lippmann equation* (9)

$$q = -\left(\frac{\partial \gamma}{\partial E}\right)_{\mu_k} \tag{11}$$

all the chemical potentials μ_k being kept constant. The subscript p and T are deleted to render the writing of equations less cumbersome. This equation also holds for unsymmetrical $z - z'$ electrolytes. Note that the subscript $\pm$ of E was dropped in Eq. 11, for it does not matter which reference electrode is used, the derivative $(\partial \gamma / \partial E)_{\mu_k}$ being independent of the reference electrode.

The charge on the electrode is a thermodynamic quantity which can be determined from the *electrocapillary curve* representing the variations of γ with E (Fig. 2-1). Since the initial, but highly accurate, work of Gouy in

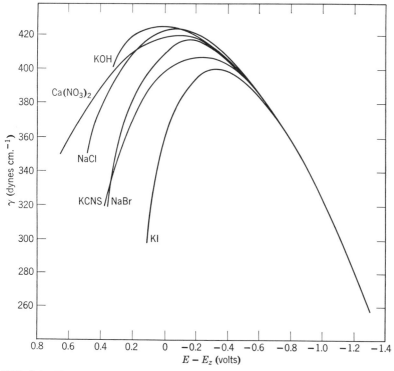

FIG. 2-1. Electrocapillary curves for mercury and different electrolytes at 18°C. Potentials referred to E_z for an electrolyte (sodium fluoride) without specific adsorption [Grahame (2)] (by permission of the American Chemical Society).

the early 1900's a number of such electrocapillary curves has been reported. The Lippmann electrometer has progressively evolved into a precise instrument. Parsons (4) quotes a number of references pertaining to instrumentation, and further details and minor improvements have been discussed in more recent papers (10–12). The γ-E curve has the general shape of a parabola, but it is not a second-degree parabola for the reason stated in Sec. 2-4. Electrocapillary curves vary markedly with the nature of the electrolyte at the more positive potentials, but they often coincide

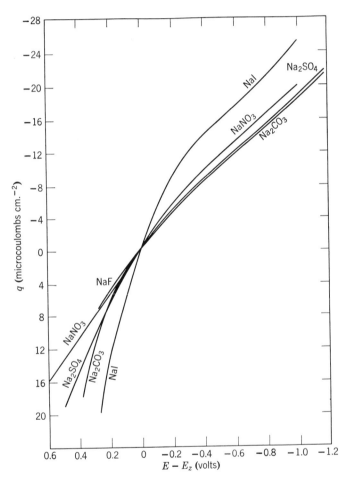

FIG. 2-2. Charge on mercury in contact with various $1M$ electrolytes at 25°C. Potentials referred to E_z for each electrolyte [Grahame (2)] (by permission of the American Chemical Society).

at markedly negative potentials. However, the curves do not coincide in the negative range of potentials for cations having sufficiently different properties, for example, alkali cations versus tetraalklyammonium cations.

The charge q is equal to zero at the apex of the parabola, and the corresponding potential is the *point of zero charge* (E_z) or the *electrocapillary maximum*. Since $q \gtrless 0$ for $E \gtrless E_z$ (Fig. 2-2), there is electrostatic

TABLE 2-1 Point of Zero Charge for Mercury and Various Electrolytes at $25°$ C[a]

Salt	Concentration mole l^{-1}	$-E_z$ volts[b]	Salt	Concentration mole l^{-1}	$-E_z$ volts[b]
NaF	0.1	0.472	NaCl	1	0.557
	1	0.472	CsCl	1	0.556
KF	0.1	0.471	KClO$_4$	0.1	0.507
KCl	0.001	0.474	KNO$_3$	0.1	0.516
	0.01	0.485	KOH	0.1	0.476
	0.1	0.505	K$_2$CO$_3$	0.05	0.473
	1	0.555	K$_2$SO$_4$	0·05	0.470
KBr	0.1	0.573			
KI	0.1	0.731			
KCNS	0.1	0.625			
KCN	0.01	0.582			
	0.1	0.684			
	1	0.790			

[a] Data from Grahame et al. (10) as compiled by Conway (14). Values vary slightly according to method being used. See Refs. 10, 13, and 14.

[b] Potentials referred to normal calomel electrode in KCl after correction for liquid junction potential.

attraction of anions by the electrode, aside from any other type of interaction with the electrode, for $q > 0$ and attraction of cations for $q < 0$. Ions that are attracted near the electrode are repelled from each other, and consequently the work needed to expand the interface is smaller than in the absence of electrostatic interaction with the electrode ($q = 0$). The interfacial tension thus decreases as $|q|$ increases.

The point of zero charge, as measured *with respect to a given reference electrode* in a cell with liquid junction, is essentially the same regardless of the nature and concentration of electrolyte for some electrolytes, whereas it varies strongly for others (Table 2-1). We shall see (Sec. 4-1) that the shift of E_z is caused by *specific adsorption* of ions. We imply by this expression that ionic surface excesses are not accounted for by simple

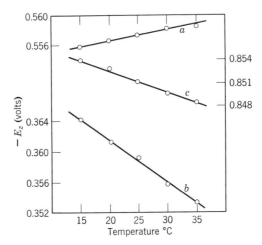

FIG. 2-3. Point of zero charge as a function of temperature for the following cells [Randles and Whiteley (15)]: (a) Hg (streaming electrode) |0.1M KCl, Hg$_2$Cl$_2$| Hg; (b) Hg (streaming electrode) |0.1M NaOH, HgO| Hg; (c) Hg (streaming electrode) |0.1M K$_2$SO$_4$, Hg$_2$SO$_4$| Hg (by permission of The Faraday Society).

electrostatic considerations of the type discussed in Chapter 3. The relationship between E_z and electrolyte activity is discussed in further detail in Sec. 4-1. Grahame (2) coined the expression *rational potential* to designate potentials which are referred to the point of zero charge for an electrolyte which does not exhibit any detectable specific adsorption at the point of zero charge (sodium fluoride).

Values of E_z have been determined with high accuracy by a number of authors (4) and particularly by Grahame and co-workers (10, 13). These authors also critically compared experimental methods for E_z determination for mercury. (See Chapter 6 for amalgams and other metals.) Rather extensive tables are given by Conway (14), who also lists values of q for a number of electrolytes in contact with mercury.

The point of zero·charge depends somewhat on temperature (Fig. 2-3), but the relationship is not a simple one and its interpretation involves nonthermodynamic arguments [Randles and Whiteley (15)].

2-3 Relative Surface Excesses

a. Determination of Relative Surface Excesses

We only consider here ionic surface excesses. Adsorption of uncharged substances is treated in Chapter 5; mixed solvents and amalgams are reserved for Chapter 6. Equation 9 allows determination of relative surface excesses, at constant cell e.m.f., from variations of interfacial tension with the chemical potential of the species whose surface excess is being determined. It is deduced (2–4) from Eq. 10, as written for a salt $C_{v+}A_{v-}$,

$$\Gamma_{\mp} = -v_{\mp}\left(\frac{\partial\gamma}{\partial\mu}\right)_{E\pm} \tag{12}$$

There μ is the chemical potential of $C_{v+}A_{v-}$ in solution, all other μ's as well as p and T being kept constant. If the charge q is known, one of the surface excesses can be obtained by difference from

$$q = -F(z_+\Gamma_+ + z_-\Gamma_-) \tag{13}$$

where z_+ and z_- are the ionic valences, with sign, of the cation and anion, respectively. As a particular case, application of Eq. 12 at the point of zero charge yields the surface excess of salt Γ_{salt} at E_z (2). Thus

$$\left(\frac{\partial\gamma}{\partial\mu}\right)_{E_z} = -\frac{(\Gamma_+)_{E_z}}{v_+} = -\frac{(\Gamma_-)_{E_z}}{v_-}$$

$$= -(\Gamma_{salt})_{E_z} \tag{14}$$

Application of Eq. 12 requires, in all rigor, a cell without liquid junction and a reference electrode which is reversible to the cation (for Γ_-) or the anion (for Γ_+). Measurements can be simplified with little or no loss of accuracy, as shown by Grahame and Soderberg (16), by the use of the following cell with liquid junction and a single reference electrode:

Hg	electrolyte at concentration c_1	electrolyte at constant concentration c_2	reference electrode

The two compartments contain the same electrolyte at the variable concentration c_1 and the constant concentration c_2. The reference electrode is, for instance, a normal calomel electrode or any other suitable electrode. The liquid junction potential between the compartments c_1 and c_2 can be accurately computed from activities and transference numbers. The liquid junction potential between the reference electrode and the compartment with the electrolyte at the concentration c_2 need not be known exactly as long as it is constant. One can then calculate the change in e.m.f. of the above cell, as c_1 varies, that corresponds to a constant E_+ or

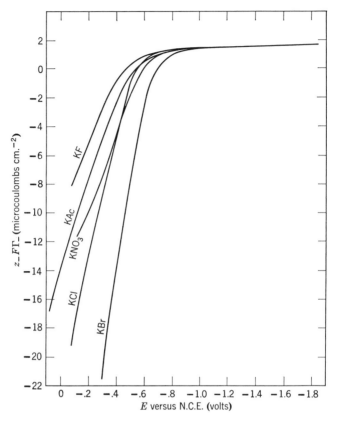

FIG. 2-4. Relative (to water) surface excesses of anions for mercury in 0.1 normal solutions of different electrolytes at 25°C. Surface excess expressed as a charge [Grahame and Soderberg (16)] (by permission of the American Institute of Physics).

E_- of a cell without liquid junction. This procedure not only simplifies measurements but also eliminates the need for a reference electrode which is reversible to one of the ions in solution. Such a reference electrode may not be available or is at best cumbersome to use for a number of ions.

Some results obtained by Grahame and Soderberg (16) are summarized in Figs. 2-4 and 2-5, and similar, but less accurate, data are given by Grahame (2). The data of Figs. 2-4 and 2-5 were not computed from Eq. 12 but were obtained by the wholly equivalent method of Sec. 2-4. We conclude from Figs. 2-4 and 2-5 that (*a*) Γ_- and Γ_+ increase when q becomes increasingly positive or negative, respectively. This is understandable in view of the increasing electrode interaction between ions and the electrode as $|q|$ increases. (b) Γ_- reaches a limiting value for increasingly negative q's. (c) A negative Γ_+ is hardly ever reached for $q > 0$ except for potassium fluoride; Γ_+ at positive electrode charge for the latter electrolyte approaches a value which is not very different, in absolute value, from the limiting cation surface excess. The rather large positive Γ_+ and the increase of Γ_+ with q for $q > 0$ are surprising. Grahame (2) explained this seemingly abnormal behavior by noting that, as a result of specific adsorption of anions on the electrode, the positive charge on the electrode is more than compensated by the charge of specifically adsorbed anions, and consequently cations are attracted.

It was assumed in the derivation of Eq. 12 that the electrolyte is completely dissociated, but this restriction can easily be removed by going over the derivation of this equation and by taking into account the lack of complete electrolyte dissociation. We then obtain two equations which are linear with respect to the three surface excesses Γ_+, Γ_- and Γ for the incompletely dissociated electrolyte. It is not possible to compute Γ_+ and Γ_- separately from thermodynamics. The case of salts of weak bases and strong acid, treated by Blomgren and Bockris (17), shows clearly this thermodynamic limitation.

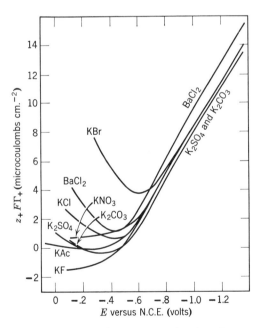

FIG. 2-5. Relative (to water) surface excesses of cations for mercury in 0.1 normal solutions of different electrolytes at 25°C. Surface excess expressed as a charge [Grahame and Soderberg (16)] (by permission of the American Institute of Physics).

b. Further Thermodynamic Correlations

Since Eq. 10 is a complete differential, we obtain by cross differentiation (18) for a $z - z$ electrolyte at constant temperature, pressure and electrode composition

$$\left(\frac{\partial q}{\partial \mu}\right)_{E_\pm} = \left(\frac{\partial \Gamma_\mp}{\partial E_\pm}\right)_\mu \tag{15}$$

$$\left(\frac{\partial E_\pm}{\partial \mu}\right)_q = -\left(\frac{\partial \Gamma_\mp}{\partial q}\right)_\mu \tag{16}$$

$$\left(\frac{\partial q}{\partial \Gamma_\mp}\right)_{E_\pm} = -\left(\frac{\partial \mu}{\partial E_\pm}\right)_{\Gamma_\mp} \tag{17}$$

$$\left(\frac{\partial E_\pm}{\partial \Gamma_\mp}\right)_q = \left(\frac{\partial \mu}{\partial q}\right)_{\Gamma_\mp} \tag{18}$$

where μ is the chemical potential of the electrolyte. The same equations hold for uncharged substances, and $E_\pm$ can then be replaced by E. Equation 17 was derived by Gouy (19) and was used by Frumkin in a number of studies of uncharged substances (Chapter 5). Equation 15 was obtained by Grahame and Soderberg (16) and applied to the analysis of double-layer capacity data (Sec. 2-4). The above correlations will also be used in Chapters 4 and 5.

2-4   Double-Layer Capacity

a. Definition

The interface electrode-solution has two equal charges of opposite signs, one on the electrode and the other on the solution side and is analogous to a capacitor. We define the *integral capacity* C^i at the potential E with respect to some reference electrode by

$$q = C^i(E - E_z) \tag{19}$$

The integral capacity varies with potential (Fig. 2-6). It is higher on the positive side of the point of zero charge than on the negative side. Variations of C^i with E are explained in Chapters 4 and 5. It is noted in passing that the electrocapillary curve would be a second-degree parabola if C^i were independent of E. This conclusion follows immediately from Eqs. 11 and 19.

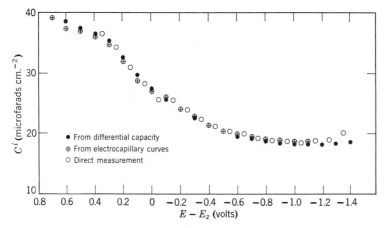

FIG. 2-6. Variations of integral capacity with potential. Mercury in $0.5M$ sodium sulfate [Grahame (2)] (by permission of the American Chemical Society).

Since C^i varies with E, it is more convenient to introduce the *differential capacity* defined by

$$C = \left(\frac{\partial q}{\partial E}\right)_\mu \tag{20}$$

The temperature, pressure, and μ are constant in Eq. 20. Capacities referred to in the text will always be differential capacities unless specified otherwise,

Differential capacities vary with potential (examples of $C - E$ curves in Chapter 3), but they can be measured provided the excursion of potential δE in measurements does not exceed a few millivolts. Differential capacities are independent of δE provided δE is small enough. Earlier measurements with mercury were grossly in error because of unsuspected contamination by traces of strongly adsorbed organic impurities in the electrolyte. This major source of error was discovered by Proskurnin and Frumkin (20) who made the first reliable measurements. Grahame introduced the systematic use of the dropping mercury electrode and was able, in this way, to minimize considerably electrode contamination. Adsorption of impurity traces is generally a slow process because of diffusion control (Chapter 5), and frequent (every few seconds) renewal of the mercury drop provides a clean surface provided solutions are reasonably purified. This technique reached a high degree of perfection in the hands of Grahame (21–24).

Measurements are generally made at frequencies of the order of 1000 c.p.s. with aqueous solutions, since conditions are then favorable for accuracy and design of the A.C. Bridge. Higher frequencies are needed in studies of adsorption (Chapter 5) and for measurements with molten salts (Chapter 6). A bridge operating up to 200 kc was designed by Melik-Gaikazyan (25), and more recently Lorenz (26) pushed the limit slightly above 1 Mc by means of a twin T-bridge.

b. Correlation between Capacity and Charge on the Electrode, Interfacial Tension, and Relative Surface Excesses

We deduce from the definition of the differential capacity

$$q = \int_{E_z}^{E} C \, dE \tag{21}$$

$$\gamma = \gamma_{E_z} - \iint_{E_z}^{E} C \, dE^2 \tag{22}$$

Application of Eqs. 21 and 22 requires independent measurement of E_z and γ_z, respectively. Grahame advocated throughout his work application of Eq. 21 for the determination of q over the computation of q from electrocapillary curve data (Eq. 11). The latter method requires differentiation of electrocapillary curves with respect to potential, and according to Grahame yields less accurate results than those obtained by integration of the differential capacity. Moreover, danger of contamination by traces of adsorbed impurities adversely affects precise determinations of surface tensions more than capacity measurements. Grahame's position on this point is possibly justified, although comparison of the two methods for the mercury-0.1M potassium chloride system by Devanathan and Peries (27) indicates good agreement. A minor cause of discrepancy resulting from a difference between the Gibbs reference surfaces in the two methods was discussed by Grahame and Parsons (28), but we need not concern ourselves with this point here. (See also Ref. 29 for a different opinion on this point.)

Grahame also extended his argument in favor of obtaining q from capacity measurements to the determination of relative surface excesses. Analysis for ions, according to Grahame and Soderberg (16), will now be given. Uncharged substances are dealt with in Chapter 5. We introduce the differential capacity components C_+ and C_- corresponding respectively to the surface excesses of cations and anions in the double layer. These capacities are related to ionic surface excesses at constant temperature, pressure, and electrode composition by

$$z_\pm F \left(\frac{\partial \Gamma_\pm}{\partial E_\mp} \right)_\mu = -C_\pm \tag{23}$$

Since the charge on the solution side is $-q$, $C_{\pm}$ is preceded by a minus sign in Eq. 23. By combining Eqs. 11 and 12 with Eq. 23, we immediately obtain

$$z_{\pm}\nu_{\pm}F\left(\frac{\partial q}{\partial \mu}\right)_{E_{\mp}} = -C_{\pm} \tag{24}$$

or, after differentiation,

$$z_{\pm}\nu_{\pm}F\left(\frac{\partial^2 q}{\partial \mu \, \partial E_{\pm}}\right) = -\left(\frac{\partial C_{\pm}}{\partial E_{\mp}}\right)_{\mu} \tag{25}$$

Recalling that C is given by Eq. 20, we write Eq. 25 in the form

$$z_{\pm}\nu_{\pm}F\left(\frac{\partial C}{\partial \mu}\right)_{E_{\mp}} = -\left(\frac{\partial C_{\pm}}{\partial E_{\mp}}\right)_{\mu} \tag{26}$$

The derivative $(\partial C/\partial \mu_{E_{\mp}}$ can be evaluated from experimental capacities for different electrolyte activities, and consequently $C_{\pm}$ can be computed by integration of Eq. 26. Integration of Eq. 23 then yields $\Gamma_{\pm}$. The constant for the first integration, namely $C_{\pm}$ at E_z, is determined by rewriting Eq. 24 as

$$z_{\pm}\nu_{\pm}F\left(\frac{\partial q}{\partial E_{\mp}}\right)_{\mu}\left(\frac{\partial E_{\mp}}{\partial \mu}\right)_{q} = -C_{\pm}$$

or

$$z_{\pm}\nu_{\pm}FC\left(\frac{\partial E_{\pm}}{\partial \mu}\right)_{q} = -C_{\pm} \tag{27}$$

Equation 27 is applied to the point of zero charge, and the derivative $(\partial E_{\mp}/\partial \mu)_{q=0}$ is determined experimentally. The quantity $C_{\pm}$ is thus known at E_z. The second integration constant, $\Gamma_{\pm}$ at E_z, is determined from electrocapillary measurements and by application of Eq. 14 at the point of zero charge. Grahame and Soderberg (16) also give an alternate method of computing the second integration constant, which is based on the theory of the double layer discussed in Chapter 3. (See Ref. 16 for details.)

The foregoing method of obtaining surface excesses is equivalent to the one based on Eq. 12 since it involves the study of the effect of variation of the chemical potential of the electrolyte on two quantities—the interfacial tension and the double layer capacity—which are readily correlated. Application of Eq. 26, however, yields, according to Grahame, more accurate results than Eq. 12. The results in Figs. 2-4 and 2-5 were obtained by the method just outlined.

REFERENCES

1. D. C. Grahame and R. W. Whitney, *J. Am. Chem. Soc.*, **64**, 1548 (1942).
2. D. C. Grahame, *Chem. Revs.*, **41**, 441 (1947).
3. R. Parsons and M. A. V. Devanathan, *Trans. Faraday Soc.*, **49**, 404 (1953).
4. R. Parsons, *Modern Aspects of Electrochemistry*, Vol. 1, J. O'M. Bockris, editor, Butterworths, London, 1954, pp. 103–179.
5. D. C. Grahame, *J. Chem. Phys.*, **16**, 1117 (1948).
6. R. Parsons, *Can. J. Chem.*, **37**, 308 (1959).
7. D. M. Mohilner, *J. Phys. Chem.*, **66**, 724 (1962).
8. F. O. Koenig, H. C. Wohlers, and D. Bandini, paper presented at the Moscow C.I.T.C.E. meeting, 1963.
9. G. Lippmann, *Ann. chim. phys.*, (5) **5**, 494 (1875).
10. D. C. Grahame, E. M. Coffin, J. I. Cummings, and M. A. Poth, *J. Am. Chem. Soc.*, **74**, 1207 (1952).
11. B. E. Conway and R. G. Barradas, *Electrochim. Acta*, **5**, 319 (1961).
12. R. S. Hansen, D. J. Kelsh, and D. H. Grantham, *J. Phys. Chem.*, **67**, 2316 (1963).
13. D. C. Grahame, R. P. Larsen, and M. A. Poth, *J. Am. Chem. Soc.*, **71**, 2978 (1949).
14. B. E. Conway, *Electrochemical Data*, Elsevier, Amsterdam, 1952, pp. 221–232.
15. J. E. B. Randles and K. S. Whiteley, *Trans. Faraday Soc.*, **52**, 1509 (1956).
16. D. C. Grahame and B. A. Soderberg, *J. Chem. Phys.*, **22**, 449 (1954).
17. E. Blomgren and J. O'M. Bockris, *J. Phys. Chem.*, **63**, 1475 (1959).
18. R. Parsons, *Proc. Second. Int. Congress Surface Activity*, Butterworths, London, **3**, 38 (1957).
19. G. Gouy, *Ann. phys.*, (9), **6**, 3 (1916); (9) **7**, 129 (1917).
20. M. Proskurnin and A. N. Frumkin, *Trans. Faraday Soc.*, **31**, 110 (1935).
21. D. C. Grahame, *J. Am. Chem. Soc.*, **63**, 1207 (1941).
22. D. C. Grahame, *ibid.*, **68**, 301 (1946).
23. D. C. Grahame, *ibid.*, **71**, 2975 (1949).
24. D. C. Grahame, *J. Phys. Chem.*, **61**, 701 (1957).
25. V. I. Melik-Gaikazyan, *Zhur. Fiz. Khim.*, **26**, 560 (1952).
26. W. Lorenz, *Z. physik. Chem.* (*Frankfurt*), **26**, 424 (1960).
27. M. A. V. Devanathan and P. Peries, *Trans. Faraday Soc.*, **50**, 1236 (1954).
28. D. C. Grahame and R. Parsons, *J. Am. Chem. Soc.*, **83**, 1291 (1961).
29. M. A. V. Devanathan and S. G. Canagaratna, *Electrochim. Acta*, **8**, 77 (1963).

CHAPTER 3

Structure of the Diffuse Double Layer in the Absence of Specific Adsorption

3-1 The Gouy-Chapman Theory

Thermodynamic analysis of the double layer yields the relative ionic surface excesses but cannot, by its very nature, give any information about ionic distribution. A model is necessary for this purpose. The early model of Helmholtz (1) and Quincke (2), in which the double layer is considered as a parallel plate capacitor, is highly simplified. The model advocated independently by Gouy (3, 4) and Chapman (5) is still, after modification by Stern (6), the basis of our present understanding of the double layer. The Gouy-Chapman theory bears close resemblance to the Debye-Hückel theory of electrolytes which, in fact, it preceded by a decade. The Gouy-Chapman-Stern model is discussed in this chapter with its implications and experimental verification of its validity. Modifications of this theory and the statistical treatment of the double layer are mentioned at the end of the chapter. Complications arising from specific adsorption are covered in Chapter 4. Reviews by Grahame (7), Parsons (8), and Overbeek (9) are available. The historical background was summarized by Grahame (7).

We can assume equilibrium between any point in the double layer and the bulk of the solution for an ideal polarized electrode. Hence we have for ionic species i

$$\bar{\mu}_i = \bar{\mu}_i^s \tag{1}$$

where $\bar{\mu}_i$ and $\bar{\mu}_i^s$ are the electrochemical potentials of species i in the double layer and in the bulk of the solution, respectively. We write Eq. 1

33

in the *approximate* form

$$c_i = c_i^s e^{-z_i f \phi} \tag{2}$$

with

$$f = \frac{F}{RT} \tag{3}$$

There, c_i and c_i^s are the concentrations of ions i at x and in the bulk of the solution, respectively; z_i is the ionic valence (with sign) of ions i; and ϕ is the potential at x with respect to the potential ϕ_s in the bulk of solution. ϕ_s is set at zero for the sake of convenience. The coordinate x is the distance from the electrode. For the time being x can have any value, however small it might be, but we shall amend this statement. Equation 2 corresponds to a Boltzmann distribution on the assumption that the work being done to bring ion i from outside the double layer at the point of coordinate x is $z_i f \phi$. This is a simplification of the actual state of affairs (see Sec. 3-6).

The Poisson equation gives the necessary correlation between c_i and ϕ. Thus

$$\frac{d^2\phi}{dx^2} = -\frac{4\pi\rho}{\epsilon} \tag{4}$$

where ρ is the charge density per unit volume and ϵ the dielectric constant. We also have

$$\rho = \sum z_i F c_i \tag{5}$$

The combination of Eqs. 2, 4, and 5 yields

$$\frac{d^2\phi}{dx^2} = -\frac{4\pi}{\epsilon} \sum z_i F c_i^s e^{-z_i f \phi} \tag{6}$$

This equation is readily solved for ϕ provided it is assumed that ϵ is independent of x. We shall make this assumption although it is really not valid because of dielectric saturation in the double layer (Sec. 3-6). It turns out, however, that this oversimplification has no disastrous consequences. By multiplying both members of Eq. 6 by $2d\,\phi/dx$ and by integrating once we find, after noting that $\phi \to 0$ and $d\phi/dx \to 0$ for $x \to \infty$,

$$\left(\frac{d\phi}{dx}\right)^2 = \frac{8\pi RT}{\epsilon} \sum c_i^s (e^{-z_i f \phi} - 1) \tag{7}$$

The charge q on the electrode per unit area is related to $d\phi/dx$ by the Gauss theorem, that is,

$$4\pi q = -\epsilon \left(\frac{d\phi}{dx}\right)_{x_2} \tag{8}$$

We should take the value of $d\phi/dx$ at $x = 0$, but anticipating the discussion of the next section, we rather write x_2. Similarly, we write $\phi = \phi_{x_2}$ for $x = x_2$ rather then $\phi_{x=0}$ in the following equation. By combination of Eqs. 7 and 8 we deduce

$$q = \pm \left[\frac{RT\epsilon}{2\pi} \sum c_i^s (e^{-z_i f \phi_2} - 1) \right]^{\frac{1}{2}} \tag{9}$$

Equation 9 allows the calculation of q as a function of ϕ or vice versa. It should be emphasized that specific adsorption was not considered, and the foregoing treatment, in its present form, is not valid when there is specific adsorption (cf. Chapter 4).

Equation 9 takes the following form for a $z - z$ electrolyte of concentration c^s

$$q = +2A \sinh \left(\frac{|z| f \phi_2}{2} \right) \tag{10}$$

$$A = +\left(\frac{RT\epsilon c^s}{2\pi} \right)^{\frac{1}{2}} \tag{11}$$

or for aqueous solutions at 25°C (7)

$$q = 11.74(c^s)^{\frac{1}{2}} \sinh (19.46 |z| \phi_2)$$

where q is in microcoulombs per square centimeter, c^s in moles per liter, and ϕ in volts. See Grahame (11) for detailed calculations for unsymmetrical electrolytes.

The interfacial tension can be deduced from Eq. 9 by integration of Eq. 2-11. The resulting interfacial tension variations with potential are in complete disagreement with experiment, as was shown by Frumkin (12), and it can be concluded that the Gouy-Chapman theory in its original form is not satisfactory.

3-2   Stern's Modification of the Gouy-Chapman Theory and its Experimental Verification

Ions are treated as point charges in the Gouy-Chapman theory, and are supposed to approach the electrode within any distance however small it might be. The corresponding calculated capacity is thus much higher than it actually is for ions of finite size, and abnormally large values of q are thus predicted by Eq. 9. Gouy (13) had already noted this oversimplification, but it was Stern (6) who made this point very clear. Stern postulated that ions cannot reach the electrode beyond the *plane of closest approach*. He also assumed that this plane of closest approach is the same for cations and anions although he indicated in a footnote, as

Grahame points out (10) that this assumption might not be valid. We shall see in Chapter 4 that indeed two planes of closest approach must be distinguished, but a model with a single plane will suffice in this chapter.

The double layer can now be divided into two regions: the *compact double layer* comprised between the electrode and the plane of closest approach and the *diffuse double layer* extending from the plane of closest approach to the bulk of the solution. The compact double layer is also referred to as *Helmholtz double layer* or *inner double layer*. The difference of potential ϕ_M between the metal and solution ($\phi_s = 0$ by convention) can now be divided into two parts (7, 8)

$$\phi_M = (\phi_M - \phi_2) + \phi_2 \tag{12}$$

where ϕ_2 is the potential in the plane of closest approach. We use the subscript "2," for we shall use later the subscript "1" for a second plane which is closer to the electrode than the one we consider here. Thus

$$\frac{\partial \phi_M}{\partial q} = \frac{\partial(\phi_M - \phi_2)}{\partial q} + \frac{\partial \phi_2}{\partial q}$$

or

$$\frac{1}{C} = \frac{1}{C_{M-2}} + \frac{1}{C_{2-s}} \tag{13}$$

where C is the double-layer differential capacity and C_{M-2} and C_{2-s} are the differential capacities corresponding to the compact and diffuse double layers, respectively. It is seen that the double layer can be regarded as two capacitors in series. The Gouy-Chapman theory allows only calculation of the capacity C_{2-s}, and this is at least one good reason for disagreement between experiment and the predictions of this theory. The differential capacity C_{2-s} is directly obtained by differentiation of Eq. 9 with respect to ϕ_2. One has for a $z - z$ electrolyte (cf. Eq. 10)

$$C_{2-s} = |z| fA \cosh\left(\frac{|z| f\phi_2}{2}\right) \tag{14}$$

or for aqueous solutions at 25°C (7)

$$C_{2-s} = 228.5 |z| (c^s)^{\frac{1}{2}} \cosh(19.46 |z| \phi_2)$$

where C_{2-s} is in microfarads per square centimeter, ϕ_2 in volts, and C^s in moles per liter.

In order to test the validity of the Gouy-Chapman theory, as modified by Stern, it is necessary to know C_{M-2}. We can measure the capacity C of Eq. 13 and deduce q by integration from E_z to E (cf. Eq. 2-23). The value of ϕ_2 corresponding to q, on the basis of the Gouy-Chapman theory, can then be computed from Eq. 9 (or Eq. 10 for a $z - z$ electrolyte), and the capacity C_{2-s} can be deduced from Eq. 14. All necessary quantities are available for the verification of Eq. 13 except C_{M-2} which is not accessible to experimental determination. We could postulate a given value of C_{M-2} as a palliative, and carry out this procedure. A better approximation is achieved if we set a somewhat higher value of C_{M-2} for markedly positive values of $E - E_z$ than for markedly negative values. This approach was followed by Frumkin (14) for potassium chloride in the range 10^{-4} to $10^{-1}M$. Calculated C versus E curves agreed very approximately with experiment, but the fit was far from good. This work was important, for it showed that the Gouy-Chapman theory, duly modified by Stern, gave capacities which were not too far from the experimental values.

Stronger evidence about the validity of the Gouy-Chapman theory was obtained by Grahame (7) by assuming that the capacity of the compact layer depends only on the charge on the electrode and not on electrolyte concentration. No particular value of C_{M-2} was postulated by Grahame, but this capacity was calculated from experimental values of C and from values of C_{2-s} that were computed from the Gouy-Chapman theory. The capacity C_{M-2} was computed for a concentrated electrolyte solution since C_{2-s} is then much higher than C_{M-2}, at least for potentials not too near the point of zero charge. (C_{2-s} increases with the square root of the electrolyte concentration; cf. Eqs. 11 and 14.) An electrolyte that exhibits as little specific adsorption as possible must be selected. Grahame adopted sodium fluoride in his work, for there is hardly any shift of the point of zero charge for this electrolyte when its concentration varies (Table 2-1). This criterion, based on the dependence of E_z on concentration, might not be very sensitive to slight specific adsorption (Sec. 4-1), but the rather good agreement with experiment obtained by Grahame in his verification of the Gouy-Chapman theory provided some additional indirect evidence that sodium fluoride is not strongly specifically adsorbed, at least for not highly positive potentials.

The first comparison between theory and experiment was reported by Grahame in 1947 (7). In two subsequent papers (1954 and 1957) he utilized more accurate experimental data at 25°C (15) than in 1947 and investigated the effect of temperature (16). Results are summarized in Figs. 3-1 to 3-5 from which we note the following points: (a) The influence of the diffuse double layer on the total capacity is indeed quite small, especially for E not too near E_z (Fig. 3-1). (b) The capacity of the compact double layer varies markedly with the charge on the electrode (Fig. 3-2), and the previous attempt (14) to verify the theory on the assumption of a constant capacity C_{M-2} could only be tentative. The variations of C_{M-2} with q are interpreted in Chapter 4. (c) Agreement between experimental and calculated capacities is very good, except at the more positive potentials at

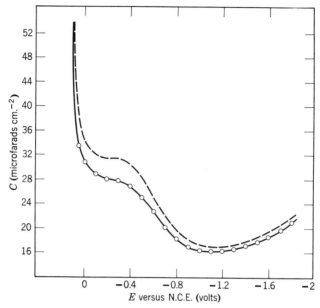

FIG. 3-1. Differential capacity of mercury in $0.916M$ sodium fluoride at $25°C$. Dashed line represents the differential capacity C_{M-2} of the compact double layer [Grahame (15)] (by permission of the American Chemical Society).

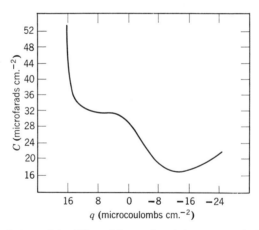

FIG. 3-2. Variations of the differential capacity of the compact double layer with the charge on the electrode. Calculated from data for $0.916M$ sodium fluoride in Fig. 3-1 [Grahame (15)] (by permission of the American Chemical Society).

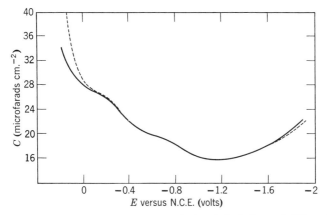

FIG. 3-3. Experimental (solid curve) and calculated (dashed curve) differential capacities of mercury in $0.1M$ sodium fluoride at 25°C [Grahame (15)] (by permission of
the American Chemical Society).

all concentrations and for the $0.001M$ solution on both sides of the point
of zero charge. Specific adsorption of fluoride ion at the more positive
potentials is possibly one cause of discrepancy. The difference between
experiment and theory for the $0.001M$ solution is probably caused, in a
major part, by experimental errors, according to Grahame (15). The
conductivity of such a solution is quite low and measurements are
increasingly inaccurate as the capacity becomes higher. (d) The capacity-
potential curve exhibits a V-shaped segment which becomes less pronounced and ultimately disappears with increasing concentrations. The

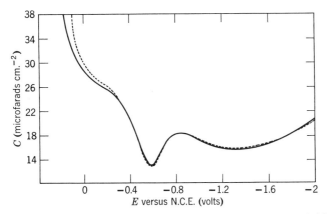

FIG. 3-4. Same results as in Fig. 3-3 but for $0.01M$ sodium fluoride at 25°C [Grahame
(15)] (by permission of the American Chemical Society).

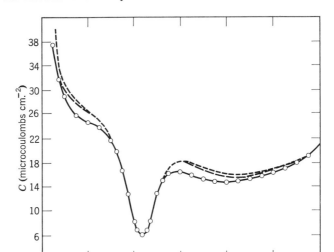

FIG. 3-5. Same results as in Fig. 3-3 but for $0.001 M$ sodium fluoride at $25°C$. See Ref. 15 for the details about calculated curves. Points are experimental capacities [Grahame (15)] (by permission of the American Chemical Society).

V-shaped segment corresponds to a predominant influence of the diffuse double-layer capacity whose dependence on ϕ_2 (cf. Eq. 14) indeed corresponds to this shape of curve. The minimum of the capacity-potential curve occurs at the point of zero charge for dilute solutions of $z - z$ electrolytes but not for $z - z'$ electrolytes (11).

An elegant way of comparing experiment with the predictions of the Gouy-Chapman theory was recently proposed independently by de Levie (54) and Parsons (55). These authors apply Eq. 13 at constant charge and plot $1/C$ against $1/C_{2-s}$ where C is the experimental capacity and C_{2-s} is calculated as a function of the charge from the Gouy-Chapman theory. A straight line of unit slope must be obtained for each value of the charge regardless of the concentration if C_{M-2} only depends on the charge and provided there is no specific adsorption. The intercept is $1/C_{M-2}$.

The previous theory can also be applied to the prediction of properties of the double layer other than the capacity, for example, the variation of E_+ at the point of zero charge with electrolyte concentration. We shall discuss this matter in Sec. 4-1.

It can be concluded from Grahame's work that the Gouy-Chapman theory predicts results which are in excellent agreement with theory provided the capacity of the compact double layer is considered. It also follows from this work that the capacity of the compact double layer depends solely on the charge on the electrode and not on the electrolyte concentration. These conclusions were reached for an electrolyte (sodium fluoride) exhibiting little specific adsorption, except probably for high positive charges on the electrode. We shall see in Chapter 4 how to apply the Gouy-Chapman theory when there is specific adsorption. It must be recognized, however, that the contribution of the diffuse double layer at high electrode charges is relatively minor, even in dilute solution, and that the excellent agreement obtained by Grahame should not lead one to conclude that the Gouy-Chapman theory is as satisfactory for a high electrode charge as it is near the point of zero charge. This point is clearly made by Joshi and Parsons (17).

3-3   Distribution of Potential

The Gouy-Chapman theory allows the calculation of the difference of potential ϕ between any point at $x \geqslant x_2$ and a point in the bulk of the solution. It suffices to integrate Eq. 7. However, we shall discuss first the calculation of the potential ϕ_2 in the plane of closest approach which was already outlined in Sec. 3-2. The method of calculation holds in the absence of specific adsorption. (See Chapter 4 for the opposite case.)

The charge on the electrode q is obtained (a) either from electro-capillary curves and application of Eq. 2-11 or (b) from differential capacity measurements together with Eq. 2-21. Conversely, the charge q is expressed as a function of ϕ_2 by Eq. 9 (or Eq. 10 for a $z - z$ electrolyte). Thus $q = f(E)$ is known from experiment and $q = f(\phi_2)$ is computed from theory. The dependence $\phi_2 = f(E)$ follows (Fig. 3-6). Extensive tables of ϕ_2 for sodium fluoride were computed by Russell (18) from Grahame's data (15). We have $\phi_2 \gtrless 0$ for $E \gtrless E_z$, and $|\phi_2|$ increases with $|E - E_z|$. This is to be expected since the perturbation of the ionic distribution by the electrode charge becomes more pronounced when $|q|$, that is, $|E - E_z|$ increases. At $E = E_z$, $q = 0$ and $\phi_2 = 0$, for there is no perturbation by the electrode on the ionic distribution. $|\phi_2|$ at a given E increases with decreasing electrolyte concentration. The $\phi_2 - E$ curves are not symmetrical with respect to E_z because $|q|$ rises more quickly with potential for $E > E_z$ than for $E < E_z$ (see Fig. 2-2).

It should be realized that values of ϕ_2 obtained by this method are *average* potentials based on the Gouy-Chapman theory. All the simplifications introduced in this theory, and in particular the treatment of ions as points carrying a charge, are in some way reflected in the potential ϕ_2.

In addition to the foregoing procedure for the calculation of ϕ_2, this potential was computed by Macdonald and Barlow (52) in the course of a detailed analysis of the compact double layer. Values of ϕ_2 for sodium

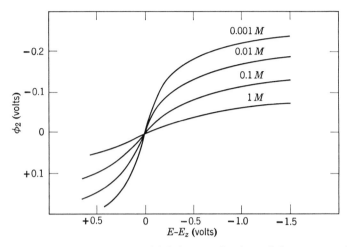

FIG. 3-6. Variations of the potential ϕ_2 between the plane of closest approach and the bulk of the solution with $E - E_z$ for the mercury in sodium fluoride solutions at 25°C. Calculated from Grahame's data (15, 16) [Parsons (19)] (by permission of Interscience).

fluoride, as computed from Grahame's data (15, 16), are not very different from those of Fig. 3-6 and are probably more accurate.

The relationship between ϕ_2 and the electrolyte concentration at constant potential E is not a simple one. An *approximate* relationship is obtained if we consider that q is independent of E (which really is not the case; see Fig. 2-2). Then for $\phi_2 < 0.1$ volt the exponential term $e^{|z|f\phi_2/2}$ in Eq. 10 (for a $z - z$ electrolyte) can be dropped. Conversely, $e^{-|z|f\phi_2/2}$ almost vanishes for $\phi_2 > 0.1$ volt. If q is supposed to be constant, Eq. 10 yields

$$\phi_2 = \text{constant} \pm \frac{1}{|z|f} \ln c^s \qquad (15)$$

where the $\pm$ sign holds for $\phi_2 \lessgtr 0$, respectively. Figure 3-7 shows that this relationship holds fairly well for sufficiently positive or negative values of $E - E_z$. Equation 15 was applied in early investigations by Frumkin and his school on the correlation between electrode kinetics (H^+ discharge on mercury especially) and double-layer structure when no accurate data on double layer properties were available. The more accurate method of computing ϕ_2 as just outlined is now universally applied.

We now consider the distribution of potential in the diffuse double layer and only quote the final result of the derivation of the potential ϕ. Details can be found in several reviews (7-9) but are not given here because they are purely mathematical in nature. The potential at any point in the diffuse double layer is

$$\phi = \frac{4}{|z|f} \tanh^{-1} e^{p - \kappa(x - x_2)} \tag{16}$$

with

$$p = \ln \tanh \left[\frac{|z| f \phi_2}{4} \right] + \kappa x_2$$

$$\kappa = + \left(\frac{8\pi z^2 F f c^s}{\epsilon} \right)^{\frac{1}{2}}$$

where x is the distance from the plane of closest approach and κ is the Debye-Hückel reciprocal length. The potential ϕ decreases almost exponentially with distance from the plane of closest approach (Fig. 3-8),

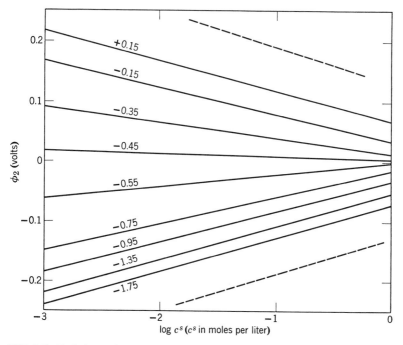

FIG. 3-7. Variations of the potential ϕ_2 between the plane of closest approach and the bulk of the solution with the logarithm of concentration for mercury in sodium fluoride solution at 25°C. Potentials referred to a normal calomel electrode. Dashed lines correspond to the slopes given by Eq. 15. Plotted from Russell's tables (18).

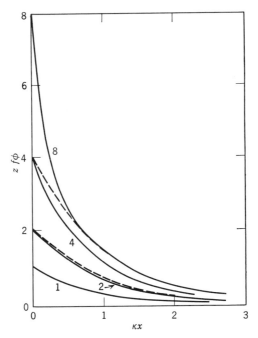

FIG. 3-8. Variations of $|z|\, f\phi$ with κx for different values of $|z|\, f\phi_2$. Dotted curve drawn according to Eq. 17 [Overbeek (9)] (by permission of Elsevier).

especially at low values of ϕ. Equation 16 in the latter case takes the simplified form

$$\phi \approx \phi_2 e^{-\kappa x} \tag{17}$$

after linearization of exponentials. It follows from Eq. 17 that the diffuse double layer can be characterized by a "thickness" $1/\kappa$ which, for aqueous solutions at room temperature, is of the order of $[3.10^7\, |z|\, (c^s)^{1/2}]^{-1}$ cm. with c^s in moles per liter. We have $1/\kappa \approx 10^{-6}$ and 3×10^{-8} cm. for $|z| = 1$ and $c^s = 10^{-3}$ and $1M$, respectively. We shall refer to the double-layer thickness when discussing mass transfer in electrode processes (Chapter 7).

The field strength in the plane of closest approach is readily obtained by combining Eqs. 8 and 10 ($z - z$ electrolytes). Equation 8 yields for aqueous solutions at 25°C (7)

$$\left(\frac{d\phi}{dx}\right)_{\phi=\phi_2} = -1.44 \times 10^5 q \text{ volts cm.}^{-1}$$

where q is in microcoulombs per square centimeter. The field strength in the plane of closest approach may reach 10^6 volts cm.$^{-1}$ or even higher values, and there is dielectric saturation. We shall return to this point in Sec. 3-6.

3-4   Ionic Concentrations in the Plane of Closest Approach and Ionic Contributions of the Diffuse Double Layer to the Total Charge

Ionic concentrations in the diffuse double layer can be calculated at this stage of the theory as functions of the distance from the plane of closest approach. It suffices to introduce into Eq. 2 the value of ϕ given by Eq. 16. It is more useful to calculate the contributions that cations and anions in the diffuse double layer make to the total charge on the solution side. These contributions will be needed in Chapter 4 to compute the amount of specifically adsorbed ions from ionic surface excesses. Before we proceed with the calculations of these contributions we shall compute the ionic concentrations in the plane of closest approach. Knowledge of these concentrations is of paramount importance in electrode kinetics, as we shall see in Chapter 9.

The ionic concentration c_i^2 in the plane of closest approach is immediately given by Eq. 2 in which ϕ is made equal to ϕ_2. Thus

$$c_i^{\,2} = c_i^{\,s} e^{-z_i f \phi_2} \tag{18}$$

There is attraction or repulsion, that is, $c_i^{\,2} \gtrless c_i^{\,s}$, when $z_i \phi_2 \lessgtr 0$. Since $\phi_2 \gtrless 0$ when $E \gtrless E_z$, cations are attracted for $E < E_z$ and are repelled for $E > E_z$ in the absence of specific adsorption. The effect is quite pronounced for $|\phi_2|$ can be as high as 0.2 volt in dilute solutions. The concentration c^2 of a strongly attracted ion can be almost independent of c^s for a single $z - z$ electrolyte ($E = -1.75$ volts, Table 3-1). The solubility for a $z - z$ electrolyte is not exceeded despite such a high electrostatic attraction because the exponential factors containing ϕ_2 for the anion and cation cancel out. This, however, is not necessarily true when there is specific adsorption, but no experimental information seems to be available on this point. One should keep in mind that the data of Table 3-1 are affected by all the approximations of the Gouy-Chapman theory. Actual concentrations may be significantly different from the calculated values, especially for large $|\phi_2|$'s.

We now turn to the derivation, according to Grahame (7), of the contributions that cations and anions make to the total charge on the solution side. These ionic components are for a $z - z$ electrolyte

$$q_+^{2-s} = \int_{x_2}^{\infty} (\rho_+ - z_+ F c^s) \, dx$$

$$q_-^{2-s} = \int_{x_2}^{\infty} (\rho_- - z_- F c^s) \, dx$$

where ρ_+ and ρ_- are the charge densities per unit volume of solution. In

TABLE 3-1   Concentration of Na^+ and F^- in the Plane of Closest Approach for NaF in Contact with Mercury at 25°C

Potential, volts versus N.C.E.	Bulk concentration, mole l^{-1}	Potential $\phi_2{}^a$, volts	$c_2^{Na^+}$ mole l^{-1}	$c_2^{F^-}$ mole l^{-1}
−1.75	0.001	−0.241	11.8	8.46×10^{-8}
	0.01	−0.184	13.1	7.62×10^{-6}
	0.1	−0.128	14.8	6.76×10^{-4}
	1	−0.074	18.1	5.52×10^{-2}
−1.35	0.001	−0.22	5.27	$1.9 \ \times 10^{-7}$
	0.01	−0.164	6.04	1.63×10^{-5}
	0.1	−0.109	7.03	1.42×10^{-3}
	1	−0.058	9.62	1.04×10^{-1}
−0.95	0.001	−0.187	1.45	6.89×10^{-7}
	0.01	−0.135	1.90	5.26×10^{-5}
	0.1	−0.0829	2.53	3.96×10^{-3}
	1	−0.039	4.56	2.19×10^{-1}
−0.55	0.001	−0.066	1.31×10^{-2}	7.64×10^{-5}
	0.01	−0.041	5.00×10^{-2}	2.00×10^{-3}
	0.1	−0.021	2.21×10^{-1}	4.42×10^{-2}
	1	−0.0085	1.41	7.18×10^{-1}
−0.45	0.001	+0.141	5.78×10^{-4}	1.73×10^{-3}
	0.01	+0.134	5.93×10^{-3}	1.69×10^{-2}
	0.1	+0.067	7.70×10^{-2}	1.30×10^{-1}
	1	+0.0024	9.11×10^{-1}	1.10

[a] From Russell's tables (18).

view of Eqs. 2 and 5 we have

$$\rho_+ = z_+ F c^s e^{-z_+ f\phi}$$

Hence

$$q_+^{2-s} = z_+ F c^s \int_{x_2}^{\infty} (e^{-z_+ f\phi} - 1) \, dx$$

In order to eliminate the variable x and integrate with respect to ϕ, we write the preceding equation in the form

$$q_+^{2-s} = z_+ F c^s \int_{x_2}^{\infty} (e^{-2z_+ f\phi} - 2e^{-z_+ f\phi} + 1)^{\frac{1}{2}} \, dx$$

$$= z_+ F c^s \int_{x_2}^{\infty} ((e^{z_+ f\phi} + e^{-z_+ f\phi} - 2)e^{-z_+ f\phi})^{\frac{1}{2}} \, dx$$

By noting that Eq. 10 can be put in the form

$$q = A(e^{z_+ + f\phi/2} - e^{-z_+ + f\phi/2})$$

$$= A(e^{z_+ + f\phi} + e^{z_+ + f\phi} - 2)^{\frac{1}{2}}$$

we obtain

$$q_+^{2-s} = -z_+ F \int_{x_2}^{\infty} q \left(\frac{2\pi c^s}{\epsilon RT} e^{-z_+ + f\phi} \right)^{\frac{1}{2}} dx$$

which yields upon combination with Eq. 8

$$q_+^{2-s} = -z_+ F \int_{\phi_2}^{0} \left(\frac{\epsilon c^s}{8\pi RT} e^{-z_+ + f\phi} \right)^{\frac{1}{2}} d\phi$$

After integration

$$q_+^{2-s} = A(e^{-z_+ + f\phi_2/2} - 1) \tag{19}$$

where A is defined by Eq. 11. Similarly,

$$q_-^{2-s} = -A(e^{-z_- - f\phi_2/2} - 1) \tag{20}$$

We have $q_+^{2-s} = q_-^{2-s} = 0$ for $\phi_2 = 0$, as one would expect at the point of zero charge. Furthermore, $q_+^{2-s}/q_-^{2-s} \approx +1$ for $|\phi_2| \ll z_+ f$; $q_+^{2-s} \to \infty$ for $\phi_2 \to -\infty$ and $q_-^{2-s} \to -\infty$ for $\phi_2 \to +\infty$; $q_+^{2-s} \to -A$ for $\phi_2 \to +\infty$ and $q_-^{2-s} \to A$ for $\phi_2 \to -\infty$. In the absence of specific adsorption we have $q_+^{2-s} = Z_+ F \Gamma_+$ and $q_-^{2-s} = z_- F \Gamma_-$, and therefore Γ_- and Γ_+ reach limiting values for the conditions just stated for q_+^{2-s} and q_-^{2-s}. This is essentially the case for Γ_- in Fig. 2-4 at potentials which are so negative that there is no anion specific adsorption and only minor specific adsorption of cations (at least for the electrolytes of this diagram). Experimental values of the limiting Γ_- in Fig. 2-4 agree quite well with calculated surface excesses. This situation is complicated for $E > E_z$ in Fig. 2-5 because of anion specific adsorption, but Γ_+ in fluoride medium also begins to approach a limiting value. Data on fluoride are not given for sufficiently positive potentials to ascertain whether or not a limiting value is reached, and there is possibly specific adsorption of fluoride at markedly positive potentials.

3-5 Mixed Electrolytes

It was pointed out at the end of Sec. 3-2 that double-layer capacity measurements do not provide a very sensitive test of the Gouy-Chapman theory for high charges on the electrode. Joshi and Parsons (17), who made this point, investigated mixtures of hydrochloric acid and barium chloride to test the theory for high electrode charges. This system was selected because activity coefficients are available. They determined the relative

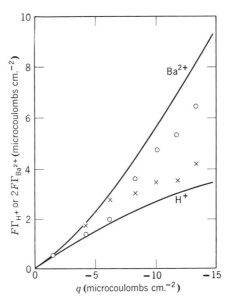

FIG. 3-9. Relative surface excesses (expressed as charges) of Ba^{++} (circles) and H^+ (crosses) against charge on the electrode for mercury in $0.2M$ hydrochloric acid plus $0.05M$ barium chloride. Curves calculated from the Gouy-Chapman theory [Joshi and Parsons (17)] (by permission of Pergamon).

surface excesses of H^+ and Ba^{++} from electrocapillary curves, and compared the results with the values predicted by the Gouy-Chapman theory for $0 > q > -13$ microcoulombs cm.$^{-2}$ (Fig. 3-9). Specific adsorption was not considered, but a number of possible causes for the discrepancy between theory and experiment, which is beyond experimental errors, were considered. No completely satisfactory explanation could be given, but it appears that the main cause of discrepancy is the difference of the planes of closest approach for Ba^{++} and H^+. The former ion is the larger of the two, and is more solvated than H^+. This causes $\Gamma_{Ba^{++}}$ to be smaller than predicted by theory and conversely Γ_{H^+} is larger than predicted. This is indeed the case (Fig. 3-9). Calculation of the effect of ionic size were made by Joshi and Parsons who also point out the need for a three-dimensional solution of the Poisson equation instead of the one-dimensional solution now available.

This work is important because it called attention to the necessity of considering differences in the planes of closest approach in mixed electrolytes as a possible cause of departure from theory. Such a difference must be kept in mind in applying the Gouy-Chapman theory in the correlation between double-layer theory and electrode kinetics (Chapter 9).

3-6   Modifications of the Gouy-Chapman Theory and Statistical Theories of the Double Layer

A number of modifications of the Gouy-Chapman theory have been proposed to eliminate some of the shortcomings of the very simple model on which it rests. Saturation of the dielectric, which is neglected in the solution of the Poisson equation, was considered by several authors (20–25, 53). Brodowsky and Strehlow (24) also considered, aside from saturation, the variation of dielectric constant with electrolyte concentration. The dielectric saturation is very pronounced at the field strength prevailing in the plane of closest approach (Fig. 3-10), but Grahame (20) concluded that its influence on measurable properties of the double layer is probably quite small. The comparison between experiment and theory of Sec. 3-2 seems to support this view. The conclusion of the rather qualitative analysis of Grahame is also supported by Macdonald's detailed quantitative treatment (53).

Attempts were also made to correct the Gouy-Chapman theory for the finite size of ions (23, 24, 27). The effect of ionic size on the potential ϕ_2, for instance, is quite pronounced (24) when the charge on the metal exceeds 10 microcoulombs cm.$^{-2}$, and the corresponding departure from

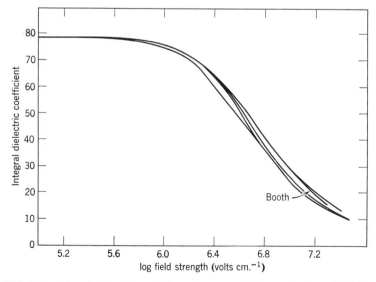

FIG. 3-10. Integral dielectric coefficient of water at 25°C as a function of field strength according to different equations given by Grahame (20) and Booth (26) [Grahame (21)] (by permission of the American Institute of Physics).

the simple Gouy-Chapman theory is relatively much greater for concentrated electrolytes ($1M$) than for dilute ones ($0.01M$). Experimental evidence supporting the validity of this correction might possibly be obtained from correlation between double-layer structure and electrode kinetics (Chapter 9). Other interactions have also been considered (28–30). Hurwitz, Sanfeld, and Steinchen-Sanfeld recently embodied the preceding corrections in a rather rigorous treatment (51) and indicated the experimental implications of their analysis.

The foregoing modifications of the Gouy-Chapman theory have their points, but a fundamentally new approach may be more fruitful, just as for the Debye-Hückel theory of electrolytes. The work of Stillinger and Kirkwood (31) and previous application of statistical mechanics to electrolytes may have provided the breakthrough in theory that allowed further advances by Levich and Krylov (32–34) and Buff and Stillinger (35). [See also the earlier summary by Levich and Kir'yanov (36).] These theories are applicable up to concentrations of $1M$ and perhaps even to higher concentrations. They lead to the conclusion that the potential ϕ for $x > x_2$ is smaller and falls off more rapidly than predicted by the Gouy-Chapman theory. Buff and Stillinger apply more general methods of statistical mechanics than Levich and Krylov but at the cost of mathematical difficulties. Application by Krylov and Levich was first made to the double layer at a dielectric-solution interface (33) and then to metal-electrolyte interfaces. (Reference 34 is not available in English translation as of this writing.) It would be of considerable interest to compare theoretical potentials ϕ_2 with the values deduced from experiment by correlation of electrode kinetics with double-layer structure (Chapter 9).

3-7   Relaxation of the Diffuse Double Layer and the Question of Frequency Dependence

The diffuse double layer should exhibit relaxation similar to the Falkenhagen relaxation of an ionic atmosphere, as was shown by Ferry (37). The corresponding frequencies are well outside the range of presently available methods, and the theory has not been verified. Since it is analogous to the corresponding treatment for electrolytes, which has been thoroughly tested, Ferry's analysis is undoubtedly satisfactory. Experimental verification, if measurements could be made, might be difficult because of complications introduced by relaxation of the compact double layer. Measurements by Melik-Gaikazyan (38) up to 200 kc showed no frequency dependence of the double-layer capacity, and the same conclusion seems to follow from Barker's study of double-layer rectification up to 1.6 Mc (39).

Some frequency dependence of the double-layer impedance is observed for the usual dropping mercury electrode at low frequencies (for example 100 c.p.s. to 10 kc). [For the equivalent effect in pulse techniques see Lorenz (50).] Grahame (40) concluded that the major cause of frequency dependence was the shielding of the mercury drop by the tip of the capillary. Frequency dependence was considerably reduced with a capillary having a fine tip (1 mm. diameter). Recent model calculations by Susbielle s (49) indicate that the frequency dependence of the measured capacity shoud be quite negligible under such conditions, even at frequencies as high as 1 Mc. Wetting of the inside wall of the capillary by creeping of solution definitely causes frequency dependence of the measured capacity, as was first shown by Rozental and Ershler (41). The phenomena occurring during the periodic formation of a drop at a dropping mercury electrode have been studied in detail (42–44), and the use of tapered capillaries was advocated (43). Barker (42) and Grantham (44) examined the electrode frequency response on the basis of a transmission line model with distributed capacity and resistance and found a frequency of the corresponding impedance. This matter is discussed further by de Levie (48). Grantham was able to eliminate the frequency dependence of the double-layer capacity with Desicote-coated glass capillaries. Teflon capillaries (47) might be considered to avoid solution creeping in conventional double-layer capacity measurements and the danger of contamination by such a coating as Desicote. Explanation (45, 46) of the supposed frequency dependence by water relaxation does not seem necessary for the effect is purely an experimental artefact at the frequencies usually prevailing in such measurements.

REFERENCES

1. H. L. F. von Helmholtz, *Ann. Physik*, (2), **89**, 211 (1853); (3), **7**, 337 (1879).
2. G. Quincke, *Pogg. Ann.*, **113**, 513 (1861).
3. G. Gouy, *J. phys. radium*, (4), **9**, 457 (1910).
4. G. Gouy, *Compt. rend.*, **149**, 654 (1910).
5. D. L. Chapman, *Phil. Mag.*, (6), **25**, 475 (1913).
6. O. Stern, *Z. Elektrochem.*, **30**, 508 (1924).
7. D. C. Grahame, *Chem. Revs.*, **41**, 441 (1947).
8. R. Parsons, *Modern Aspects of Electrochemistry*, Vol. 1, J. O'M. Bockris, editor, Butterworths, London, 1954, pp. 103–179.
9. J. T. G. Overbeek, *Colloid Science*, Vol. 1, H. R. Kruyt, editor, Elsevier, Amsterdam, 1952, pp. 115–193.
10. D. C. Grahame, *Z. Elektrochem.*, **59**, 773 (1955).
11. D. C. Grahame, *J. Chem. Phys.*, **21**, 1054 (1953).
12. A. N. Frumkin, *Phil. Mag.*, (6), **40**, 375 (1920).
13. G. Gouy, *Ann. Phys., Paris*, **7**, 163 (1917).
14. A. N. Frumkin, *Trans. Faraday Soc.*, **36**, 117 (1940).

15. D. C. Grahame, *J. Am. Chem. Soc.*, **76**, 4819 (1954).
16. D. C. Grahame, *ibid.*, **79**, 2093 (1957).
17. K. M. Joshi and R. Parsons, *Electrochim. Acta.*, **4**, 129 (1961).
18. C. D. Russell, *J. Electroanal. Chem.*, **6**, 486 (1963). Potentials are referred to N.C.E. and not S.C.E., as stated erroneously.
19. R. Parsons, *Advances in Electrochemistry and Electrochemical Engineering*, Vol. 1, P. Delahay, editor, Interscience, New York, 1961, pp. 1–64.
20. D. C. Grahame, *J. Chem. Phys.*, **18**, 903 (1950).
21. D. C. Grahame, *ibid.*, **21**, 1054 (1953).
22. B. E. Conway, J. O'M. Bockris, and I. A. Ammar, *Trans. Faraday Soc.*, **47**, 756 (1951).
23. M. J. Sparnaay, *Rec. trav. chim.*, **77**, 872 (1958).
24. H. Brodowsky and H. Strehlow, *Z. Elektrochem.*, **63**, 262 (1959).
25. A. Sanfeld, A. Steinchen-Sanfeld, H. Hurwitz and R. Defay, *J. chim. phys.*, **59**, 139 (1962).
26. F. Booth, *J. Chem. Phys.*, **19**, 391 (1951).
27. V. Freise, *Z. Elektrochem.*, **56**, 822 (1952).
28. J. J. Bikerman, *Phil. Mag.*, (7), **33**, 884 (1942).
29. A. L. Loeb, *J. Colloid Sci.*, **6**, 75 (1951).
30. W. E. Williams, *Proc. Phys. Soc.*, **66A**, 372 (1953).
31. F. H. Stillinger and J. G. Kirkwood, *J. Chem. Phys.*, **33**, 1282 (1960).
32. V. G. Levich and V. S. Krylov, *Doklady Akad. Nauk S.S.S.R.*, **141**, 1403 (1961).
33. V. S. Krylov and V. G. Levich, *Zhur. Fiz. Khim.*, **37**, 106 (1963).
34. V. S. Krylov and V. G. Levich, *ibid.*, **37**, 2273 (1963).
35. F. P. Buff and F. H. Stillinger, *J. Chem. Phys.*, **39**, 1911 (1963).
36. V. G. Levich and V. A. Kir'yanov, *Doklady Akad. Nauk S.S.S.R.*, **131**, 1134 (1960).
37. J. D. Ferry, *J. Chem. Phys.*, **16**, 737 (1948).
38. V. I. Melik-Gaikazyan, *Zhur. Fiz. Khim.*, **26**, 560 (1952).
39. G. C. Barker, *Transactions of the Symposium on Electrode Processes*, E. Yeager, editor, Wiley, New York, 1961, pp. 325–365
40. D. C. Grahame, *J. Am. Chem. Soc.*, **68**, 301 (1946).
41. K. I. Rozental' and B. V. Ershler, *Zhur. Fiz. Khim.*, **22**, 1344 (1948).
42. G. C. Barker, *Anal. Chim. Acta.*, **18**, 118 (1958).
43. W. D. Cooke, M. T. Kelley, and D. J. Fisher, *Anal. Chem.*, **33**, 1209 (1961).
44. D. M. Grantham, Dissertation, Iowa State University (1962); *Diss. Abstr.*, **23**, 3646 (1963).
45. J. O'M. Bockris and B. E. Conway, *J. Chem. Phys.*, **28**, 716 (1958).
46. D. A. Hickson, Dissertation, Iowa, State University (1962); *Diss. Abstr.*, **19**, 2241 (1959).
47. H. P. Raaen, *Anal. Chem.*, **34**, 1714 (1962).
48. R. de Levie, *J. Electroanal. Chem.*, in press.
49. G. Susbielles, unpublished work.
50. W. Lorenz, *Z. physik Chem.* (*Leipzig*), **205**, 311 (1956).
51. H. D. Hurwitz, A. Sanfeld, and A. Steinchen-Sanfeld, *Electrochim. Acta*, **9**, 929 (1964).
52. J. R. Macdonald and C. A. Barlow, *J. Chem. Phys.*, **36**, 3062 (1962).
53. J. R. Macdonald, *ibid.*, **22**, 1857 (1954).
54. R. de Levie, personal communication.
55. R. Parsons, personal communication.

CHAPTER 4

Structure of the Double Layer with Specific Adsorption

4-1 Criteria for Specific Adsorption

a. The Esin and Markov Effect

It was pointed out in Sec. 2-2 that the point of zero charge, as measured against a given reference electrode (that is, in a cell with liquid junction), varies with electrolyte concentration when there is electrolyte specific adsorption. We examine this effect, according to Parsons (3), on the basis of Eq. 2-16, namely,

$$\left(\frac{\partial E_{\pm}}{\partial \mu}\right)_q = -\left(\frac{\partial \Gamma_{\mp}}{\partial q}\right)_\mu$$

at constant temperature, pressure, and electrode composition. There $E_{\pm}$ is the potential measured against a reference electrode which is reversible to the cation (E_+) or anion (E_-) in a cell without liquid junction. This equation gives the dependence of $E_{\pm}$ on the chemical potential μ of the electrolyte at constant charge, that is, the shift of the point of zero charge with electrolyte activity or, for that matter, the shift of any potential, at constant charge, along the electrocapillary curve as the electrolyte activity varies.

The preceding equation can be written as

$$\left(\frac{\partial E_{\pm}}{\partial \ln a}\right)_q = -\frac{1}{z_{\mp}f}\left(\frac{\partial q_{\mp}}{\partial q}\right)_a \tag{1}$$

$$f = \frac{F}{RT} \tag{2}$$

where a is the electrolyte activity and $q_\mp$ is the charge in solution contributed by anions (q_-) or cations (q_+). If a reference electrode of constant electrolyte activity is used, we have for a $z - z$ electrolyte upon variation of the activity of the electrolyte in contact with the ideal polarized electrode

$$E_r = E_\pm \pm \frac{1}{|z|f} \ln a_\pm + \text{constant}$$

provided the liquid junction potential is constant. There E_r is the potential measured against the reference electrode in a cell with liquid junction, and $a_\pm$ is the mean activity $[a_\pm = a^{\frac{1}{2}}$ for a $z - z$ electrolyte]. Equation 1 now becomes

$$\left(\frac{\partial E_r}{\partial \ln a_\pm^2}\right)_q = \pm \frac{1}{|z|f}\left[\left(\frac{\partial q_\mp}{\partial q}\right)_a + \frac{1}{2}\right] \tag{3}$$

It follows from Eqs. 1 and 3 that the shift of E_r with $\ln a$ (or $\ln a_\pm^2$) at constant q depends on $(\partial q_\mp/\partial q)_a$. In the absence of specific adsorption $q_\mp$ can be computed from the Gouy-Chapman theory, and comparison of experimental and predicted shifts of potential provides a means of verifying the validity of this theory. We have in the absence of specific adsorption (cf. Eqs. 3-19 and 3-20)

$$q_\pm = q_\pm^{2-s} = \pm A(e^{z\pm f\phi_2/2} - 1)$$

with (cf. Eq. 3-11)

$$A = \left(\frac{RT\epsilon c^s}{2\pi}\right)^{\frac{1}{2}}$$

Furthermore, we have

$$q = -(q_+ + q_-)$$

and, in the absence of specific adsorption,

$$q = -(q_+^{2-s} + q_-^{2-s})$$

Hence

$$-\left(\frac{\partial q_-}{\partial q}\right)_a = '\left(\frac{\partial q_-^{2-s}}{\partial q^{2-s}}\right)_a$$

$$= -|z|f\left(\frac{\partial E_+}{\partial \ln a_\pm^2}\right)_q$$

$$= \tfrac{1}{2}\exp\left[\sinh^{-1}\left(-\frac{q^{2-s}}{2A}\right)\right]\left[1 + \left(\frac{q^{2-s}}{2A}\right)^2\right]^{-\frac{1}{2}} \tag{4}$$

Results for sodium fluoride, calculated by application of Eq. 4 to Grahame's data (4), are plotted in Fig. 4-1. We deduce from Eq. 4:

$$\left(\frac{\partial q_-}{\partial q}\right)_a \to 0 \quad \text{for} \quad q^{2-s} \to \infty \quad (q \to -\infty)$$

$$\left(\frac{\partial q_-}{\partial q}\right)_a \to -1 \quad \text{for} \quad q^{2-s} \to -\infty \quad (q \to +\infty)$$

These two limiting slopes are essentially verified in Fig. 4-1. Furthermore,

$$(\partial q_-/\partial q)_a = -\tfrac{1}{2} \quad \text{for} \quad q^{2-s} = 0 \quad (q = 0)$$

and consequently the point of zero charge is independent of electrolyte activity when it is measured against a reference electrode of constant electrolyte concentration in a cell with liquid junction.

This calculation provides a way of verifying the validity of the Gouy-Chapman theory in the absence of specific adsorption, but the qualification

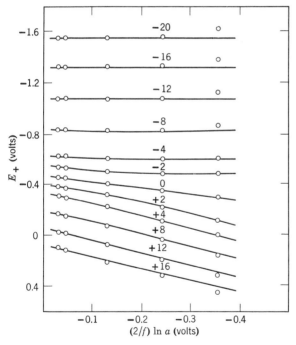

FIG. 4-1. Variations of E_+ with $(2/f)\ln a$ for mercury in sodium fluoride solutions at 25°C. Points are Grahame's experimental values; lines are calculated according to Eq. 4 and fitted at the highest concentration. Charge on electrode, in microcoulombs per square centimeter, indicated on each curve [Parsons (3)] (by permission of Butterworths).

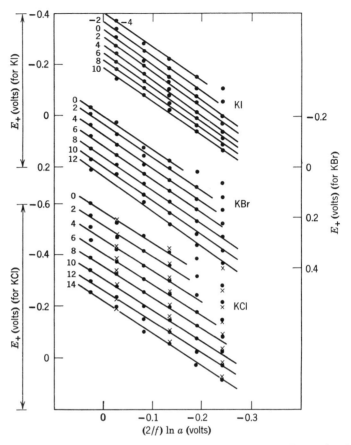

FIG. 4-2. Variations of E_+ with $(2/f)\ln a$ for mercury in solutions of potassium halide at 25°C. Solid circles are data from Devanathan and Peries (6); crosses are from Grahame data (5). Charge on electrode, in microcoulombs per square centimeter, indicated on each curve [Parsons (3)] (by permission of Butterworths).

made at the end of Sec. 3-2 also applies. The good agreement between theory and experiment is most convincing not too far from the point of zero charge; it does not provide a very sensitive test of the theory at high electrode charges because the contribution of the diffuse double layer is then relatively minor. The same comment applies to the use of plots such as Fig. 4-1 for detection of specific adsorption. Departure from predicted behavior could be attributed to defects of the Gouy-Chapman theory rather than specific adsorption. Such an argument could be advanced only for borderline cases for the shift of E_z (Eq. 3) is very definite for electrolytes with significant specific adsorption.

When there is specific adsorption we can divide $q_{\mp}$ into two parts corresponding to specifically adsorbed ions and to ions in the diffuse double layer ($q_{\mp}^{2-s}$), respectively. Anticipating the next section, we shall designate the first of these contributions by $q_{\mp}^1$. Thus

$$\left(\frac{\partial q_{\mp}}{\partial q}\right)_a = \left(\frac{\partial q_{\mp}^{2-s}}{\partial q}\right)_a + \left(\frac{\partial q_{\mp}^1}{\partial q}\right)_a$$

Evaluation of the second term on the right-hand side requires information on the dependence of $q_{\mp}^1$ on the charge q and the electrolyte activity a, that is, on the adsorption isotherm. Conversely, the application of Eq. 1 to experimental shifts of potential provides information about the isotherm. Whether or not this procedure allows unambiguous assignment of a particular isotherm is another matter. We shall reserve this question for Chapter 5 and limit ourselves to the descriptive aspects.

It was observed by Esin and Markov (2) that the point of zero charge varies linearly with the logarithm of electrolyte concentration. This observation seems to apply to potentials at any constant charge q as shown in Fig. 4-2. This diagram was prepared by Parsons (3) on the basis of Grahame's capacity data and the electrocapillary curves reported by Devanathan and Peries (6). The slope of the lines in Fig. 4-2 seems quite independent of the charge q, whereas this is not so in the absence of specific adsorption (Fig. 4-1). Esin and Markov (2) pointed out that the magnitude of the shift of the point of zero charge is not consistent with Stern's theory (7) of the double layer. Grahame (1) coined the expression "Esin and Markov effect" for this seemingly abnormal shift of the point of zero charge. We shall not consider this matter in detail as Stern's treatment of specific adsorption is now superseded by more recent work. The argument is given by Parsons (8) together with an account of Stern's theory.

The point of zero charge shifts toward increasingly negative potentials for predominant anion specific adsorption (Fig. 4-2) and toward positive potentials for predominant cation adsorption (Fig. 4-3). When both anions and cations are strongly adsorbed, the sign of the shift of potential may be reversed as the concentration changes (Table 4-1).

The existence of anion specific adsorption was already realized by Gouy (11) who, however, did not pursue the idea, as Grahame noted (12), and it was Stern (7) who reintroduced the idea and treated it quantitatively. Grahame stressed anion specific adsorption throughout his work, and specific adsorption of cations on mercury was recognized only rather recently. (Specific adsorption of large organic cations such as the tetraalkylammonium ions was well known before.) Frumkin and co-workers (10, 13–15) showed by analysis of electrocapillary curves that Tl^+

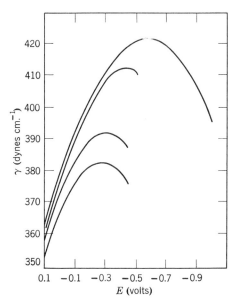

FIG. 4-3. Electrocapillary curves for mercury in $1M$ KNO$_3$ + $0.01M$ nitric acid + 0, 0.01, 0.1, and $0.2M$ thallium (I) nitrate (from top to bottom) [Frumkin (15)] (by permission of John Wiley).

ions are strongly adsorbed on mercury, and this conclusion is confirmed by kinetic studies of the discharge of Tl$^+$ ions on thallium amalgam (60, 61). Adsorption of Cs$^+$ at high negative charges was also inferred by Frumkin, Damaskin, and Nikolaeva-Fedorovich (16, 17) from the influence of this ion on the electrochemical reduction of peroxydisulfate and from double-layer capacity measurements in presence of iodide. [See review in (17a).]

TABLE 4-1   Point of Zero Charge for Tetramethyl-ammonium Iodide in Aqueous Solution in Contact with Mercury at $25°$ C[a]

Concentration, mole l^{-1}	Potential E_z, volts versus AgI/Ag in solution
0.005	−0.337
0.01	−0.350
0.02	−0.362
0.03	−0.358
0.1	−0.350
0.2	−0.342

[a] From Devanathan and Fernando (9).

This view was challenged by Grahame, Higinbotham, and Deane (18), but present evidence on the role of Cs^+ in electrode kinetics (Chapter 9) supports the view that this ion is specifically adsorbed. In conclusion, it is safe to assume that all ions are specifically adsorbed for favorable sign and value of the charge on the electrode. Fortunately, specific adsorption can be ignored as a *first approximation* in a number of cases.

b. Dependence of $dC_{\pm}/dE$ on Potential

In Sec. 2-4 we introduced the capacities C_+ and C_- corresponding to the cations and anions in the double layer and we showed how, according to Grahame and Soderberg (19), these capacities can be related to the measured double layer capacity. One has for a $z - z$ electrolyte (cf. Eq. 2-26) at constant temperature, pressure, and electrode composition

$$z_{\pm}F\left(\frac{\partial C}{\partial \mu}\right)_{E_{\mp}} = -\left(\frac{\partial C_{\pm}}{\partial E_{\mp}}\right)_{\mu} \tag{5}$$

In the absence of specific adsorption

$$C = -\left(\frac{\partial q_+^{2-s}}{\partial E}\right)_{\mu} - \left(\frac{\partial q_-^{2-s}}{\partial E}\right)_{\mu} \tag{6}$$

The subscript $\pm$ on E is dropped in Eq. 6 because it does not matter which reference electrode is being used. The quantities q_+^{2-s} and q_-^{2-s} can be computed from the Gouy-Chapman theory, and Eq. 5 thus provides a way of verifying this theory. Details of the calculation, which involves a number of steps but is quite straightforward, are given by Grahame (20). Thus

$$\left(\frac{\partial C_+}{\partial E}\right)_{\mu} = \frac{C}{2(1+v^2)^{1/2}}\left\{[(1+v^2)^{1/2} + v]\frac{1}{C}\left(\frac{\partial C}{\partial E}\right) - \frac{C}{2A(1+v^2)}\right\} \tag{7}$$

where

$$v = -\frac{q}{2A}$$

and A was already defined in Sec. 4-1a (see also Eq. 3-11). (The last term was preceded by a plus sign as the result of a misprint in Grahame's original paper (20); correction was made in Ref. 19.) Grahame and Soderberg (19) compared predictions from Eqs. 5 and 7 and similar equations for unsymmetrical electrolytes with experiment for a number of electrolytes and showed that good agreement only prevailed in the absence of specific adsorption (Fig. 4-4). The comments made in Sec. 4-1a also apply here to the significance of this test on the Gouy-Chapman theory.

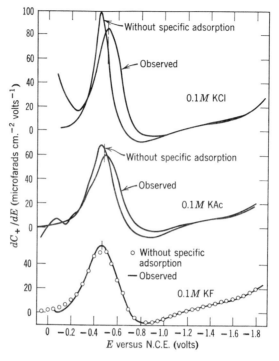

FIG. 4-4. Observed and calculated values of $(\partial C_+/\partial E)_\mu$ for three electrolytes in contact with mercury at 25°C. Calculated curves were computed from Eq. 7 on the assumption of no specific adsorption [Grahame and Soderberg (19)] (by permission of the American Institute of Physics).

4-2   Amount of Specifically Adsorbed Ions

The amount of a given specifically adsorbed ion can be computed from experimental surface excesses and the Gouy-Chapman theory provided it is assumed that ions of the opposite sign are not specifically adsorbed. The procedure, according to Grahame and Soderberg (19), will be outlined for anions. *It is assumed that cations are not specifically adsorbed* in the range of potential being considered. Then

$$q_+^{2-s} = z_+ F \Gamma_+ \tag{8}$$

where Γ_+ is determined experimentally as indicated in Secs. 2-3 and 2-4. The charge q_+^{2-s} is correlated to the potential ϕ_2 in the plane of closest approach by Eq. 3-19, that is,

$$q_+^{2-s} = A(e^{-z_+ f\phi_2/2} - 1) \tag{9}$$

Application of Eqs. 8 and 9 thus yields ϕ_2 and consequently the charge q_-^{2-s} (Eq. 3-20)

$$q_-^{2-s} = -A(e^{-z_-f\phi_2/2} - 1) \qquad (10)$$

Setting now

$$q_- = z_- F\Gamma_-$$
$$= q_-^1 + q_-^{2-s} \qquad (11)$$

where q_-^1 is the charge corresponding to the specifically adsorbed anions, we can compute q_-^1 since q_-^{2-s} is given by Eq. 10 and Γ_- is deduced from experimental data by purely thermodynamic argument. Grahame and Soderberg gave a plot of q_-^1 against potential for a number of electrolytes. The more recent, similar diagram prepared by Parsons from Grahame's data and which was reported by Mott and Watts-Tobin (21) is reproduced in Fig. 4-5. Results for a given electrolyte can also be plotted as an isotherm at constant charge on the electrode (or at constant electrode potential). We shall discuss in Sec. 5-2 the selection of the most suitable electrical parameter in the plotting of such an isotherm, and we limit ourselves here to giving two examples for chloride (22) and iodide (23) (Figs. 4-6 and 4-7). Some capacity data on potassium chloride in the 2 to 4 molar range (24) and on isocyano-chromium (III) complexes (63, 64) may also be examined in this connection.

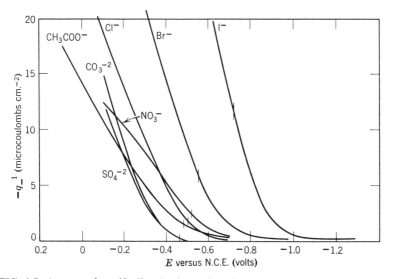

FIG. 4-5. Amount of specifically adsorbed anions for various electrolytes (0.1 normal) in contact with mercury at 25°C. Curves computed by Parsons from Grahame's data. Vertical lines indicate point of zero charge [Mott and Watts-Tobin (21)] (by permission of Pergamon).

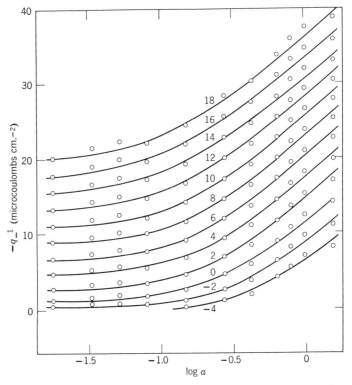

FIG. 4-6. Amount of specifically adsorbed chloride for mercury in potassium chloride at 25°C as a function of the logarithm of activity. Different charges on the electrode, in microcoulombs per square centimeter [Grahame and Parsons (22)] (by permission of the American Chemical Society).

The foregoing analysis is not valid when there is specific adsorption of cations and this led Devanathan and Canagaratna (25) to cast some doubt about the validity of the calculation of q_-^1 made by Grahame and Soderberg (19). Actually, the error is probably small especially for $q > 0$ since specific adsorption of cations is then probably minor. Calculation of the amounts of specifically adsorbed cations and anions for simultaneous specific adsorption has not been attempted. This calculation would require a relationship between the amount of specifically adsorbed ions and the charge to replace Eq. 8 which is not valid in such a case.

Reference should be made here to Devanathan's method (26) of computing ionic components of the double layer. This nonthermodynamic method was applied by its originator to potassium halides by using the data of Devanathan and Peries (27). Grahame (1) questioned the need for

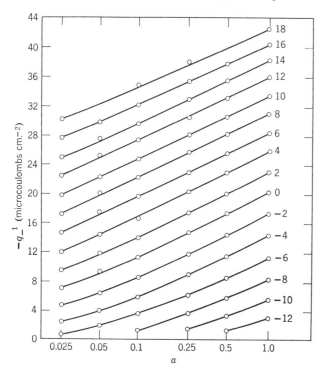

FIG. 4-7. Same plot as in Fig. 4-6 but for potassium iodide [Grahame (23)] (by permission of the American Chemical Society).

such an approach and indicated that good agreement with experiment might not depend markedly on some of the novel features of the model advocated by Devanathan. The theory, as applied to the adsorption of uncharged substances, was also criticized by Frumkin and Damaskin (28). These criticisms seem hard to refute, but further examination of models such as the one used by Devanathan might prove of value. A detailed analysis of Devanathan's method is also given by Macdonald and Barlow (65).

4-3 Grahame's Model of the Double Layer and Nature of Specific Adsorption

Strong specific adsorption of most anions led Grahame (29) to modify Stern's model (7) by introducing the *inner plane of closest approach* within which anions can approach the electrode. This plane is located at a distance x_1 from the electrode which is smaller than the distance x_2 within which cations approach the electrode. The plane at x_2 is now called the *outer plane of closest approach*. The notation q_-^1 introduced in Sec. 4-1a followed from the assumption made by Grahame about the inner plane. Grahame's model differs from that of Stern because it involves two distinct planes of closest approach, whereas a common plane was postulated by Stern. This author, however, pointed out in a footnote, as Grahame noted (12), that two planes might have to be considered, but he did not develop the corresponding model.

TABLE 4-2　Primary Hydration Numbers[a]

Cation	Hydration Number	Anion	Hydration Number
Li^+	5	F^-	4
Na^+	5	Cl^-	1
K^+	4	Br^-	1
Rb^+	3	I^-	1
Cs^+	0		

[a] From Bockris, Devanathan, and Müller (32).

Grahame (29) assumed the existence of some covalent bonding between specifically adsorbed anions and mercury. He gave as supporting evidence (30) the essentially linear relationship between the differential capacity for various anions, at the limit of positive potentials at which measurements can be made, and the logarithm of mercurous ion concentration of the salts corresponding to the anions being tested. This interpretation of the nature of specific adsorption was rejected by Levine, Bell, and Calvert (31), who suggested image energy (cf. Sec. 4-4) as the origin of specific adsorption and by Bockris, Devanathan, and Müller (32) who advocated the degree and type of ionic hydration as the principal factor to be considered. The latter group of authors advanced as argument against Grahame's interpretation the discrepancy between mercury-halide bond strengths (32, 23, 17, and 7 kcal. mole^{-1} from fluoride to iodide) and the degree of adsorbability of halides on mercury. These data pertain to conditions very different from those prevailing at the mercury-solution interface, but this qualification can hardly account for the discrepancy. Bockris *et al.* believe that ions with a high primary hydration number show little tendency to specific adsorption, whereas ions with low primary hydration number undergo strong specific adsorption when electrostatic repulsion is not too strong. [For a distinction between primary and secondary hydration see Conway and Bockris (33).] The trend (Table 4-2) agrees with the tendency for specific adsorption to increase from Li^+ to Cs^+ and from F^- to I^-. Factors other than hydration undoubtedly must be considered, but the interpretation of Bockris, Devanathan, and Müller seems more plausible than that of Grahame. This question was further discussed by Andersen and Bockris (32a).

4-4 Distribution of Potentials

a. Distribution of Potential in the Diffuse Double Layer

We consider first the variations of the potential ϕ_2 in the outer plane as a function of potential E. The method of calculation of ϕ_2 was already indicated in Sec. 4-2 for the case in which only one ionic species is specifically adsorbed. Results obtained by Grahame and Soderberg (19) are summarized in Fig. 4-8. The potential ϕ_2 is identical at markedly negative potentials in Fig. 4-8 for all electrolytes with univalent cations, that is, in a region where there is no anion specific adsorption. For $E > E_z$, ϕ_2 becomes markedly positive only for potassium fluoride, for this anion shows little tendency toward specific adsorption (except probably for high positive charges on the electrode). Other electrolytes display mostly negative ϕ's in the positive range of $E-E_z$. This is in agreement with the explanation advanced for the data of Fig. 2-5 where the positive charge on the electrode is more than compensated by the charge of the specifically adsorbed anions. The reservation made about the calculation of the amount of specifically adsorbed anions in Sec. 4-2 is also valid here. Results of the type in Fig. 4-8 are important in correlating electrode kinetics and double-layer structure (Chapter 9).

Once ϕ_2 is known, we can readily calculate the difference of potential $\phi_M - \phi_2$ which can be equated to $E - E_z - \phi_2$, where E_z is the point of zero charge for an electrolyte without specific adsorption. Values of $\phi_M - \phi_2$ computed in this way are rational potentials according to Grahame's definition (29). Values of $\phi_M - \phi_2$ were computed by Grahame (23) for potassium iodide and later by Grahame and Parsons (22) for potassium chloride. Results can be displayed as a plot of $\phi_M - \phi_2$ against the amount of specifically adsorbed ions q_-^1 for different values of the charge q on the electrode. Figure 4-9 shows that $\phi_M - \phi_2$ is a function of q_-^1 and q. Hence we may formally divide (22, 23) $\phi_M - \phi_2$ into two components $_{q^1}(\phi_M - \phi_2)$ and $_q(\phi_M - \phi_2)$ which depend solely on q^1 and on q respectively. We drop the subscript "$-$" on q^1 here and in subsequent equations whenever they are applicable regardless of ionic valence [notation according to Parsons (34)]. Thus

$$\phi_M - \phi_2 = {}_{q^1}(\phi_M - \phi_2) + {}_q(\phi_M - \phi_2) \tag{12}$$

where the subscripts q^1 and q indicate the charge component on which the component of $\phi_M - \phi_2$ depends.

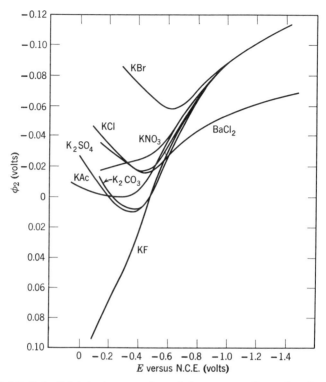

FIG. 4-8. Potential ϕ_2 in the outer plane of closest approach as a function of potential for mercury in tenth-normal aqueous solutions at 25°C [Grahame and Soderberg (19)] (by permission of the American Institute of Physics).

We now define the corresponding integral capacities $_{q^1}C^i$ and $_qC^i$ according to Grahame and Parsons (22) by (cf. Eq. 2-21)

$$q^1 = \,_{q^1}C^i\,_{q^1}(\phi_M - \phi_2) \tag{13}$$

$$q = \,_qC^i\,_q(\phi_M - \phi_2)$$

The capacity $_{q^1}C^i$ is given by the slope of the lines in Fig. 4-9 and varies somewhat with q^1. Similarly, $_qC^i$ is obtained from Eq. 13 and Fig. 4-9. Values of $_qC^i$ for potassium chloride (22) are compared in Fig. 4-10 with the integral capacity of the compact double layer for potassium fluoride in the absence of specific adsorption. [See Fig. 3-2 for the variations of the differential capacity of the compact double layer for sodium fluoride.] It is remarkable that the two capacities are nearly the same, and this may indicate, according to Grahame (23), that the dielectric constant in the compact layer is not strongly affected by the field of specifically adsorbed

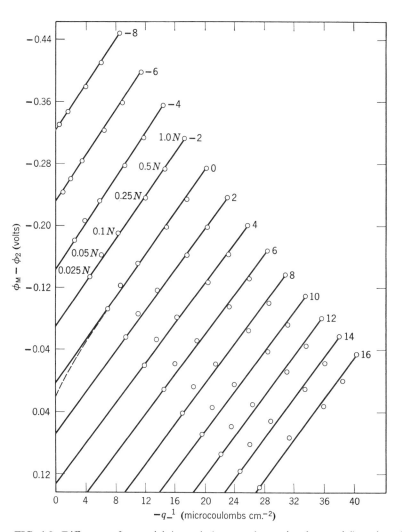

FIG. 4-9. Difference of potential $\phi_M - \phi_2$ (expressed as rational potential) against the amount of specifically adsorbed iodide for mercury in potassium iodide solutions at 25°C. Charge on the electrode in microcoulombs per square centimeter. Each point corresponds to a given concentration [Grahame (23)] (by permission of the American Chemical Society).

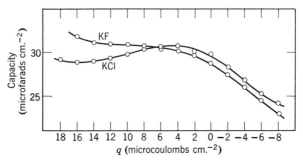

FIG. 4-10. Integral capacity $_qC^i$ (Eq. 13) of the compact double layer against the charge on the electrode for potassium chloride in contact with mercury at 25°C. Comparison with the differential capacity C_{M-2} for potassium fluoride [Grahame and Parsons (22)] (by permission of the American Chemical Society).

anions. This conclusion, however, is open to further inquiry. Results similar to those of Fig. 4-10 are given by Grahame (23) for potassium iodide, but they are expressed as the differential capacities corresponding to the integral capacities $_{q1}C^i$ and $_qC^i$ of Eq. 13. The capacity component depending on q for iodide is not very different from the capacity of the compact double layer in the absence of specific adsorption, just as for chloride.

b. Distribution of Potential in the Compact Double Layer

Two methods were worked out by Grahame (23) to calculate the potential ϕ_1 in the inner plane: the first method makes use of a linear isotherm for anion adsorption and is only very tentative; the second method takes into account the discreteness of charge in the inner plane. The strating point of the first method is the isotherm

$$q_-^{\ 1} = Kae^{-zf\phi_1} \tag{14}$$

where the charge dependent quantity K is related to Stern's adsorption potential and ϕ_1 is the micropotential discussed below. Details are unimportant here, for Eq. 14 is open to question, as we shall see, and Stern's theory has been superseded. Equation 14 was derived by Grahame in an elaborate fashion, but it amounts simply to a linear isotherm [cf. Sec. 5-1]. The difference of potential $\phi_1 - \phi_2$ is now set as being equal to some fraction $\lambda(0 < \lambda < 1)$ of the difference of potential $\phi_M - \phi_2$ already computed. Thus

$$\phi_1 - \phi_2 = \lambda(\phi_M - \phi_2) \tag{15}$$

Actually, Grahame (23) assumed a linear distribution of potential in the compact layer and equated λ to $(x_2 - x_1)/x_2$, where x_1 and x_2 are the distances between the inner and outer planes and the electrode, respectively. We do not make this assumption and introduce the factor λ in view of the comments made later.

Equations 14 and 15 now yield

$$\ln \frac{q^1}{a} + zf\phi_2 = \ln K - zf\lambda(\phi_M - \phi_2) \tag{16}$$

The data of Fig. 4-9 can be plotted according to Eq. 16. Straight lines are obtained (22) which yield the values of λ plotted in Fig. 4-11. The quantity λ is smaller for iodide than for chloride, and we conclude that the fraction of $\phi_M - \phi_2$ in the region between the metal and the inner plane is greater for iodide than for chloride. Once λ is known we can revert to Eq. 15 and calculate ϕ_1 from previously determined values of ϕ_2 and $\phi_M - \phi_2$.

Equation 14 is only a coarse approximation because adsorption is accounted for by a linear isotherm only at low coverages (Chapter 5). This point was made by Parry and Parsons (36), who used the Langmuir isotherm [already discussed by Grahame (29)]. They write instead of Eq. 14

$$\frac{q_-^1}{q_{\text{sat}}^1 - q_-^1} = ae^{(\Phi/RT) - zf\phi_1} \tag{17}$$

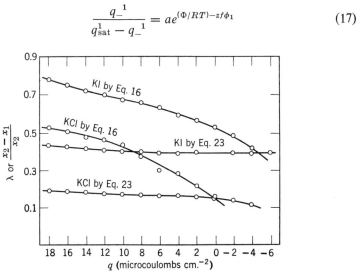

FIG. 4-11. Variations of λ and $(x_2 - x_1)/x_2$, as computed from Eqs. 16 and 23, with the charge on the electrode for potassium chloride and iodide [Grahame and Parsons (22)] (by permission of the American Chemical Society).

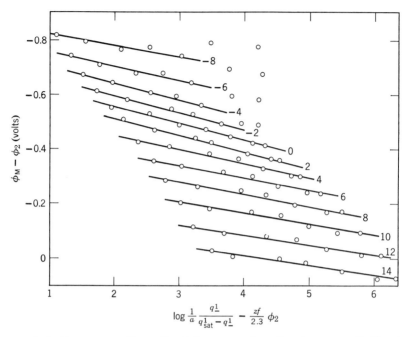

FIG. 4-12. Plot corresponding to Eq. 18 for mercury in sodium benzene *m*-disulfonate solutions at 30°C. Charge on the electrode in microcoulombs per square centimeter [Parry and Parsons (36)] (by permission of The Faraday Society).

where Φ is related to Stern's adsorption potential. Equation 16 now becomes

$$\ln \frac{1}{a} \frac{q_-^{\;1}}{q_{sat}^1 - q_-^{\;1}} - zf\phi_2 = \Phi - zf\lambda(\phi_M - \phi_2) \tag{18}$$

The plots corresponding to Eq. 18 for sodium benzene *m*-disulfate are linear (Fig. 4-12) and λ, at constant q, is thus constant. On the other hand, the ratio λ, as deduced from Eq. 18 and the slope of the lines in Fig. 4-12, increases with the charge q on the electrode and approaches unity (Fig. 4-11). We shall explain these variations of λ with q later after discussing another method for the calculation of ϕ_1. Further comments on the validity of this calculation will also be made there.

We now turn to the second method of evaluating ϕ_1 and begin with some considerations on the effect of discreteness of charge in the inner plane. It was pointed out in Sec. 4-1a that the seemingly abnormal Esin and Markov effect for strong specific adsorption was ascribed to the influence of discreteness of charge. Credit for the idea was given by Esin and Markov (2) to Frumkin (37), and it may be added that de Boer (38), as Parsons noted (34), independently advanced a similar idea for metal-gas adsorption. The problem was reexamined by Grahame (35), who also reviewed previous work by Esin and Shikov (39) and Ershler (40). A concise and lucid review was prepared by Parsons (34). A general analysis of discreteness effects is given by Macdonald and Barlow (65). These authors recently outlined various methods of calculation of these effects (66).

Esin and Shikhov (39) used as a model of the double layer two parallel layers of discrete charges of opposite sign. These authors noted that the distribution of potential for such an array (Fig. 4-13) is different from the linear variation of potential for two parallel layers of uniformly smeared out charges. They then proceeded to correlate these two potential distributions. Ershler (40) noted that this model is oversimplified in that the regular array of cations which is postulated for the outer plane is certainly disorganized by thermal motion. He proposed a model in which the layer of specifically adsorbed anions in the inner plane lies between two parallel reflecting planes. Thus the solution in the diffuse double layer is considered as a polarizable medium just as the metal. Ershler revised the earlier calculation of Esin and Shikov and showed that the difference of potential $\phi_M - \phi_2$ *solely due* to the charge q^1 of specifically adsorbed ions is

$$_{q^1}(\phi_M - \phi_2) = \frac{4\pi q^1(x_2 - x_1)}{\epsilon_1} \tag{19}$$

There ϵ_1 is the dielectric constant of the compact double layer, which is supposed to be independent of x. This simplification about ϵ_1 may be quite drastic. The subscript q^1 preceding $\phi_M - \phi_2$ denotes that this equation gives only the component of $\phi_M - \phi_2$ due to q^1. Equation 19, which was derived by Ershler and by Grahame by the method of images, shows that $_{q^1}(\phi_M - \phi_2)$ is one-half the difference of potential for a layer of charge q^1 and its image with respect to the plane ϕ_2. The distance between plane 1

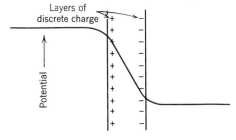

FIG. 4-13. Schematic representation of the potential distribution near a pair of parallel layers of discrete charges [Grahame (35)] (by permission of the Bunsengesellschaft).

and its image with respect to plane 2 is indeed $2(x_2 - x_1)$. [See Grahame's comments (35) on the derivation of Eq. 19; serious errors in Grahame's treatment were pointed out by Barlow and Macdonald (62, 65, 67).]

The difference of potential $_{q^1}(\phi_1 - \phi_2)$ due to the charge q^1 may now be expressed, as a first approximation, by assuming a linear drop of potential for $_{q^1}(\phi_M - \phi_2)$. Thus

$$_{q^1}(\phi_1 - \phi_2) = {}_{q^1}(\phi_M - \phi_2) \frac{x_2 - x_1}{x_2} \tag{20}$$

or, in view of Eq. 19,

$$_{q^1}(\phi_1 - \phi_2) = \frac{4\pi q^1}{\epsilon_1} \frac{(x_2 - x_1)^2}{x_2} \tag{21}$$

Since $x_1 < x_2$, comparison of Eqs. 19 and 21 shows that

$$|_{q^1}(\phi_1 - \phi_2)| < |_{q^1}(\phi_M - \phi_2)|$$

Hence the shift of point of zero charge, which is related to the change of $_{q^1}(\phi_M - \phi_2)$, on variation of anion concentration is greater than the change of the potential $_{q^1}(\phi_1 - \phi_2)$ affecting the adsorbed anions. This accounts qualitatively for the discrepancy noted by Esin and Markov (2) between experimental shifts of the point of zero charge and the prediction of Stern's theory.

By considering the metal surface and the outer plane as a parallel plate capacitor, one has

$$_q(\phi_M - \phi_2) = \frac{4\pi q x_2}{\epsilon_1}$$

Combination of this equation with Eqs. 13 and 19 yields for a supposedly constant ϵ_1

$$\frac{x_2 - x_1}{x_2} = \frac{_{q^1}(\phi_M - \phi_2)}{_q(\phi_M - \phi_2)} \frac{q}{q^1} \tag{22}$$

$$\frac{x_2 - x_1}{x_2} = \frac{_q C^i}{_{q^1} C^i} \tag{23}$$

Results for potassium chloride and iodide, which are plotted in Fig. 4-11, indicate that $(x_2 - x_1)/x_2$ hardly varies with q, whereas λ is strongly dependent on q. This discrepancy was analyzed by Parry and Parsons (36), who concluded that Eq. 23 should give a better approximation to the ratio of distances $(x_2 - x_1)/x_2$ than the values of λ computed from Eqs. 15 or 17. They point out that the capacities in Eq. 23 depend on average values of the potentials ϕ_M, ϕ_1, and ϕ_2 which, as noted by Watts-Tobin (41) are not affected by the extent of charge discreteness. The ratio of the integral capacities in Eq. 23 can be equated to the ratio of the dielectric thicknesses provided the dielectric constant is assumed to be independent of x. In contrast, the potential ϕ_1 appearing in Eqs. 15 and 17 is not an average potential and depends on discreteness of charge. At low values of q^1, $\lambda \approx (x_2 - x_1)/x_2$, as the assumption of a linear distribution of potential, is quite reasonable. At high values of q^1, however, the electrode resembles more a model with smeared out charges, and the relative importance of $_q^1(\phi_1 - \phi_2)$ increases (21). Hence $\lambda > (x_2 - x_1)/x_2$. These considerations are borne out by the results of Fig. 4-11. The analysis of Parry and Parsons (36) is also examined in detail by Macdonald and Barlow (65).

The potential ϕ_1 can now be computed, according to Parry and Parsons (36), by dividing $\phi_1 - \phi_2$ into two components depending on q and q^1, respectively. Thus

$$\phi_1 - \phi_2 = {_q}(\phi_M - \phi_2)\frac{x_2 - x_1}{x_2} + {_q}^1(\phi_M - \phi_2)\lambda$$

or, in view of Eqs. 13 and 23,

$$\phi_1 = \frac{q + \lambda q^1}{_q{}^1 C^i} + \phi_2 \tag{24}$$

The potential ϕ_2 in Eq. 24 can be expressed as a function q (Sec. 4-4a), and ϕ_1 is thus obtained as a function of q and q^1.

In conclusion, the foregoing analysis is quite tentative, but it has given some insight into the structure of the inner layer. The models at the basis of the foregoing treatments are oversimplified for a number of reasons, among which the following ones may be mentioned. (a) The average distance between specifically adsorbed ions is such that one-dimensional analysis is open to question (see Sec. 3-5 and Ref. 62). (b) One would expect specifically adsorbed ions to "squeeze" nonspecifically adsorbed ions away from the electrode as the coverage increases, that is, x_2 should increase with q_-^1 and $(x_2 - x_1)/x_2$ should not necessarily be independent of the charge on the electrode. Further progress may follow by possible refinements of the model of discreteness or perhaps from a new approach. Further work on this problem is discussed in the recent papers of Levich and co-workers (42, 43), and Yalamov (44). The detailed analysis of the potential distribution in the inner plane by Levine, Bell, and Calvert (31) and particularly the application of methods of calculation from crystal field theory by Barlow and Macdonald (62, 67) may have reached the ultimate rigor that can be expected for this type of approach. [See also further application to air-water interfaces (45).]

4-5   Structure of the Compact Double Layer

The differential capacity C_{M-2} of the compact double layer was computed in Sec. 3-2 on the assumption that this capacity is solely a function of the charge on the electrode and not of the electrolyte concentration. Good agreement between experimental capacities and the Gouy-Chapman theory was obtained on the basis of this hypothesis. It was noted that C_{M-2} varies markedly with the charge on the electrode and the explanation of this effect was reserved for this chapter, for it had to await a deeper understanding of the compact double layer. Additional data on C_{M-2} obtained by Grahame (46) for different temperatures are given in Fig. 4-14 of which the following features must be explained: (a) the increase of C_{M-2} with an increasingly positive charge, (b) the increase in capacity for large negative charges, and (c) the *hump* and its disappearance at higher temperature.

These effects were interpreted quantitatively by Macdonald (47) and Macdonald and Barlow (48). [See also related papers by Macdonald and co-workers (49–52).] The decrease of capacity (Fig. 4-14) for $q < 0$ is interpreted as being caused by the drop in dielectric constant because of increasing saturation as the charge on the electrode becomes more negative. This effect is more than compensated at high negative charges by compression of the layer of water between $x = 0$ and x_1 as the field increases

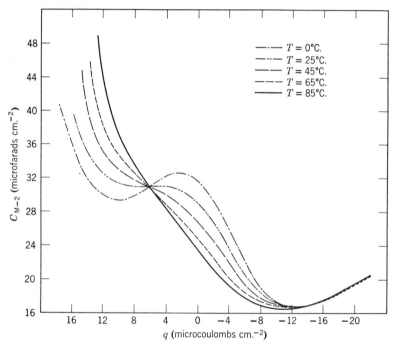

FIG. 4-14. Calculated capacity C_{M-2} of the compact double layer for mercury in 0.8M sodium fluoride at several temperatures [Grahame (46)] (by permission of the American Chemical Society).

(electrostriction). Macdonald and Barlow set up a model to account for these two effects and treated it in detail. Theoretical curves fit quite well experimental capacity-potential curves for $q < 0$, but they do not do so for $q > 0$. The theory predicts a drop in C_{M-2} followed by an increase as q is made more positive. A continuous increase of C_{M-2} with potential (or with q) for $q > 0$ was actually deduced by Grahame from his measurements at higher temperature (Fig. 4-14), and C_{M-2} at the lower temperature also increases quite rapidly with potential (or with q) beyond the hump. Macdonald and Barlow (48) also considered dipole image forces corresponding to physical adsorption of the solvent and were able to improve agreement between theory and experiment for aqueous solutions of sodium fluoride and also for methanol solutions of potassium fluoride. Experimental results for the latter system are available from Grahame's work (53). Some results are given in Fig. 4-15, and similar curves are given in Ref. 53 for the data of Fig. 4-14 at other temperatures and for methanol. The complete discrepancy at high positive charges was ascribed by Macdonald and Barlow to specific adsorption of fluoride ion. Possible support for this explanation can be found in the discrepancy found by Grahame between experimental capacities and the values predicted by the Gouy-Chapman theory on the assumption of no specific adsorption (Chapter 3). Macdonald and Barlow pointed out more recently (65) that a source of discrepancy is the discreteness of the solvent molecules and the induced polarizability of discrete solvent molecules. They elaborated on their previous work in two recent papers (67, 68) and improved the fitting of experimental and theoretical capacities.

The structure of the compact double layer was also discussed by several other authors (21, 32, 41, 54). Mott and Watts-Tobin (21) are in agreement with Macdonald's treatment, but they suggest as a possible explanation of the rise in capacity at markedly positive charges the adsorption of hydroxyl ions. This, however, was disproved by Austin and Parsons (55), who hardly found any influence of hydroxyl ions on capacity up to pH 11. [See also Payne's recent study (69).] Frumkin (56) pointed out that Grahame's capacities at highly positive charge are too high, possibly because of the contamination produced by glass attack by fluoride (formation of SiF_6^{--}?). Work in his laboratory in Teflon cells gave lower capacities for highly positive charge on the electrode.

Macdonald and Barlow (48) account for the hump in the C_{M-2} versus q curve (Fig. 4-14) at the lower temperature by the interplay of specific adsorption of fluoride ion and dielectric saturation. Mott and Watts-Tobin (21) are in agreement with this view. Saturation is not so complete at the maximum of the hump as on either side of the hump maximum. Hence, the dielectric constant, and consequently the capacity, decreases on

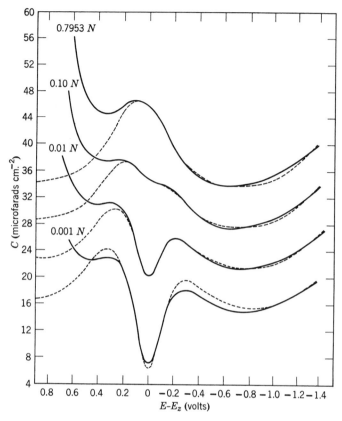

FIG. 4-15. Comparison between experimental and calculated differential capacities of the double layer for mercury in sodium fluoride solutions at 0°C. Solid curves from Grahame's data; dotted curves according to theory [Macdonald and Barlow (48)] (by permission of the American Institute of Physics).

either side of the hump. Mott and Watts-Tobin explain the disappearance of the hump at higher temperature (Fig. 4-14) by means of a model composed of a capacitor with a monolayer of water. They showed that the capacity for this model exhibits a slower drop with increasing field at higher temperatures than at lower ones.

The maximum of the hump is not observed at the point of zero charge but at small positive charge. Mott and Watts-Tobin ascribe this shift of the hump maximum to specific adsorption. It must be recognized, however, that specific adsorption of fluoride ion in this region is probably very weak since agreement between experiment and the Gouy-Chapman theory is still quite satisfactory (Chapter 3) in the region of the hump. [See also further results bearing on this point in Grahame (46).] Such an agreement is significant because the contribution of the diffuse double layer is important in the hump region, and it may not suffice to invoke specific adsorption and dielectric saturation to account satisfactorily for the hump. The same reservation can be made about the interpretation of Bockris, Devanathan, and Müller (32). These authors questioned the foregoing interpretation of the hump and advocated an explanation based primarily on specific adsorption. They attempted a quantitative evaluation of capacity from an isotherm they derive for specific adsorption. Agreement with experiment, however, was quite poor.

Damaskin, Schwartz, and Frumkin (57, 58) reexamined the interpretation of Mott and Watts-Tobin and pointed out that it did not account for the absence of a hump for potassium hydroxide and potassium carbonate. Watts-Tobin (41) thought that the absence of a hump for these electrolytes resulted from strong specific adsorption much in the same way as no hump is observed for iodide. Thus the capacity rises too quickly with q for $q > 0$ for a hump to be observed. This explanation does not hold because points of zero charge for potassium hydroxide and potassium carbonate are not very different from that of fluoride (Table 2-1) and are not strongly concentration dependent. Damaskin, Schwartz, and Frumkin suggest on the basis of measurements for potassium ferrocyanide that water orientation in the compact layer is profoundly affected by the presence of highly polarizable ions. When the charge on the electrode becomes more positive, anion concentration in the double layer increases and the water orientation changes. The effect is particularly pronounced with highly hydrated ions such as ferrocyanide. A sharp rise in capacity is then observed as the charge on the electrode becomes more positive. A detailed treatment based on this idea is available (58).

Another feature of the compact double layer must be explained, namely, the lack of strong dependence of the experimental differential capacity on the nature of cations (Fig. 4-16). Experimental evidence substantiating this point was gathered by Grahame (59). Mott, Parsons, and Watts-Tobin (54) explain these observations by assuming that the dielectric constant of water rises very rapidly with the distance from the electrode, and therefore the size of the cation is unimportant. Cation specific adsorption might also have to be considered in a more detailed explanation than that advanced by these authors.

In conclusion, the structure of the compact double layer is fairly well understood from a qualitative point of view. Quantitative interpretation is more tentative than for the diffuse double layer.

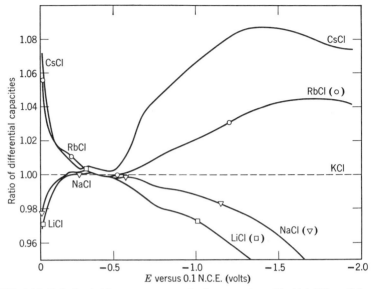

FIG. 4-16. Relative (with respect to capacity for potassium chloride) differential capacity for mercury in $0.1 M$ alkali chloride solutions [Grahame (59)] (by permission of The Electrochemical Society).

REFERENCES

1. D. C. Grahame, *Ann. Rev. Phys. Chem.*, **6**, 337 (1955).
2. O. A. Esin and B. F. Markov, *Acta Physicochim. U.R.S.S.*, **10**, 353 (1939).
3. R. Parsons, *Proc. 2nd Int. Congress Surface Activity*, Butterworths, London, **3**, 38 (1957).
4. D. C. Grahame, *J. Am. Chem. Soc.*, **76**, 4819 (1954).
5. D. C. Grahame, unpublished data communicated to R. Parsons.
6. M. A. V. Devanathan and P. Peries, *Trans. Faraday Soc.*, **50**, 1236 (1954).
7. O. Stern, *Z. Elektrochem.*, **30**, 508 (1924).
8. R. Parsons, *Modern Aspects of Electrochemistry*, Vol. 1, J. O'M. Bockris, editor, Butterworths, London, 1954, pp. 103–179.
9. M. A. V. Devanathan and M. J. Fernando, *Trans. Faraday Soc.*, **58**, 368 (1962).
10. A. N. Frumkin and A. S. Titievskaja, *Zhur. Fiz. Khim.*, **31**, 485 (1957).
11. G. Gouy, *Compt. rend.*, **146**, 1374 (1908).
12. D. C. Grahame, *Z. Elektrochem.* **59**, 773 (1955).
13. A. N. Frumkin and N. S. Polyanovskaya, *Zhur. Fiz. Khim.*, **32**, 157 (1958).
14. A. N. Frumkin, *Surface Phenomena in Chemistry and Biology*, J. F. Danieli, K. G. A. Pankhurst, and A. C. Riddiford, editors, Pergamon, London, 1958, pp. 189–194.
15. A. N. Frumkin, *Transactions of the Symposium on Electrode Processes*, E. Yeager editor, Wiley, New York, 1961, pp. 1–12.
16. A. N. Frumkin, B. B. Damaskin, and N. Nikolaeva-Fedorovich, *Doklady Akad. Nauk S.S.S.R.*, **115**, 751 (1957).
17. A. N. Frumkin, Ref. 15, pp. 207–208.

17a. A. N. Frumkin, *Electrochim. Acta.*, **5**, 265 (1961).

18. D. C. Grahame, A. E. Higinbotham, and F. R. M. Deane, Ref. 15, pp. 197–207.

19. D. C. Grahame and B. A. Soderberg, *J. Chem. Phys.*, **22**, 449 (1954).

20. D. C. Grahame, *ibid.*, **21**, 1054 (1953).

21. N. F. Mott and R. J. Watts-Tobin, *Electrochim. Acta.*, **4**, 79 (1961).

22. D. C. Grahame and R. Parsons, *J. Am. Chem. Soc.*, **83**, 1291 (1961).

23. D. C. Grahame, *ibid.*, **80**, 4201 (1958).

24. J. R. Sams, C. W. Lees, and D. C. Grahame, *J. Phys. Chem.*, **63**, 2032 (1959).

25. M. A. V. Devanathan and S. G. Canagaratna, *Electrochim. Acta*, **8**, 77 (1963).

26. M. A. V. Devanthan, *Trans. Faraday Soc.*, **50**, 373 (1954).

27. M. A. V. Devanathan and P. Peries, *ibid.*, **50**, 1236 (1954).

28. A. N. Frumkin and B. B. Damaskin, *Modern Aspects of Electrochemistry*, Vol. 3, J. O'M. Bockris, editor, Butterworths, London, in press.

29. D. C. Grahame, *Chem. Revs.*, **41**, 441 (1947).

30. D. C. Grahame, M. A. Poth, and J. I. Cummings, *J. Am. Chem. Soc.*, **74**, 4422 (1952).

31. S. Levine, G. M. Bell, and D. Calvert, *Canad. J. Chem.*, **40**, 518 (1962).

32. J. O'M. Bockris, M. A. V. Devanathan, and K. Müller, *Proc. Roy. Soc.*, **274A**, 55 (1963).

32a. T. N. Anderson and J. O'M. Bockris, *Electrochim. Acta*, **9**, 347 (1964).

33. B. E. Conway and J. O'M. Bockris, see Ref. 8, p. 62.

34. R. Parsons, *Advances in Electrochemistry and Electrochemical Engineering*, Vol. 1, P. Delahay, editor, Interscience, New York, 1961, pp. 1–64.

35. D. C. Grahame, *Z. Elektrochem.*, **62**, 264 (1958).

36. J. M. Parry and R. Parsons, *Trans. Faraday Soc.*, **59**, 241 (1963).

37. A. N. Frumkin, *Uspekhi Khim.*, **4**, 938 (1935); *Chem. Abstr.*, **31**, 2941 (1937).

38. J. H. de Boer, *Electron Emission and Adsorption Phenomena*, Cambridge University Press, London, 1935.

39. O. A. Esin and V. Shikhov, *Zhur. Fiz. Khim.*, **17**, 236 (1943).

40. B. V. Ershler, *ibid.*, **20**, 679 (1946).

41. R. J. Watts-Tobin, *Phil Mag.*, **6**, 133 (1961).

42. V. G. Levich, V. A. Kir'yanov, and V. S. Krylov, *Doklady Akad. Nauk S.S.S.R.*, **135**, 1425 (1960).

43. V. G. Levich and V. S. Krylov, *ibid.*, **142**, 123 (1962).

44. Yu. I. Yalamov, *Zhur. Fiz. Khim.*, **37**, 1393, 1429 (1963).

45. S. Levine, J. Mingins, and G. M. Bell, *J. Phys. Chem.*, **67**, 2095 (1963).

46. D. C. Grahame, *J. Am. Chem. Soc.*, **79**, 2093 (1957).

47. J. R. Macdonald, *J. Chem. Phys.*, **22**, 1857 (1954).

48. J. R. Macdonald and C. A. Barlow, Jr., *ibid.*, **36**, 3062 (1962).

49. J. R. Macdonald, *ibid.*, **22**, 763 (1954).

50. J. R. Macdonald, *ibid.*, **22**, 1317 (1954).

51. J. R. Macdonald and M. K. Brachman, *ibid.*, **22**, 1314 (1954).

52. J. R. Macdonald, *ibid.*, **25**, 364 (1956).

53. D. C. Grahame, *Z. Elektrochem.*, **59**, 740 (1955).

54. N. F. Mott, R. Parsons and R. J. Watts-Tobin, *Phil. Mag.*, **7**, 483 (1962).

55. M. J. Austin and R. Parsons, *Proc. Chem. Soc.*, 239 (1961).

56. A. N. Frumkin, Ref. 15, pp. 207–208.

57. B. B. Damaskin, E. Schwartz, and A. N. Frumkin, *Doklady Akad. Nauk S.S.S.R.*, **140**, 630 (1961).

58. E. Schwartz, B. B. Damaskin, and A. N. Frumkin, *Zhur. Fiz. Khim.*, **36**, 2419 (1962).

59. D. C. Grahame, *J. Electrochem. Soc.*, **98,** 343 (1951).
60. G. C. Barker, Ref. 15, pp. 325–365.
61. M. Rehbach and J. H. Sluyters, *Rec. trav. chim.*, **80,** 469 (1961); **81,** 301 (1962).
62. C. A. Barlow, Jr. and J. R. Macdonald, *J. Chem. Phys.*, **40,** 1535 (1964).
63. E. Fischerová and O. Fischer, *Coll. Czechoslov. Chem. Commun.*, **26,** 2570 (1961).
64. N. Tanaka, E. Kyuno, G. Sato, and R. Tamamushi, *J. Phys. Chem.*, **66,** 2706 (1962).
65. J. R. Macdonald and C. A. Barlow, *Proceedings of the First Australian Conference on Electrochemistry*, A. Friend and F. Gutmann, editors, Pergamon, Oxford, 1964, pp. 199–247.
66. J. R. Macdonald and C. A. Barlow, *J. Phys. Chem.*, **68,** 2737 (1964).
67. C. A. Barlow and J. R. Macdonald, *J. Chem. Phys.*, in press.
68. J. R. Macdonald and C. A. Barlow, *ibid.*, **39,** 412 (1963).
69. R. Payne, *J. Electroanal. Chem.*, **7,** 343 (1964).

CHAPTER 5

Adsorption at an Ideal Polarized Electrode

5-1 Isotherm and Equations of State

Some sections of the previous chapters dealt with the determination of the surface concentration of an adsorbed substance at an ideal polarized electrode. The treatment in Sec. 4-2 enables us to calculate the amount of a given specifically adsorbed ion when no other ionic species is specifically adsorbed. Equation 2-12 gives the relative surface excess of an uncharged species which may be taken for not too concentrated a solution to be equal to the surface concentration of that substance on the reasonable assumption that there is hardly any diffuse double layer for uncharged substances. We now turn to the interpretation of the results that can be obtained by the previously outlined methods. More specifically, we concern ourselves with particle-particle and particle-electrode interactions (1) and consider the corresponding equilibrium conditions and, to a much lesser extent, kinetics. We begin with a general isotherm for an ideal polarized electrode and then discuss briefly the most common isotherms.

Reference is made to the copious literature on metal-gas adsorption for details on isotherms and in particular to the rather recent books of Hayward and Trapnell (2) and Young and Crowell (3) and to Honig's review (4). An extensive review of adsorption at an ideal polarized electrode was recently prepared by Frumkin and Damaskin (5). Certain aspects of the problem are treated in Parson's review (6).

When there is equilibrium between a species in the adsorbed state and in the bulk of the solution at an ideal polarized electrode, the corresponding electrochemical potentials are equal. Thus

$$\bar{\mu}_A^* + RT \ln [f(\Gamma)] - \bar{\mu}^* - RT \ln a = 0$$

where the $\bar{\mu}_A^*$ and $\bar{\mu}^*$ are the electrochemical potentials in the adsorbed state and in solution, respectively, at the exclusion of the activity terms. The quantity $f(\Gamma)$ which is a function of the surface concentration Γ represents the activity of the adsorbate, and a is the corresponding activity in the bulk of the solution. The symbol Γ is used here and throughout this chapter to designate the surface concentration unless specified otherwise. This is common practice, and confusion with surface excess, also represented by Γ, hopefully will not arise. We rewrite the preceding equation as

$$f(\Gamma) = ae^{-\overline{\Delta G^0}/RT}$$

where $\overline{\Delta G^0} = \bar{\mu}_A^* - \bar{\mu}^*$ is the *standard free energy of adsorption*. We now define the parameter β for the sake of conciseness.

$$\beta = e^{-\overline{\Delta G^0}/RT} \tag{1}$$

and write the isotherm in the form

$$\Gamma = \Gamma(\beta a) \tag{2}$$

Equation 2 shows that the isotherm is some function $\Gamma(\beta a)$ of the product of the bulk activity and the quantity β, which depends on some electrical parameter characterizing conditions at the ideal polarized electrode. Parsons (7) has consistently used Eqs. 1 and 2 as starting point in his work.

The explicit form of the isotherm of Eq. 2 depends on particle-particle and particle-electrode interactions. In many instances it is convenient to start with the *surface pressure P* and then derive the corresponding isotherm. The surface pressure for an ideal polarized electrode is defined as the change of the quantity $\xi = \gamma + qE$ for the electrolyte without the adsorbate to the value of the same quantity in presence of the adsorbate (7). Thus at constant charge

$$P = \xi_b - \xi$$
$$= (\gamma_b - \gamma) + q(E_b - E) \tag{3}$$

where the subscript "b" refers to the solution in the absence of the adsorbate.

The most common isotherms with which we need concern ourselves here and in Chapter 10 are listed in Table 5-1. This list, prepared by Parsons (8, 9), is inspired from Everett's work (10) on adsorption. The different equations of state and/or isotherms will be briefly examined. Further details can be found in treatments of metal-gas adsorption (2–4), the

TABLE 5-1 Equations of State and Isotherms[a]

Name	Equation of State	Isotherm
Henry's Law	$P = RT\Gamma$	$\beta a = RT\Gamma$
Virial	$P = RT\Gamma + g\Gamma^2$	$\beta a = RT\Gamma e^{2g\Gamma/RT}$
Langmuir	$P = -RT\Gamma_s \ln\left(1 - \dfrac{\Gamma}{\Gamma_s}\right)$	$\beta a = \dfrac{\Gamma}{\Gamma_s - \Gamma} = \dfrac{\theta}{1 - \theta}$
Frumkin	$P = -RT\Gamma_s \ln\left(1 - \dfrac{\Gamma}{\Gamma_s}\right) + g\Gamma^2$	$\beta a = \dfrac{\theta}{1 - \theta} e^{2g\Gamma/RT}$
Volmer	$P = RT\dfrac{\Gamma}{1 - b\Gamma}$	$\beta a = \dfrac{\Gamma}{1 - b\Gamma} e^{b\Gamma/1 - b\Gamma}$
Helfand, Frisch, and Lebowitz modified by Parsons ("modified H.F.L.")	$P = RT\dfrac{\Gamma}{(1 - b\Gamma)^2} + g\Gamma^2$	$\beta a = \dfrac{\theta}{1 - \theta}\dfrac{b}{0.907}\exp\left[g\theta + \dfrac{1}{1 - \theta} + \dfrac{1}{(1 - \theta)^2} - 2\right]$
Temkin $(0.2 < \theta < 0.8)$	$P = g\Gamma^2$	$\beta a = e^{2g\Gamma/RT}$

[a] According to Parsons in Ref. 8 for all isotherms except for the modified H.F.L. equation of state and isotherm which are from Ref. 9.

83

original literature, and in Parsons' paper (8). Henry's law follows directly from the assumption that the adsorbate can be treated as a two-dimensional ideal gas. The virial equation is a modified form of Henry's law in which particle-particle interaction is accounted for by the empirical term $g\Gamma^2$ in the corresponding equation of state. This term was originally introduced by Frumkin (11) in the equation of state corresponding to the Langmuir isotherm. The parameter g is positive for attraction and negative for repulsion. Thus particle-particle repulsion decreases the surface pressure ($g < 0$) and attraction increases it ($g > 0$). The Volmer equation treats adsorption as a two-dimensional fluid of rigid particles and so does the Helfand, Frisch, and Lebowitz (H.F.L.) isotherm (12). The parameter b in the latter equation is the molecular area and $0.907/b$ is the saturation coverage for a closed-packed layer of hard spheres. The H.F.L. equation of state in Table 5.1 contains the additional term $g\Gamma^2$ which was introduced by Parsons (9) to account for particle-particle interaction in the same way as in the virial and Frumkin equations. Finally, the logarithmic Temkin isotherm is derived by assuming that the heat of adsorption varies linearly with coverage. The equation in Table 5-1 for this isotherm corresponds to intermediate coverage and a more complete equation [cf., for example (2)] is available. [See also Frumkin's recently stated views on the question of isotherms (74).]

There are two schools of thought concerning the interaction parameter g: (a) Parsons, in agreement with Frumkin's original suggestion, considers that g is independent of the potential or the charge on the electrode; the effect of the electrical field at the interface appears solely in the term β of Eq. 1. (b) Damaskin (Sec. 5-7) retains the dependence of β on potential, but he also assumes that g is a function of potential. These two approaches are discussed in Secs. 5-6 and 5-7. Part of the difficulty in settling this question is in the convenient but somewhat artificial division into electrode-particle and particle-particle interactions.

The virial isotherm in Table 5-1 can be rewritten as Henry's law by multiplying both members by $e^{-2g\Gamma/RT}$ and by defining β by

$$\beta = \beta_{\theta=0} e^{-2g\Gamma/RT} \tag{4}$$

The same transformation can be applied to the Frumkin isotherm which takes then the form of a Langmuir isotherm with the factor β defined by Eq. 4. A similar transformation can also be made for the modified H.F.L. isotherm, but the dependence of β on coverage is more involved than that predicted by Eq. 4. It follows from Eq. 4 that analysis of isotherms as a deviation from Henry's law or a Langmuir isotherm should lead to a linear variation of the standard free energy of adsorption with coverage provided that either the virial or the Frumkin isotherm can be applied.

Some results given by Blomgren, Bockris, and Jesch (13) show that this correlation is fairly well obeyed, at least when the coverage is not too high (Fig. 5-1).

Expressions for the particle-particle interaction other than the term $g\Gamma^2$ in the equations of state of Table 5-1 can be derived by transposition of the corresponding treatments for metal-gas adsorption. The only attempt made thus far, it would seem, is that of Blomgren and Bockris (14), who

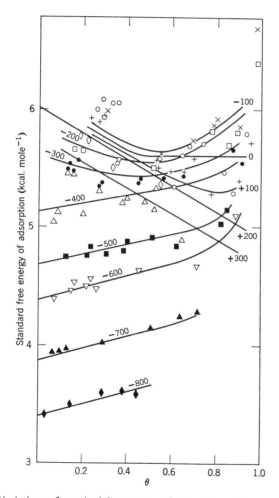

FIG. 5-1. Variations of standard free energy of adsorption with coverage for phenol in 0.1M hydrochloric acid. Potentials in millivolts referred to hydrogen electrode at atmospheric pressure in 0.1M hydrochloric acid. [Blomgren, Bockris, and Jesch (13)] (by permission of the American Chemical Society).

started with the Langmuir isotherm and corrected the standard free energy of adsorption, in the case of ion adsorption, for coulombic interaction and dispersive forces. (See Refs. 3 and 4 for the corresponding treatments of metal-gas adsorption.) Blomgren and Bockris obtained for ion adsorption the following β-factor in the Langmuir isotherm (Table 5-1)

$$\beta = \beta_{\theta=0} e^{-(p_1\theta^{1/2}-p_2\theta^3)} \tag{5}$$

where p_1 and p_2 are parameters whose explicit forms they give. Similarly, Conway and Barradas (15) wrote the Langmuir isotherm in Table 5-1 with the following β-factor for dipole-dipole interaction in the adsorption of an uncharged substance

$$\beta = \beta_{\theta=0} e^{-(p_3\theta^{3/2}-p_2\theta^3)} \tag{6}$$

p_3 being given in explicit form. If θ is not too close to unity, the term $\theta^{1/2}$ in Eq. 5 and the term in $\theta^{3/2}$ in Eq. 6 are predominant. The corresponding plots are shown in Fig. 5-2 to 5-4. The $\overline{\Delta G}{}^0$ versus $\theta^{1/2}$ plots are quite

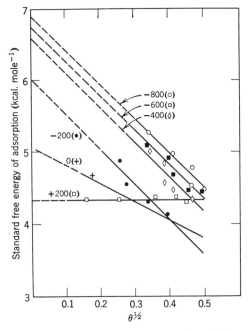

FIG. 5.2. Variations of standard free energy of adsorption with square root of coverage for aniline in $0.1M$ hydrochloric acid at $25°C$. Potentials in millivolts referred to hydrogen electrode at atmospheric pressure in $0.1M$ hydrochloric acid [Blomgren and Bockris (14)] (by permission of the American Chemical Society).

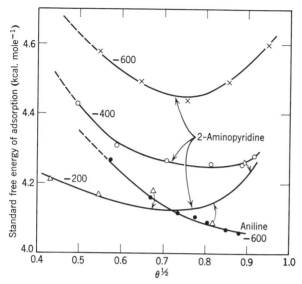

FIG. 5-3. Same plot as in Fig. 5-2 but for 2-aminopyridine and aniline in $1M$ hydrochloric acid at 25°C. Potential in millivolts referred to the normal calomel electrode [Barradas and Conway (16)] (by permission of Pergamon).

linear in Fig. 5-2, but there is considerable departure from linearity at high coverages in Fig. 5-3, as one would expect from Eq. 5. The $\overline{\Delta G^0}$ versus $\theta^{3/2}$ linear relationship holds well in Fig. 5-4 except at high coverages (cf. Eq. 6). These relationships are interesting, but it remains to be seen whether a simple model for physical metal-gas adsorption can be transposed to physical adsorption at a metal-electrolyte interface. Study in an electrolyte without strong ion specific adsorption (no chloride!) would be desirable.

5-2 Dependence of Standard Free Energy of Adsorption on Electrical Variable

a. Selection of Electrical Variable

Ideally we should select experimental conditions in the investigation of isotherms for which the "electrical part" of β is kept constant. Several approaches, which are reviewed by Parsons (9) and discussed further by Damaskin (75), have been followed. Stern (17) suggested isotherms at constant potential in the plane of closest approach. He did not make a

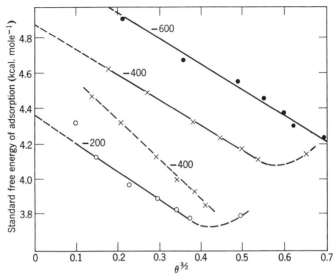

FIG. 5-4. Variations of standard free energy adsorption with $\frac{3}{2}$ power of coverage for aniline in $1M$ potassium chloride at $25°C$. Potentials in millivolts referred to normal calomel electrode. Solid curves for a saturation surface concentration of 7.1×10^{-10} mole cm.$^{-2}$; dotted line for 8.8×10^{-10} mole cm.$^{-2}$ [Conway and Barradas (15)] (by permission of Pergamon).

distinction between inner and outer planes, but his suggestion in terms of Grahame's model amounts to keeping the potential ϕ_1 constant in the inner plane. Stern thought that the diffuse double-layer component of the difference of potential ϕ_M was eliminated by this procedure. However, this is not the case at constant ϕ_1 because this potential includes a component depending on the charge q^1 of specifically adsorbed ions in the inner plane (Chapter 4).

Frumkin (11) advocated the use of constant ϕ_M, that is, constant E, but the diffuse double-layer contribution to ϕ_M is not constant under these conditions when the amount of adsorbed substance varies. This point is discussed in Chapter 4 for specifically adsorbed ions and in this chapter for uncharged species. The effect is perhaps not very significant for uncharged substances.

Parsons (7) suggested that constant electrode charge maintains electrode-particle interactions nearly constant. He added later (9) that these interactions might still vary somewhat, even at constant charge, as a result of a variation of the dielectric constant in the compact layer with the amount of adsorbed substance. Parsons also noted (9) that constancy of the charge on the metal is also achieved in gas-metal adsorption since this charge is then equal to zero, whereas the surface potential varies. Damaskin (75), however, strongly argued against Parsons' views for uncharged substances and recommended constancy of potential E, as initially suggested by Frumkin. (See also comment at the end of Sec. 5-3 about the equation used by Damaskin as a starting point.) It seems hard to refute Parsons' argument that adsorption of an uncharged particle changes the diffuse double-layer contribution to ϕ_M but, on the other hand, Parsons did not prove his point beyond the considerations just stated. This uncertainty in the selection of an electrical variable is a reflection of the present lack of detailed knowledge of the double layer for an electrode with uncharged adsorbate. It is not excluded that none of these suggestions is entirely satisfactory. We shall express results at constant E and constant q. [See also Parsons' recent reply (76) to the criticisms of Frumkin (74) and Damaskin (75).]

b. *Ions*

The dependence of the standard free energy of adsorption for specifically adsorbed ions can be found from some of the results of Chapter 4 by an analysis given by Parsons (18). We begin with Eq. 2-18, which we write for a univalent anion for constant temperature, pressure, and electrode composition. Thus

$$\left(\frac{\partial E_+}{\partial \Gamma_-}\right)_q = \left(\frac{\partial \mu}{\partial q}\right)_{\Gamma_-}$$

$$= RT\left(\frac{\partial \ln a_\pm}{\partial q}\right)_{\Gamma_-} \tag{7}$$

We can express E_+ as a function of the potential E_r versus some reference electrode in a cell with liquid junction (cf. Sec. 4-1a). We have on the assumption that the liquid junction is negligible

$$E_+ = E_r - \frac{1}{f}\ln a_\pm$$

We now divide E_r into ϕ_{M-2} and ϕ_2, that is,

$$E_r = \phi_{M-2} + \phi_2 + \text{constant}$$

Equation 7 becomes

$$\left(\frac{\partial \phi_{M-2}}{\partial \Gamma_-}\right)_q + \left(\frac{\partial \phi_2}{\partial \Gamma_-}\right)_q - \left(\frac{1}{2F}\frac{\partial \mu}{\partial \Gamma_-}\right)_q = \left(\frac{\partial \mu}{\partial q}\right)_{\Gamma_-^1} - \left(\frac{\partial \mu}{\partial \Gamma_-}\right)_q\left(\frac{\partial \Gamma_-}{\partial q}\right)_{\Gamma_-^1}$$

where we have introduced the surface concentration Γ_-^1 of specifically adsorbed anions. The right-hand side of this equation was transformed to express the partial derivatives at constant Γ_-^1 rather than at constant

Γ_-. By multiplying this equation by $(\partial\Gamma_-/\partial\Gamma_-{}^1)_q$, we obtain

$$\left(\frac{\partial\phi_{M-2}}{\partial\Gamma_-{}^1}\right)_q = \left(\frac{\partial\mu}{\partial q}\right)_{\Gamma_-{}^1}\left(\frac{\partial\Gamma_-{}^1}{\partial\Gamma}\right)_q - \left(\frac{\partial\phi_2}{\partial\Gamma_-{}^1}\right)_q + \left[\frac{1}{2F} - \left(\frac{\partial\Gamma_-}{\partial q}\right)_{\Gamma_-{}^1}\right]\left(\frac{\partial\mu}{\partial\Gamma_-{}^1}\right)_q$$

Or, in view of Eqs. 1 and 2,

$$\left(\frac{\partial\phi_{M-2}}{\partial q_-{}^1}\right)_q = \frac{1}{f}\left(\frac{\partial\ln\beta}{\partial q}\right)\left(\frac{\partial q_-{}^1}{\partial q_-}\right)_q - \left(\frac{\partial\phi_2}{\partial q_-{}^1}\right)_q + \frac{1}{F}\left[\frac{1}{2} - \left(\frac{\partial q_-}{\partial q}\right)_{q_-{}^1}\right]\left(\frac{\partial\mu}{\partial q_-{}^1}\right)_q \quad (8)$$

where q_- is the charge corresponding to Γ_-. Equation 8 allows the determination of the dependence of the standard free energy of adsorption on the charge q (term $\partial\ln\beta/\partial_q$) from available quantities. A simpler form of Eq. 8 had been derived previously by Parsons (19), namely

$$\left(\frac{\partial\phi_{M-2}}{\partial q_-{}^1}\right)_q = \frac{1}{f}\left(\frac{\partial\ln\beta}{\partial q}\right) \quad (9)$$

but this result, as he noted (18), is only approximate because it does not take into account the contribution of the diffuse double layer.

The quantity $(\partial\phi_{M-2}/\partial q_-{}^1)_q$ was calculated for potassium iodide by Grahame (20, cf. his Table 4), who obtained constancy within $\pm10\%$. Parsons (18) stated without further comment that Eq. 8 is in good agreement with experiment, and we may infer, on the basis of Grahame's results

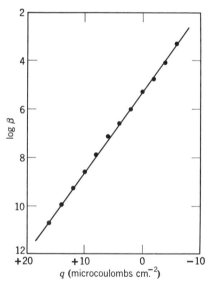

FIG. 5-5. Variations of the standard free energy of adsorption (expressed as $\log\beta$) with the charge on the electrode for iodide adsorption on mercury at 25°C [Parsons (19)] (by permission of the Faraday Society).

and the approximate equation 9 that ∂ in $\beta/\partial q$ is independent of the charge in this particular instance. The standard free energy of adsorption in this case should be essentially a linear function of the charge (Fig. 5-5). We shall consider that the iodide behavior is typical of ion specific adsorption and accept as a *working hypothesis* a linear dependence of the standard free energy of adsorption on the charge. This result can be interpreted, according to Parsons (1), on the basis of a simple model in which the compact double layer behaves as a parallel plate capacitor of constant thickness with a dielectric of constant properties.

c. Uncharged Substances

Two treatments, due to Frumkin (11) and to Butler (21) respectively, are available for the dependence of the standard free energy of adsorption on potential (or charge). We begin with the former treatment and divide $\overline{\Delta G^0}$ according to

$$\overline{\Delta G^0} = \Delta G^0 + \tfrac{1}{2}(C - C')(\Delta\phi)^2 A + \left(\frac{\mu}{l} - \frac{\mu'}{l'}\right)\Delta\phi \qquad (10)$$

where the superscript "prime" indicates saturation of the electrode surface by the adsorbate and the absence of this superscript denotes that no adsorbate is present. C is the double-layer capacity of an element of area A; $\Delta\phi$ is the difference potential across the capacity; l is the distance between the plates of the capacitor; and μ is the component of dipole moment of the element of capacity perpendicular to the capacitor plates. Details on Eq. 10 are given by Frumkin in his original paper (11) and in his recent review with Damaskin (5). The notations and subsequent treatment follow Parsons (1).

The first term on the right-hand side of Eq. 10 accounts for the variation of energy due to a decrease in dielectric constant and an increase in plate separation when the adsorbate is introduced. The second term corresponds to the change in dipole moment. It may be noted that Frumkin wrote this term $C'(\Delta E_z)(E - E_{z,\theta=0})$ where ΔE_z is the shift of E_z from $\theta = 0$ to $\theta = 1$; the first term was written as $\tfrac{1}{2}(C - C')(E - E_{z,\theta=0})$; Eq. 10 is simply another formulation of Frumkin's ideas. Equation 10 can be transformed further by selecting either the potential as electrical variable (Frumkin) or the charge on the electrode (Parsons). Both treatments will be given.

According to Eq. 10 there is maximum adsorption when

$$\Delta\phi = \Delta\phi_{max} = -\frac{\dfrac{\mu}{l} - \dfrac{\mu'}{l'}}{(C - C')A}$$

and the corresponding $\overline{\Delta G^0}$ is

$$\overline{\Delta G^0_{max}} = \Delta G^0 - \frac{\left(\dfrac{\mu}{l} - \dfrac{\mu'}{l'}\right)^2}{2(C - C')A}$$

Equation 10 can now be rewritten

$$\overline{\Delta G^0} = \overline{\Delta G^0_{max}} + \tfrac{1}{2}(C - C')A(E - E_{max})^2 \qquad (11)$$

where E is the usual potential and E_{max} the potential for maximum adsorption. We thus obtain $\overline{\Delta G^0}$ as a function of directly measurable quantities.

Transposition of Frumkin's treatment in terms of the charge q is immediate (1). There is maximum adsorption for

$$q_{max} = -\frac{4\pi(\mu/\epsilon - \mu'/\epsilon')}{(1/C' - 1/C)A}$$

and

$$\overline{\Delta G^0_{max}} = \Delta G^0 - \frac{[4\pi(\mu/\epsilon - \mu'/\epsilon')]^2}{2(1/C' - 1/C)A}$$

Hence

$$\overline{\Delta G^0} = \overline{\Delta G^0_{max}} + \frac{1}{2}\left(\frac{1}{C'} - \frac{1}{C}\right)A(q - q_{max})^2 \qquad (12)$$

Butler (21) calculated the electrical part of $\overline{\Delta G^0}$ from the work done when an element of volume V of solvent 1 is replaced by the same volume element V of adsorbate 2. Thus

$$\overline{\Delta G^0} = \Delta G^0 + \tfrac{1}{2}(\alpha_2 - \alpha_1)X^2V + (P_2 - P_1)XV$$

where α is the polarizability, P the permanent polarization per unit volume, and X the field strength. We can treat this equation exactly as Eq. 10 and show that $\overline{\Delta G^0}$ is the sum of $\overline{\Delta G^0_{max}}$ for maximum adsorption and a term varying with X^2. The field strength is not a directly measurable quantity, and it is necessary to express X in terms of $E - E_{max}$ (or $q - q_{max}$). This was done by Butler, who obtained a term in $(E - E_{max})^2$ just as in Eq. 11. The transformation from X to E involves some assumptions which are avoided when we start directly from Eq. 10. The Butler treatment uses a very simple model, but it has the disadvantage, as Frumkin and Damaskin (5) pointed out, of involving quantities which are not directly measurable. The water-competition theory of Butler was further examined by Bockris, Devanathan, and Müller (22), who also considered lateral interaction.

5-3   Charge-Coverage Relationship

The relationship between charge and coverage can be established provided the dependence of β on q is introduced in the isotherm of Table 5-1. Alternatively, we can postulate a charge-coverage relationship for some model and verify the validity of any particular isotherm by making use of Eq. 2-16, namely for a constant chemical potential of the electrolyte

$$\left(\frac{\partial E}{\partial \mu}\right)_q = -\left(\frac{\partial \Gamma}{\partial q}\right)_\mu \tag{13}$$

Equation 13 is written for adsorption of an uncharged substance, and we can then substitute surface concentration for the surface excess. Furthermore, we write E instead of E_+ because the potential need not be referred to an electrode that is reversible to the cation or anion is solution.

Frumkin (11) assumed that the double layer can be represented by a model composed of two capacitors in parallel corresponding to the plate areas which are uncovered and covered with adsorbate, respectively. The charge on the electrode is then

$$q = q_{\theta=0}(1 - \theta) + q_{\theta=1}\theta \tag{14}$$

where θ is the coverage. From Eqs. 13 and 14 we would predict a linear plot of E against μ at constant charge. Such Esin and Markov plots (cf. Figs. 4-1 and 4-2) do not seem to have been reported with the exception of the results of Barradas and Conway (16) in Fig. 5-6. Even so these results pertain to organic ions rather than uncharged substances. Plots in Fig. 5-6 seem to be fairly linear. Similar Esin and Markov plots for different values of the charge on the electrode were also obtained in the writer's laboratory by Mohilner and Tidwell (23) for n-amyl alcohol adsorption in sodium fluoride and were fairly linear. However, the argument is only tentative because this test does not appear to be very sensitive, as Mohilner and Tidwell concluded.

Equation 14 can be tested directly by comparison of the θ's, deduced from experimental surface excesses, with the values of θ computed from this equation on the basis of experimental values of q. Such a verification does not involve any assumption about the isotherm. Breiter and Delahay (24) made such a comparison for n-amyl alcohol in perchloric acid and found fair agreement. However, affecting errors θ, which can be as large as 10% even with good technique (13, 14), do not make such a comparison wholly convincing.

Hansen, Minturn, and Hickson (25) used Eq. 14 in conjunction with the Frumkin isotherm to account for the adsorption of n-valeric acid in $0.1 M$ perchloric acid. Hansen, Kelsh, and Grantham (26) returned to this problem and obtained agreement near the point of zero charge for the

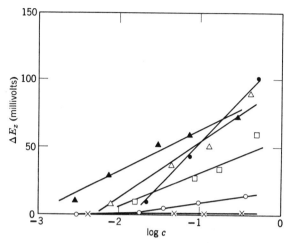

FIG. 5-6. Variations of the point of zero charge with the logarithm of concentration for various aminium ions in $1M$ hydrochloric acid at $25°C$; $\bigcirc$—anilinium; $\bullet$—piperidinium; $\blacktriangle$—2-chloropyridinium; $\times$—2-aminopyridinium; $\triangle$—1,2,3,6-tetrahydropyridinium; $\square$—pyridinium [Barradas and Conway (16)] (by permission of Pergamon).

adsorption of n-amyl alcohol in perchloric acid. Adsorption of phenol in perchloric acid, however, could be described satisfactorily only by inclusion of a term in θ^3 in the equation for the charge. Similarly, Damaskin and Grigorjev (27) did not obtain satisfactory agreement between experiment for the adsorption of ter-amyl alcohol and the results predicted from a combination of Eq. 14 with the Frumkin isotherm.

Equation 14 can be written in terms of differential capacities by differentiation with respect to E, and the resulting equation can be applied, as a first approximation, to the interpretation of differential capacities.

An objection to the simple model of two parallel capacitors was raised by Parsons (19) who showed that Eq. 14 implies that adsorption must obey, among the most common isotherms, either Henry's law or the Freundlich isotherm. These two isotherms do not predict any saturation value of θ, and their use therefore is not self-consistent with Eq. 14. Application of this equation requires caution as it is only approximate and definitely not of thermodynamic character. Arguments based on Eq. 14, as those given by Damaskin (75) in favor of the choice of the potential E as electrical variable (Sec. 5-2a), lose some of their rigor because of the approximate nature of this equation.

Consideration of interaction between the terms corresponding to $\theta = 0$ and $\theta = 1$ might improve Eq. 14, as suggested by Macdonald and Barlow (77). Parsons' objection might then be removed.

5-4   Isotherm Assignment from Surface Excesses

The assignment of an isotherm would appear rather straightforward since surface excesses can be determined by thermodynamic argument. Surface excesses can be identified with surface concentrations for uncharged substances or, for ions, can be corrected for the diffuse double-layer contribution (Chapter 4). This thermodynamic approach has been applied since the early studies of Gouy, Frumkin, Butler, and others. Valuable results, which are briefly reviewed next, were gathered, but the assignment of isotherms is hampered by errors affecting surface excesses (9). More sensitive criteria than isotherm plots are needed to discriminate between different isotherms, especially for adsorption of uncharged substances. Such criteria follow from the determination of surface pressure (Sec. 5-5) and double-layer capacity (Sec. 5-6).

Sets of electrocapillary curves for a typical aliphatic substance, n-amyl alcohol, and a typical aromatic substance, phenol, are shown in Figs. 5-7 and 5-8 respectively. The charge-potential curves corresponding to Fig. 5-8 are given in Fig. 5-9. There is an appreciable decrease of interfacial tension on addition of adsorbate and a shift of the point of zero charge toward positive potentials for n-amyl alcohol and toward negative potentials for phenol. Frumkin (5, 28, 29) concluded that this shift for aliphatic compounds is caused by dipole orientation, dipoles having their negative end closest to mercury. He also compared the shift of the point of zero charge with the variation of the adsorption potential at an air-solution interface and obtained a good correlation for aliphatic compounds. Discrepancies between these two sets of data are observed, however, for aromatic substances, as was shown by Gerovich and co-workers (30–32). This discrepancy was explained by assuming interaction of π-electrons and the electrode. Adsorbed molecules are assumed to lie flat on the electrode and are not desorbed for increasingly positive charges (Fig. 5-8), whereas aliphatic compounds are desorbed for sufficiently positive and negative charges (Fig. 5-7). Interaction between the electrode and π-electrons is also discussed by Bockris and co-workers (13, 14) and by Conway and Barradas (15, 16), and further details are given by Frumkin and Damaskin (5) and by Frumkin (33). (For a discussion of gas-electrolyte interfaces in the absence of organic adsorbate see, for example, Refs. 34–36.)

From results such as those of Figs. 5-8 and 5-9, we can deduce the variations of surface concentration with potential or with charge at constant bulk concentration of adsorbate (Fig. 5-10). The isotherm at constant charge or constant potential may be plotted from data such as those of Fig. 5-10. A variety of substances has been studied, and the Frumkin isotherm has been shown to fit experimental data in numerous cases

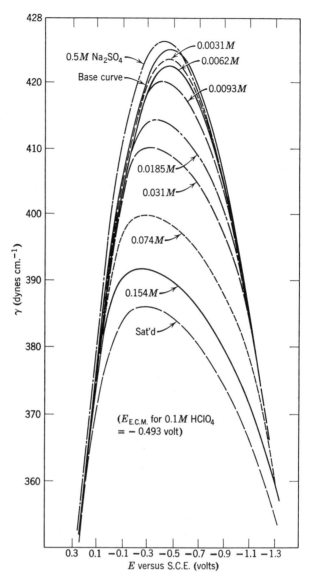

FIG. 5-7. Electrocapillary curves for mercury in $0.1M$ perchloric acid plus n-amyl alcohol of different concentrations at $25°C$ [Hansen, Kelsh, and Grantham (26)] (by permission of the American Chemical Society).

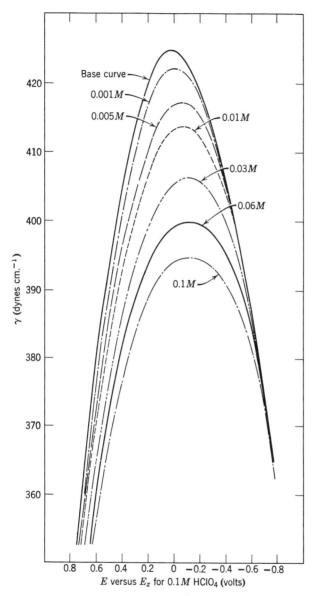

FIG. 5-8. Electrocapillary curves for mercury in $0.1M$ perchloric acid plus phenol at different concentrations at 25°C [Hansen, Kelsh, and Grantham (26)] (by permission of the American Chemical Society).

provided the interaction constant g is supposed to be a function of potential (Sec. 5-7). A detailed review is available (5) and we shall only emphasize the following three points. (*a*) Surface excesses are generally computed from plots of interfacial tension against the logarithm of the bulk concentration of adsorbate. Concentrations are thus substituted for activities to avoid activity coefficient determinations. This procedure may lead to serious errors, as noted by Frumkin (5), when results are compared for different electrolyte concentrations because of the salting-out effect. (*b*) The coverage θ is generally taken equal to Γ/Γ_s, where Γ_s is the saturation value of Γ. This definition of θ implies two assumptions which may not be justified at high coverages (5): monolayer formation and

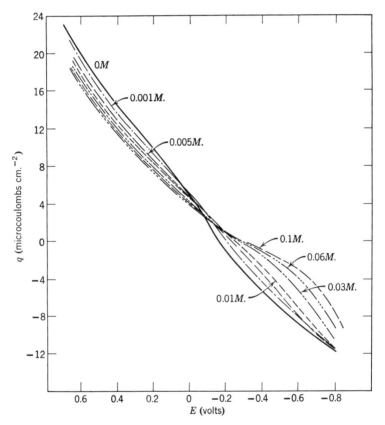

FIG. 5-9. Variations of charge on the electrode with potential for the data of Fig. 5-8. Potentials referred to hydrogen electrode at atmospheric pressure in $0.1M$ perchloric acid [Hansen, Kelsh, and Grantham (26)] (by permission of the American Chemical Society).

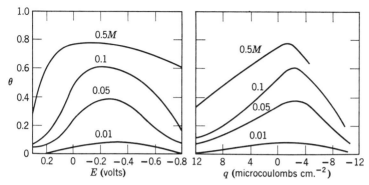

FIG. 5-10. Coverage versus potential (left) and charge (right) on the electrode for adsorption of *n*-butyl alcohol, at different concentrations, on mercury in $0.1M$ hydrochloric acid at 25°C. Potentials referred to hydrogen electrode at atmospheric pressure in $0.1M$ hydrochloric acid [Bockris, Devanathan, and Müller (22)] (by permission of The Royal Society).

constant covered area per molecule. (*c*) Multilayer adsorption and micelle formation in the adsorbed layer may interfere, especially for large adsorbed molecules (5, 37, 38). The existence of multilayers can be inferred from the shape of capacity-potential curves, and several examples have been reported (38).

5-5 Isotherm Assignment from Surface Pressures

The uncertainty in the determination of surface excesses prompted Parsons (7) to suggest analysis of surface pressure data for the assignment of isotherms. Figure 5-11 shows that different isotherms may have nearly

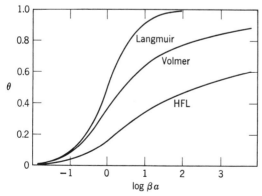

FIG. 5-11. Coverage against the logarithm of bulk activity (plotted as βa) for the Langmuir, Volmer, and HFL isotherms [Parsons (9)] (by permission of Elsevier).

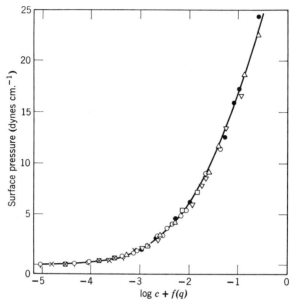

FIG. 5-12. Surface pressure for adsorption of thiourea in $0.1M$ sodium fluoride on mercury at 25°C for different charges on the electrode. The points for different charges are shifted parallel to the $\log c$ axis by an amount depending on q to fall on a common curve. Values of q in microcoulombs cm.$^{-2}$: ● (0), △ (-2), ▽(-4), ○ (-6), □ (-8), ○̣ (-10), × (-12) [Parsons (39)] (by permission of The Royal Society).

the same shape, and therefore sources of error in the analysis of data should be avoided as much as possible. The evaluation of the surface pressure from Eq. 3 eliminates the differentiation of the γ versus μ curves needed in the computation of Γ, and improved accuracy can be expected. Equation 3 can be applied directly to uncharged substances. For ions, however, it is necessary to take into account the contribution of the charge in the diffuse double layer. The calculations are given by Parsons (7) and follow directly from the material in Sec. 4-2.

The surface pressure P is plotted against $\log a$ for ionic specific adsorption or versus $\log c$ for an uncharged substance ($\log a$, if possible) at constant charge (or potential). It was noted by Parsons (39) that the P versus $\log c$ curves at constant charge have practically the same slope for a given surface pressure, regardless of the charge, and these curves can be superimposed by translation along the abscissa axis. Results are plotted in Fig. 5-12 for thiourea (39) from data reported by Schapink et al. (40). A diagram similar to Fig. 5-12 is given by Parry and Parsons (18) for the adsorption of benzene m-sulfonate on mercury in aqueous solution. The

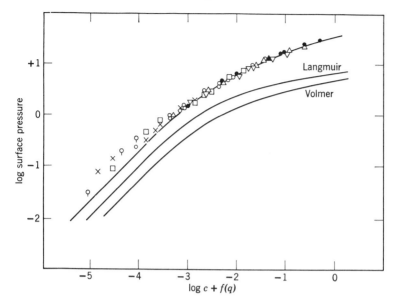

FIG. 5-13. Data of Fig. 5-12 plotted as $\log P$ against $\log c + f(q)$. Comparison between the virial (through points), Langmuir, and Volmer equations of state [Parsons (39)] (by permission of the Royal Society).

isotherm can be tested, via the equation of state, by the replotting of data such as those of Fig. 5-12 in the way shown in Fig. 5-13 for three isotherms. The best fit is obtained for the virial equation of state in this particular instance, but agreement is not fully satisfactory for low values of $\log c + f(q)$. Subsequent analysis based on double-layer capacity (Sec. 5-6) indicates that the Frumkin isotherm is more satisfactory. The differences in shape between the curves of Fig. 5-13 for different equations of state are not considerable, and this hampers somewhat unambiguous assignment of a particular isotherm. This conclusion, which was reached by Parsons (9), led him to prefer analysis from double-layer capacity data (Sec. 5-6).

5-6 Analysis Based on Double-Layer Capacity and Assignment of Isotherms

a. Correlation between Capacity and the Isotherm Parameter Depending on Charge or Potential

The charge on the electrode at constant solution and electrode composition, constant temperature and pressure is solely a function of the

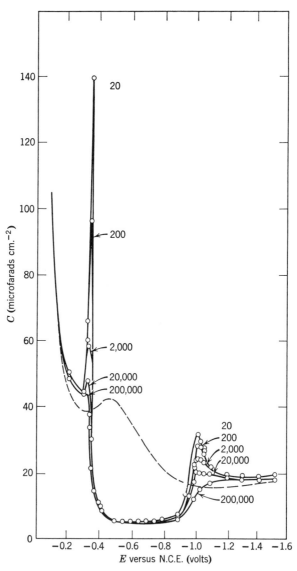

FIG. 5-14. Variations of differential capacity with potential for adsorption of $10^{-2}M$ n-amyl alcohol in $1M$ potassium chloride on a hanging mercury drop at 25°C at different frequencies (in cycles per second). Dotted curve for $1M$ potassium chloride [Melik-Gaikazyan (41); cf. Frumkin (33)] (by permission of *Nova Acta Leopoldina*).

potential and the relative surface excess of the adsorbed species. Hence

$$dq = \left(\frac{\partial q}{\partial E}\right)_\Gamma dE + \left(\frac{\partial q}{\partial \Gamma}\right)_E d\Gamma$$

The differential capacity $C = (\partial q/\partial E)_\mu$ is

$$C = \left(\frac{\partial q}{\partial E}\right)_\Gamma + \left(\frac{\partial q}{\partial \Gamma}\right)_E \left(\frac{d\Gamma}{dE}\right)_\mu \tag{15}$$

The quantity $(\partial q/\partial \Gamma)_E$ in Eq. 15 is given by Eq. 2-17, that is,

$$\left(\frac{\partial q}{\partial \Gamma}\right)_E = -\left(\frac{\partial \mu}{\partial E}\right)_\Gamma$$

Measured capacities correspond to the thermodynamic value given by Eq. 15 only when equilibrium conditions prevail. The potential E includes a periodic component in measurements with the A.C. bridge, and consequently Γ varies periodically with time. The term $(d\Gamma/dE)_\mu$ in Eq. 15 does not necessarily reach its equilibrium value (corresponding to the bulk concentration of adsorbate not near the electrode) because of slow mass transfer and, possibly, slow adsorption. Measurements in which $(\partial \Gamma/dE)_\mu \rightarrow 0$ would correspond to constant coverage. They would yield the capacity $(\partial q/\partial E)_\Gamma$. This capacity is sometimes called the "true capacity," but the expression is misleading since the capacity C of Eq. 15 is truly the thermodynamic capacity (6). The term $(\partial q/\partial E)_\Gamma$ may be called the "constant coverage capacity" or, as Parsons suggests (6), the "infinite frequency capacity." The former expression seems preferable as it does not refer to any particular technique. This capacity would be observed if the frequency in the measurement of C were to approach infinity or for equivalent conditions in pulse techniques. The frequency effect is illustrated by the results of Melik-Gaikazyan (41) in Fig. 5-14 who was the first to make a detailed experimental study of the frequency dependence. [Grahame reported this frequency dependence somewhat earlier (79) but did not make a detailed quantitative study.]

Capacity-potential curves for most uncharged substances and for a number of bulky organic ions exhibit two peaks (Fig. 5-14) which correspond to the two regions of the θ versus E curve (Fig. 5-10) in which coverage varies rapidly with potential. The capacity is the same as that of the electrolyte alone at sufficiently positive or negative potentials for most substances which then are completely desorbed. This, however, is not always the case (for example, substances with π-electron interaction with the electrode). The two peaks in the capacity-potential curves are readily interpreted from the *approximate* Eq. 14. We have by differentiation with respect to E

$$C = C_{\theta=0}(1 - \theta) + C_{\theta=1}\theta + (q_{\theta=1} - q_{\theta=0})\frac{d\theta}{dE} \qquad (16)$$

The last term in this equation is always positive. We have for $E > E_z$, $q_{\theta=1} < q_{\theta=0}$, and $d\theta/dE < 0$; conversely, for $E < E_z$, $q_{\theta=1} > q_{\theta=0}$, and $d\theta/dE > 0$ (cf. Figs. 5-9 and 5-10). The sharpness of the two peaks in C versus E curves depends, of course, on $(d\theta/dE)_\mu$ at equilibrium. It also depends on frequency when equilibrium does not prevail.

The region between the peaks in the $C - E$ curves, which corresponds to the top of the θ versus E curves (Fig. 5-10), is not strongly frequency dependent (Fig. 5-14) because the contribution of the term $d\theta/dE$ in Eq. 16 is rather minor in that range of potential. These considerations are only qualitative because they are based on an approximate charge-coverage relationship (Eq. 14), but they provide a simple explanation of the general shape of capacity-potential curves. *Further considerations in this section deal solely with the thermodynamic capacity C of Eq.* 15.

The capacity of Eq. 15 can be obtained from electrocapillary curves. Double-layer capacity measurements by the bridge method can also be applied with a sufficiently small excursion of potential but results must be corrected for mass transfer. The effect of adsorption on capacity can also be studied qualitatively from the so-called tensammetric waves obtained by A.C. polarography, according to the approach advocated by Breyer and Bauer (42). It has been noted (43) that A.C. polarography is really a method of obtaining a combination of the resistive and capacitive components of the *cell* impedance, whereas bridge measurements allow the separation of these components for the *electrode* impedance. Frumkin and Damaskin (44) emphasized this point of view. [See also (45).] The determination of "tensammetric waves" with an A.C. polarograph is more rapid than bridge measurements and might be thought of as being interesting in analytical determinations. As an analytical tool, however, the method has very poor selectivity.

Capacity-potential curves were examined by Lorenz and co-workers (46–51) and later by Damaskin and co-workers (27, 52–56) and by Parsons (1, 9, 19). A detailed review which, however, does not cover some of the aspects discussed later is given by Frumkin and Damaskin (5). We shall limit ourselves to the essential points, and we shall begin with a general relationship between the double-layer capacity and the isotherm parameter β according to Parsons (9).

We take as starting point Eq. 2-15, which we write for an uncharged substance. Thus we have at constant temperature, pressure, constant electrolyte activity, and constant electrode composition

$$\left(\frac{\partial q}{\partial \mu}\right)_E = \left(\frac{\partial \Gamma}{\partial E}\right)_\mu$$

or, by introducing β (Eq. 2) which is independent of μ,

$$\frac{1}{RT}\left(\frac{\partial q}{\partial \ln a}\right)_E = \left(\frac{\partial \Gamma}{\partial \beta}\right)_\mu \frac{\partial \beta}{\partial E}$$

$$q - q_b = RT\frac{\partial \beta}{\partial E}\int_0^a \left(\frac{\partial \Gamma}{\partial \beta}\right)_\mu d \ln a$$

where the subscript b corresponds to the electrolyte alone. Since the quantities β and a appear as their product βa in the isotherm (Eq. 2),

$$\frac{1}{\beta}\left(\frac{\partial \Gamma}{\partial a}\right)_\beta = \frac{1}{a}\left(\frac{\partial \Gamma}{\partial \beta}\right)_a$$

Hence

$$q - q_b = \frac{RT}{\beta}\frac{\partial \beta}{\partial E}\int_0^a \left(\frac{\partial \Gamma}{\partial a}\right)_E da$$

$$= RT\Gamma\left(\frac{\partial \ln \beta}{\partial E}\right)$$

Introducing now the differential capacities corresponding to q and q_b, we write

$$C - C_b = RT\left[\frac{\partial}{\partial E}\left(\Gamma\frac{\partial \ln \beta}{\partial E}\right)\right]_\mu$$

or

$$C - C_b = RT\left[\Gamma\frac{\partial^2 \ln \beta}{\partial E^2} + \left(\frac{\partial \Gamma}{\partial \ln \beta}\right)_\mu\left(\frac{\partial \ln \beta}{\partial E}\right)^2\right] \tag{17}$$

Similarly, we deduce by selecting the charge as the electrical variable (19)

$$\frac{1}{C} - \frac{1}{C_b} = -RT\left[\Gamma\frac{\partial^2 \ln \beta}{\partial q^2} + \left(\frac{\partial \Gamma}{\partial \ln \beta}\right)_\mu\left(\frac{\partial \ln \beta}{\partial q}\right)^2\right] \tag{18}$$

Since the capacities C and C_b can be measured, an isotherm can be assigned, in principle, provided the dependence of Γ on β is known. The procedure will be developed further by assuming that the standard free energy of adsorption is either a linear or a quadratic function of potential or charge (cf. Sec. 5-2).

b. Capacity-Potential Relationship for a Standard Free Energy Varying Linearly with Potential or Charge

In this case

$$\ln \beta = \ln \beta_{max} - l(E - E_{max}) \tag{19}$$

where β_{max} and E_{max} correspond to maximum adsorption and l is a parameter independent of E. This relationship seems to hold primarily for ionic specific adsorption, but it can be applied to certain uncharged substances (for example, thiourea; see the following) which are strongly bonded to mercury. The term $\partial^2 \ln \beta/\partial E^2$ then vanishes, and Eq. 17 yields

$$C - C_b = RTl^2 \left(\frac{\partial \Gamma}{\partial \ln \beta} \right)_\mu \tag{20}$$

Parsons (1) calculated $(\partial \Gamma/\partial \ln \beta)_\mu$ for the isotherms of Table 1, except the Frumkin and modified H.F.L. isotherms, and compared the predictions of such calculations with experimental values of $C - C_b$. Good agreement was obtained with a Temkin isotherm for the data of Barker and Faircloth (57) on adsorption of chloride and bromide in $1.5M$ perchloride acid. [Values of C_b for perchloric acid were used.] Correlation was equally good for adsorption of thiourea in $0.1M$ sodium fluoride for the data of Schapink et al. (40). The agreement, however, was less satisfactory when $-\ln \beta$ was taken as a linear function of the charge instead of potential.

If we choose the charge q as electrical variable, we write Eq. 18 with linear dependence of $\ln \beta$ on q

$$\frac{1}{C} - \frac{1}{C_b} = -RT \frac{\partial \Gamma}{\partial \ln \beta} \left(\frac{\partial \ln \beta}{\partial q} \right)^2$$

or in terms of the coverage θ,

$$\frac{1}{C} - \frac{1}{C_b} = -\frac{RT}{\Gamma_s} \frac{\partial \theta}{\partial \ln \beta} \left(\frac{\partial \ln \beta}{\partial q} \right)^2 \tag{21}$$

where Γ_s is the saturation value of Γ. The term $\partial \theta/\partial \ln \beta$ can be evaluated for each isotherm of Table 5-1 and this was done by Parsons (9) for the Frumkin and modified H.F.L. isotherms. We have for the Frumkin isotherm

$$\frac{\partial \theta}{\partial \ln \beta} = \left[\frac{1}{\theta(1 - \theta)} + M \right]^{-1} \tag{22}$$

and for the modified H.F.L. isotherm

$$\frac{\partial \theta}{\partial \ln \beta} = \left[\frac{1 + \theta}{(1 - \theta)^3 \theta} + M \right]^{-1} \tag{23}$$

where M is a constant depending on the factor g of these two isotherms (Table 5-1). The capacity according to Eqs. 21 and 22 includes the constant capacity proportional to $1/M$ and the coverage-dependent capacity [term in $\theta(1 - \theta)$]. This point was also noted by Conway and Gileadi (58). A similar remark applies to the modified H.F.L. isotherm.

We have according to Eq. 22 $\partial\theta/\partial \ln \beta = 0$ for $\theta = 0$ and $\theta = 1$. Furthermore, $\partial\theta/\partial \ln \beta$ is maximum at $\theta = 0.5$. The plot of $\partial\theta/\partial \ln \beta$, that is, of $(1/C) - (1/C_b)$, against θ is given by a parabola-shaped curve with a maximum at $\theta = 0.5$ for the Frumkin isotherm. The same plot for the modified H.F.L. isotherm is definitely asymmetrical and has a maximum at $b\Gamma = 0.215$ or ($\Gamma_s = 0.907/b$) at $\theta = 0.237$. Examination of the plot of $(1/C) - (1/C_b)$ against θ provides a direct experimental criterion to distinguish between the Frumkin and modified H.F.L. isotherms. Other isotherms, of course, cannot be ruled out. The curves in Fig. 5-15 for the adsorption of benzene m-disulfonate (9) are definitely asymmetrical and favor the modified H.F.L. isotherm rather than the Frumkin isotherm. The maximum in Fig. 5-15 occurs (for $\theta = 0.237$) for approximately 10 microcoulombs cm.$^{-2}$, that is, for a close-packing coverage of 38 microcoulombs cm.$^{-2}$. Parsons (9) compared this value with the saturation

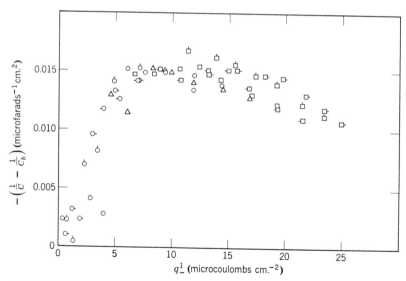

FIG. 5-15. Plot of the change in reciprocal capacity, at constant electrode charge, as a function of specifically adsorbed charge for the adsorption of benzene m-disulfonate on mercury at 20°C. Data from Parry and Parsons (18). Charge on the electrode in microcoulombs.cm^{-2}: O- (−8), Ȯ (−6), -O (−4), O (−2), △ (0), □ (2), -□ (4), □ (6), □- (8) [Parsons (9)] (by permission of Elsevier).

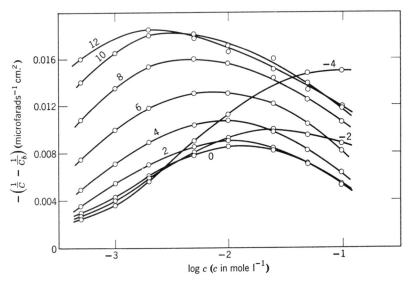

FIG. 5-16. Plot of the change in reciprocal capacity, at constant electrode charge (in microcoulombs cm.$^{-2}$), against the logarithm of thiourea concentration for the adsorption of this substance on mercury in potassium nitrate. Data from unpublished work by Parsons and Symons [(Parsons (9)] (by permission of Elsevier).

coverage of 34.5 microcoulombs cm.$^{-2}$ he calculated on the assumption that ions lie flat on the electrode and rotate freely.

This method of distinguishing between isotherms requires coverage computation with all its inherent uncertainties. This difficulty is avoided, as Parsons (9) suggested, when $(1/C) - (1/C_b)$ is plotted against the logarithm of bulk activity (concentration) of adsorbate. This plot is symmetrical for the Frumkin isotherm and asymmetrical for the modified H.F.L. isotherm. Results for thiourea in Fig. 5-16 suggest validity of the Frumkin isotherm in this particular instance.

c. Capacity-Potential Relationship for a Standard Free-Energy Quadratic in the Potential or the Charge

We now apply Eq. 11, which we write by analogy with Eq. 19,

$$\ln \beta = \ln \beta_{max} - \frac{s}{2}(E - E_{max})^2 \tag{24}$$

with

$$s = \frac{(C - C')A}{RT}$$

Similarly,

$$\ln \beta = \ln \beta_{max} - \frac{s'}{2}(q - q_{max})^2 \tag{25}$$

with

$$s' = \frac{(1/C' - 1/C)A}{RT}$$

Hence, Eqs. 17 and 18 yield (1, 9)

$$C - C_b = RT\left\{-s\Gamma + [s(E - E_{max})]^2\left(\frac{\partial\Gamma}{\partial\ln\beta}\right)_\mu\right\} \tag{26}$$

$$\frac{1}{C} - \frac{1}{C_b} = RT\left\{s'\Gamma - [s'(q - q_{max})]^2\left(\frac{\partial\Gamma}{\partial\ln\beta}\right)_\mu\right\} \tag{27}$$

The quantity $C - C_b$ goes through a minimum for $E = E_{max}$, that is, at maximum adsorption, and $(1/C) - (1/C_b)$ exhibits a maximum at this point. The potential E_{max} and the charge q_{max} can be obtained directly from capacity measurements, and Γ_{max} can be computed from capacities. Thus, at Γ_{max}

$$C - C_b = -sRT\Gamma_{max} \tag{28}$$

$$\frac{1}{C} - \frac{1}{C_b} = s'RT\Gamma_{max} \tag{29}$$

These equations hold regardless of the isotherm and depend only on Eqs. 2 and 25 or 26. Equation 28 was originally derived by Lorenz and Möckel (46). Parsons (9) in a further examination of Eq. 27 gives a method, similar to that of Sec. 5-6b, for distinguishing between the Frumkin and modified H.F.L. isotherms. Comparison with experiment was only tentative.

The two peaks in the capacity-potential curves (Fig. 5-14) correspond to (1, 9)

$$s(E_p - E_{max})^2 = \frac{3}{(\partial/\partial\Gamma)(\partial\Gamma/\partial\ln\beta)_\mu} \tag{30}$$

or

$$s'(q_p - q_{max})^2 = \frac{3}{(\partial/\partial\Gamma)(\partial\Gamma/\partial\ln\beta)_\mu} \tag{31}$$

where E_p and q_p correspond to the peaks. The peaks are symmetrical with respect to E_{max} when capacities are plotted against $s^{1/2}(E - E_{max})$. The dependence of E_p or q_p on the bulk activity (concentration) of adsorbate is obtained by introducing in Eqs. 30 and 31 the dependence of Γ on $\ln \beta$ as computed from the isotherm on the basis of Eqs. 24 or 25. It is then

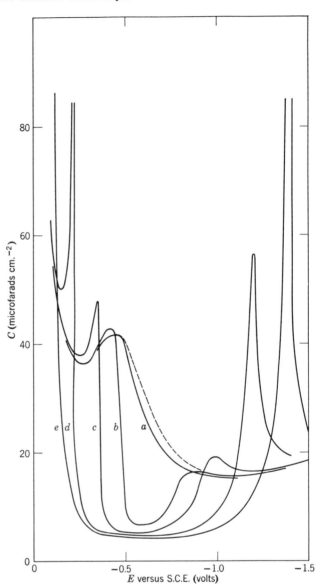

FIG. 5-17. Influence of bulk concentration on differential capacity for adsorption of triethylamine on mercury in $1M$ potassium chloride at 25°C. Dotted curve for $1M$ potassium chloride. Triethylamine concentration in mole l^{-1}: curve a (10^{-3}); b (2×10^{-3}); c (4×10^{-3}); d (2×10^{-2}); and e (10^{-1}). *The frequency was* 1.59 *kc and capacities do not have their thermodynamic values.* [Lorenz, Möckel, and Müller (48)] (by permission of *Z. physik. Chem. (Frankfurt)*).

easy to show, as Parsons did (9), that at high bulk activities $(E_p - E_{max})^2$ and $(q_p - q_{max})^2$ vary with the logarithm of the bulk activity. The dependence of $E_p - E_{max}$ on activity is more complicated at low bulk activities. The previous result holds regardless of the isotherm provided that Eqs. 2, 24, or 25 (that is, Eqs. 2, 10, and 11) are valid (9). The relationship between $(E_p - E_{max})^2$ and log a was also derived by Lorenz and Möckel (46) and Senda and Tachi (59) but for more restrictive conditions on the nature of the isotherm than in Parsons' treatment (9). Some experimental results are given in Figs. 5-17 and 5-18.

The correlation between capacity and isotherm was studied in detail by Parsons (1) by introducing in Eq. 26 values of $(\partial \Gamma / \partial \ln \beta)_\mu$ for a number of isotherms. The general shape of capacity-potential curves could be accounted for, but no definite experimental confirmation was possible for lack of suitable experimental data. Parsons later remarked (9) that the equations needed in this approach are rather cumbersome to handle and that the method discussed in Sec. 5-6b to discriminate between the Frumkin and the modified H.F.L. isotherms may be preferable.

In conclusion, the foregoing work has improved our knowledge on the morphology of capacity-potential curves, but its value in the assignment of isotherms still remains to be proved. The lack of definitive conclusion about the validity of any particular isotherm is somewhat disappointing, but it is probably too early to assess the ultimate value of Parsons' approach, for this work is still in progress. It is to be hoped that the collection of

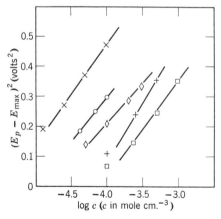

FIG. 5-18. Variation of peak potentials with bulk concentration for adsorption of different substances on mercury at 25°C in $1M$ potassium chloride. Frequency, 1.59 kc. Substances: ×—cyclohexanol, ○—isoamylalcohol, ◇—n-butanol, +—methylethylketone, □—n-butyric acid [Lorenz and Möckel (46)] (by permission of the Bunsengesellschaft).

more accurate data and further testing of isotherms will remove present ambiguity. The question as to whether the interaction parameter g in the isotherm is potential-independent must also be settled (Sec. 5-7). It might turn out that unambiguous answers about the validity of any isotherm and the constancy, or lack of constancy, of g can hardly be obtained by analysis of experimental data without further theoretical work. This is more easily said than done!

5-7   Application of the Frumkin Isotherm with Potential-Dependent Interaction Parameter

It was noted in Sec. 5-3 that application of Eq. 14 in conjunction with the Frumkin isotherm did not give good agreement with experiment. Damaskin attributed the discrepancy to variation of the interaction parameter g (Table 5-1) with potential and took this effect into account in the description of adsorption by the Frumkin isotherm. His approach is discussed in several papers (27, 52–55) and is reviewed by Frumkin and Damaskin (5). A good summary is given by Damaskin (56). The application to the adsorption of pyridine is striking and will be briefly discussed. It has been known since Gierst's (60) observations that the shape of the isotherm for pyridine adsorption on mercury varies considerably with potential (Fig. 5-19). Such variations can be accounted for by a Frumkin isotherm with a

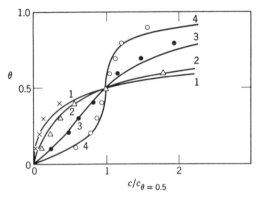

FIG. 5-19. Isotherms for adsorption of pyridine on mercury in $0.1 M$ potassium chloride at different potentials. Points are experimental coverages; solid curves represent coverages calculated from the Frumkin isotherm with allowance for variation of the interaction parameter g with potential. Potentials: -0.15, -0.45, -1.05, and -1.45 volts versus normal calomel electrode for curves 1 to 4. Ratios of the concentration to the concentration at $\theta = 0.5$ are plotted in abscissa [Damaskin (56)] (by permission of Pergamon).

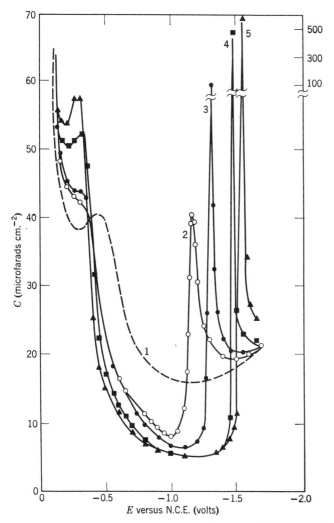

FIG. 5-20. Variations of differential capacity with potential for the adsorption of pyridine on mercury in 0.5M potassium chloride at a frequency of 400 c.p.s. Pyridine concentrations in mole l^{-1}: 0 (curve 1); 0.06 (2); 0.1 (3); 0.2 (4); and 0.3 (5) [Damaskin (56)] (by permission of Pergamon).

variable interaction parameter that can be determined from capacity-potential curves at different concentrations (Fig. 5-20). Agreement between calculated and experimental isotherms is good. There is strong attraction between pyridine molecules at markedly negative potentials and some repulsion at sufficiently positive potentials.

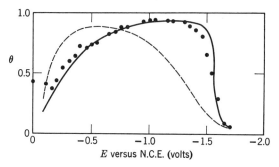

E versus N.C.E. (volts)

FIG. 5-21. Variations of coverage with potential for adsorption of $0.3M$ pyridine in $0.1M$ potassium chloride. Points are experimental coverages: Solid curve represents calculated values by the method applied in Fig. 5-19. Dotted curve corresponds to $g = 0$ (no particle-particle interaction) [Damaskin (56)] (by permission of Pergamon).

The coverage-potential curve is highly asymmetrical (Fig. 5-21) and drops off quite abruptly at negative potentials. This asymmetry of the θ versus E curve is also apparent from the capacity curves (Fig. 5-20) which exhibit a much sharper peak for $q < 0$ than for $q > 0$. The discrepancy between the calculated and experimental θ versus E curves for $q > 0$ is attributed by Damaskin to interaction between π-electrons and the electrode. He points out that the peak in the C versus E curves for $q > 0$ is not caused by desorption, as is usually the case for aliphatic compounds, but results from a change in orientation of adsorbed pyridine molecules which lie flat on the electrode at sufficiently positive charges. Because of strong π-electron-electrode interaction, the double-layer capacity is primarily determined by the interface structure beyond the adsorbed layer and is not very different from that observed in the absence of pyridine (extreme left part of Fig. 5-20).

In conclusion, Damaskin's approach is definitely successful in describing adsorption by the Frumkin isotherm, but it requires fitting experimental capacity-potential curves by means of a potential-dependent interaction parameter. It remains to be seen whether some of the other isotherms in Table 5-1 would fit experimental results just as well as the Frumkin isotherm provided a potential-dependent parameter is introduced. Indeed, it may well be that enough adjustable parameters are available to allow rather good fit with experiment for *reasonable* order of magnitude for these parameters. A study of this type might prove of interest. Ultimately, selection of an isotherm, be it the Frumkin or any other isotherm, may have to rest on a firmer basis than present theory allows.

5-8   Distribution of Potential

We consider the distribution of potential in the double layer for adsorption of uncharged substances. (See Chapter 4 for specifically adsorbed ions.) *As a first approximation* we apply the Gouy-Chapman theory to the diffuse double layer on the assumption that the presence of uncharged substances in solution is of no consequence. The method outlined in Chapter 3 can thus be applied to the computation of the potential ϕ_2. Thus the charge on the electrode is obtained as a function of potential from electrocapillary curves or double-layer capacity measurements. The charge is also calculated as a function of the potential ϕ_2 in the outer plane by applying the Gouy-Chapman theory, and the combination of these two sets of data gives ϕ_2 as a function of E. This procedure was suggested by Parsons (6), but does not seem to have been widely used. The curves of Fig. 5-22 which do not correspond to an actual example but were calculated for a compact double layer of constant capacity show that ϕ_2 is depressed by addition of the organic adsorbate. (Compare with Fig. 3-6.)

The drop of rational potential across the compact double layer can be computed from ϕ_2 exactly as was done in Chapter 4 for specifically adsorbed ions. Results of such a calculation, which was carried out by Parsons (39), are given in Fig. 5-23. The remarkable linear variation of ϕ_{M-2} with Γ obtained in this case suggests, according to Parsons, that the

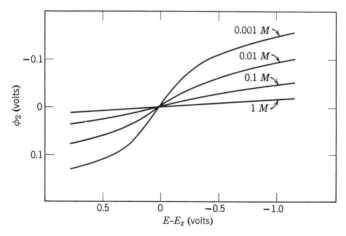

FIG. 5-22. Variations of the potential ϕ_2 in the outer plane with $E - E_z$ for sodium fluoride in contact with mercury at 25°C and an uncharged adsorbate for which it is *assumed* that the compact double layer has a constant capacity of 4 microfarads cm.$^{-2}$ [Parsons (6)] (by permission of interscience).

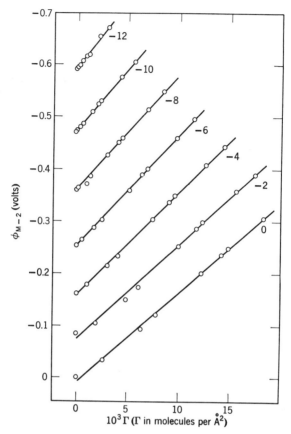

FIG. 5-23. Potential (rational) drop across the compact double layer as a function of the amount of adsorbed thiourea on mercury in 0.1M sodium fluoride at 25°C. Charge in microcoulombs cm.$^{-2}$ [Parsons (39)] (by permission of the Royal Society).

orientation of adsorbed thiourea molecules is not modified by variation of the charge on the electrode. This constancy of orientation is probably caused by strong bonding between thiourea and mercury. Other explanations might possibly be offered.

The results of Fig. 5-23 suggest, according to Parsons (39), that ϕ_{M-2} is of the form

$$\phi_{M-2} = \frac{q}{C^i_{\Gamma=0}} + \frac{\Gamma}{C''}$$

where $C^i_{\Gamma=0}$ is the integral capacity of the compact layer for $\Gamma = 0$ and C'' is the counterpart of the capacity at constant q for specifically adsorbed ions (Chapter 4). The capacity C'' can be interpreted on the basis of the equation for the potential drop D caused by a layer of oriented dipole (dipole moment μ), that is,

$$D = \frac{4\pi\mu}{\epsilon}$$

Since the plots in Fig. 5-23 are linear, it would seem that ϵ and μ are independent of coverage. The variation of the slope with the charge may be interpreted as being caused by a change of dielectric constant with the charge. An earlier application of the equation for D was made by Frumkin (29), and a detailed treatment was given by Macdonald and Barlow (78).

The drop of potential across the compact layer was also considered by Devanathan (61), who applied his model (62) of the double layer to adsorption of uncharged substances. This approach is not discussed here in view of the comments made in Sec. 4-2, and the reader is referred to the original paper.

5-9 Adsorption Kinetics

a. Control by Adsorption Rate

Equilibrium properties are emphasized throughout double-layer studies and only one attempt has been made to derive a general rate equation for adsorption kinetics. Delahay and Mohilner (63), using a phenomenological approach, calculated the rate of adsorption when equilibrium is disturbed for a process obeying the Temkin logarithmic isotherm (64) (Table 5-1). They obtained in the absence of mass-transfer control

$$\frac{d\,\delta\Gamma}{dt} = v^0\left\{e^{-(\lambda b_T/RT)\,\delta\Gamma}e^{-(\rho/RT)\,\delta\overline{\Delta G_q^0}} - e^{[(1-\lambda)b_T]/RT\,\delta\Gamma}e^{[(1-\rho)/RT]\,\delta\overline{\Delta G_q^0}}\right\} \quad (32)$$

for the logarithmic Temkin isotherm of the form

$$b_T\Gamma = -(\Delta G^0 + \overline{\Delta G_q^0}) + RT\ln a \quad (33)$$

The notations are: $\delta\Gamma$ variation in surface concentration; v^0 adsorption exchange rate prevailing before perturbation from equilibrium; λ and ρ are parameters with values lying between zero and unity which characterize the transition state with respect to coverage and the charge-dependent part $\overline{\Delta G_q^0}$ of the standard free energy of adsorption. An explicit form of the adsorption exchange rate v^0 was given by Delahay and Mohilner, who also pointed out the similitude between their treatment and the corresponding analysis of electrode kinetics (Chapter 7). The change in surface concentration can be correlated to the change in potential, and equations have been worked out to account for mass transfer (65).

Some measurements of adsorption rates have been reported (see later), but the usefulness of this treatment has not yet been demonstrated. Physical adsorption is too rapid a process for its kinetics at electrodes to be investigated by present methods (Chapter 10). Electrode chemisorption can be quite slow (Chapter 10), but its description by isotherms possibly may not require introducing an electrical variable (potential of charge) as a first approximation. It is possible that this treatment is applicable to intermediate cases in which there is some bonding at the electrode to slow down adsorption but not to the extent of rendering negligible the effect of the electrical variable. Transposition of this treatment to other isotherms might be attempted, if such intermediate cases were found.

Mention should be made here of another approach to adsorption kinetics in which no attempt is made to derive a rate equation for adsorption and only a small departure from equilibrium is considered. The adsorption rate is written in terms of the partial derivatives of the rate with respect to surface and bulk concentrations and potential. Details will not be given here since this book is not concerned with methodology. A brief review is given by Parsons (6) and details can be found in a paper by Lorenz (66) who gave the most satisfying analysis. Reference is also made to Frumkin and Melik-Gaikazyan (41, 67), who were the first to study the application of A.C. techniques to adsorption kinetics. It can be concluded from results obtained thus far that adsorption on mercury in aqueous solution is a fast process which is generally controlled by mass transfer. Lorenz (66) reported adsorption rates for conditions corresponding to almost total control by diffusion, and the question arises whether he really measured the effect of relatively slow adsorption.

Rectification of the double layer may possibly provide a method for the exploration of a frequency range in which A.C. bridges no longer can be applied to double-layer capacity measurements (68). Interpretation of the results, however, appears involved (69).

b. Control by Diffusion

Since adsorption at an ideal polarized mercury electrode in aqueous solution is generally controlled by diffusion (Sec. 5-8a), it is of interest to determine the time that is required practically to reach equilibrium. Such an inquiry is of practical interest in measurements with the electro-capillary electrometer, the dropping mercury electrode, etc., so that errors arising from the lack of equilibrium attainment can be avoided. The problem was attacked for simplifying conditions (70,71) and a solution was reported later for the Langmuir isotherm (72). Such calculations are primarily of interest in methodology and will not be discussed. [See Parsons (6) for a review.]

It suffices to state here that adsorption with diffusion control is very slow for strongly adsorbed substances at low bulk concentrations. Convection generally speeds up the process. Sufficient time must be allowed for attainment of equilibrium in measurements with the electrocapillary electrometer. The hanging mercury drop electrode is generally preferable to the dropping mercury electrode in double-layer capacity measurements whenever there is danger of interference by diffusion control. Finally, methods in which the potential is scanned quite rapidly (73) yield erroneous results unless diffusion control is considered whenever necessary.

REFERENCES

1. R. Parsons, *J. Electroanal. Chem.*, **5**, 397 (1963).
2. D. O. Hayward and B. M. W. Trapnell, *Chemisorption*, 2nd edition, Butterworths, London, 1964.
3. D. M. Young and A. D. Crowell, *Physical Adsorption of Gases*, Butterworths, London, 1962.
4. J. M. Honig, *Ann. New York Acad. Sci.*, **58**, 741 (1954).
5. A. N. Frumkin and B. B. Damaskin, *Modern Aspects of Electrochemistry*, Vol. 3, J. O'M. Bockris, editor, Butterworths, London, in press.
6. R. Parsons, *Advances in Electrochemistry and Electrochemical Engineering*, Vol. 1, P. Delahay, editor, Interscience, New York, 1961, pp. 1–64.
7. R. Parsons, *Trans. Faraday Soc.*, **51**, 1518 (1955).
8. R. Parsons, *Reports of the Fourth Soviet Conference on Electrochemistry*, English translation, Consultants Bureau, New York, 1958, pp. 18–22.
9. R. Parsons, *J. Electronal. Chem.*, **7**, 136 (1964).
10. D. H. Everett, *Trans. Faraday Soc.*, **46**, 453, 942 (1950).
11. A. N. Frumkin, *Z. Physik*, **35**, 792 (1926).
12. E. Helfand, H. L. Frisch, and J. L. Lebowitz, *J. Chem. Phys.*, **34**, 1037 (1961).
13. E. Blomgren, J. O'M. Bockris, and C. Jesch, *J. Phys. Chem.*, **65**, 2000 (1961).
14. E. Blomgren and J. O'M. Bockris, *ibid.*, **63**, 1475 (1959).
15. B. E. Conway and R. G. Barradas, *Electrochim. Acta*, **5**, 319 (1961).
16. R. G. Barradas and B. E. Conway, *ibid.*, **5**, 349 (1961).
17. O. Stern, *Z. Elektrochem.*, **30**, 508 (1924).
18. J. M. Parry and R. Parsons, *Trans. Faraday Soc.*, **59**, 241 (1963).
19. R. Parsons, *ibid.*, **55**, 999 (1959).
20. D. C. Grahame, *J. Am. Chem. Soc.*, **80**, 4201 (1958).
21. J. A. V. Butler, *Proc. Royal Soc.*, **A122**, 399 (1929).
22. J. O'M. Bockris, M. A. V. Devanathan, and K. Müller, *Proc. Royal Soc.*, **274A**, 55 (1963).
23. D. M. Mohilner and T. H. Tidwell, unpublished results.
24. M. Breiter and P. Delahay, *J. Am. Chem. Soc.*, **81**, 2938 (1959).
25. R. S. Hansen, R. E. Minturn, and D. A. Hickson, *J. Phys. Chem.*, **60**, 1185 (1956); **61**, 953 (1957).
26. R. S. Hansen, D. J. Kelsh, and D. H. Grantham, *ibid.*, **67**, 2316 (1963).
27. B. B. Damaskin and N. B. Grigorjev, *Doklady Akad. Nauk S.S.S.R.*, **147**, 135 (1962).
28. A. N. Frumkin, A. Donde, and R. Kulvarskii, *Z. physik. Chem.*, **123A**, 321 (1926).
29. A. N. Frumkin, *Ergebn. exakt. Naturwiss.*, **7**, 235 (1928).

30. M. A. Gerovich and O. G. Ol'man, *Zhur. Fiz. Khim.*, **28**, 19 (1954).
31. M. A. Gerovich, *Doklady Akad. Nauk S.S.S.R.*, **96**, 543 (1954); **105**, 1278 (1955).
32. M. A. Gerovich and G. F. Rybalchenko, *Zhur. Fiz. Khim.*, **32**, 109 (1958).
33. A. N. Frumkin, *Nova Acta Leopoldina, Neue Folge*, **19**, No 132, 1957, pp. 1–19.
34. J. E. B. Randles, *Advances in Electrochemistry and Electrochemical Engineering*, Vol. 3, P. Delahay, editor, Interscience, Wiley, New York, 1963, pp. 1–30.
35. A. N. Frumkin, Z. A. Iofa, and M. A. Gerovich, *Zhur. Fiz. Khim.*, **30**, 1455 (1956).
36. B. S. Gurenkov, *ibid.*, **30**, 1830 (1956).
37. A. N. Frumkin, A. Gorodetzkaja, and P. Chugunov, *Acta Physicochim. U.R.S.S.*, **1**, 12 (1934).
38. V. I. Melik-Gaikazyan, *Zhur. Fiz. Khim.*, **26**, 1184 (1952).
39. R. Parsons, *Proc. Royal Soc.*, **261A**, 79 (1961).
40. F. W. Schapink, M. Oudeman, K. W. Leu, and J. N. Helle, *Trans. Faraday Soc.*, **56**, 415 (1960).
41. V. I. Melik-Gaikazyan, *Zhur. Fiz. Khim.*, **26**, 560 (1952).
42. B. Breyer and H. H. Bauer *Alternating Current Polarography and Tensammetry*, Interscience, Wiley, New York, 1963.
43. P. Delahay, *New Instrumental Methods in Electrochemistry*, Interscience, New York, 1954, pp. 171–172.
44. A. N. Frumkin and B. B. Damaskin, *J. Electroanal. Chem.*, **3**, 36 (1962).
45. B. Breyer and H. H. Bauer, *ibid.*, **3**, 45 (1962).
46. W. Lorenz and F. Möckel, *Z. Elektrochem.*, **60**, 507 (1956).
47. W. Lorenz, *Z. physik. Chem. (Frankfurt)*, **18**, 1 (1958).
48. W. Lorenz, F. Möckel, and W. Müller, *ibid.*, **25**, 145 (1960).
49. W. Lorenz and W. Müller, *ibid.*, **25**, 161 (1960).
50. W. Lorenz, *ibid.*, **26**, 424 (1960).
51. W. Lorenz and G. Krüger, *Z. physik. Chemie (Leipzig)*, **221**, 231 (1962).
52. B. B. Damaskin, *Doklady Akad. Nauk S.S.S.R.*, **144**, 1073 (1962).
53. B. B. Damaskin, S. Wawrzyczka, and N. B. Grigorjev, *Zhur. Fiz. Khim.*, **36**, 2530 (1962).
54. B. B. Damaskin, *ibid.*, **37**, 2483 (1963).
55. B. B. Damaskin and G. A. Tedoradze, *Doklady Akad. Nauk S.S.S.R.*, **152**, 1151 (1963).
56. B. B. Damaskin, *Electrochim. Acta*, **9**, 231 (1964).
57. G. C. Barker and R. L. Faircloth, *Advances in Polarography*, Vol. 1, I. S. Longmuir, editor, Pergamon, London, 1960, pp. 313–329.
58. B. E. Conway and E. Gileadi, *Trans. Faraday Soc.*, **58**, 2493 (1962).
59. M. Senda and I. Tachi, *Rev. Polarography (Japan)*, **10**, 79 (1962).
60. L. Gierst, *Transactions of the Symposium on Electrode Processes*, E. Yeager, editor, Wiley, New York, 1961, pp. 294–298.
61. M. A. V. Devanathan, *Proc. Royal Soc.*, **264A**, 133 (1961).
62. M. A. V. Devanathan, *Trans. Faraday Soc.*, **50**, 373 (1954).
63. P. Delahay and D. M. Mohilner, *J. Am. Chem. Soc.*, **84**, 4247 (1962).
64. M. I. Temkin, *Zhur. Fiz. Khim.*, **15**, 296 (1941).
65. P. Delahay, *J. Phys. Chem.*, **67**, 135 (1963).
66. W. Lorenz, *Z. Elektrochem.*, **62**, 192 (1958).
67. A. N. Frumkin and V. I. Melik-Gaikazyan, *Doklady Akad. Nauk S.S.S.R.*, **77**, 855 (1951).
68. G. C. Barker, Ref. 60, pp. 325–365.
69. M. Senda and P. Delahay, *J. Am. Chem. Soc.*, **83**, 3763 (1961).

70. J. Koryta, *Collection Czechoslov. Chem. Commun.*, **18**, 206 (1956).
71. P. Delahay and I. Trachtenberg, *J. Am. Chem. Soc.*, **79**, 2355 (1957).
72. W. H. Reinmuth, *J. Phys. Chem.*, **65**, 473 (1961).
73. J. W. Loveland and P. J. Elving, *ibid.*, **56**, 935, 941, 945 (1952).
74. A. N. Frumkin, *J. Electroanal. Chem.*, **7**, 152 (1964).
75. B. B. Damaskin, *ibid.*, **7**, 155 (1964).
76. R. Parsons, *ibid.*, **8**, 93 (1964).
77. J. R. Macdonald and C. A. Barlow, *Proceedings of the First Australian Conference on Electrochemistry*, A. Friend and F. Gutmann, editors, Pergamon, Oxford, 1964 pp. 199–247.
78. J. R. Macdonald and C. A. Barlow, *J. Chem. Phys.*, **39**, 412 (1963).
79. D. C. Grahame, *J. Am. Chem. Soc.* **68**, 301 (1946).

CHAPTER 6

The Electrical Double Layer for Other Systems Than the Mercury-Aqueous Solution Interface

6-1 Liquid Metallic Phase in Aqueous Solution

Investigation of a liquid metal in aqueous solution would not be expected to reveal any new information about the diffuse double layer that cannot be obtained with mercury, but might provide new information on the compact double layer. Gallium is suitable, for it behaves essentially as an ideal polarized electrode. The range of potentials that can be explored is similar to that for mercury, but is shifted by approximately −0.4 volt toward more negative potentials. Electrocapillary curves were investigated by Frumkin and Gorodetzkaja (1) and Murtazaev and Gorodetzkaja (2) and double-layer capacity measurements were made by Grahame (3) and Leikis and Sevastyanov (4). No striking difference in behavior is observed between mercury and liquid gallium. Capacity-potential curves for gallium are shifted approximately by −0.4 volt with respect to the corresponding curves for mercury (Fig. 6-1). This shift of potential is of the order of magnitude of the difference between the electronic work functions of the two metals. (See discussion of this point in Sec. 6-2.) The similitude of the capacity data for the two metals at potentials at which there is strong anion specific adsorption lends some support to the view that chemical bonding is not the principal factor in the nature of specific adsorption (Chapter 4). It does not seem very likely that the bond energies of chloride and iodide are similar for mercury and gallium. Experimental data on gallium, however, are not sufficiently abundant to allow further argument.

The effect of transition from liquid to solid gallium was investigated by Leikis and Sevastyanov (4), who observed essentially no difference in $0.5M$

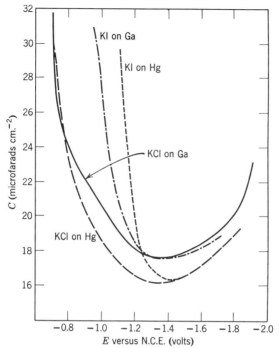

FIG. 6-1. Differential capacity of mercury and gallium in aqueous solution of potassium chloride and potassium iodide (concentration not stated by author). The curves for mercury are shifted by 0.4 volt to the right [Grahame (3)] (by permission of the American Chemical Society).

sodium sulfate $+0.01M$ hydrochloric acid. They also examined the capacity behavior in presence of n-hexyl alcohol and found no appreciable difference. One might have expected broadening of the capacity peak for solid gallium as a result of variation of the point of zero charge for crystal faces with different orientation in solid gallium, but this effect was not observed. Leikis and Sevastyanov also examined the capacity of Wood's alloy, previously studied by Karpachev, Ladygin, and Zykov (5), and attributed the 10 to 15% increase in capacity that is observed on solidification to a variation of effective area. Similar studies on liquid and solid mercury in a 50% supersaturated aqueous solution of potassium carbonate by Gorodetskaja and Proskurnin (6) and Kheifets and Krasikov (7) might also be mentioned here. Capacity-potential curves were the same for liquid and solid mercury except at markedly negative potentials at which a difference produced by amalgam formation is observed. Capacity peaks for adsorption of ethyl alcohol were identical for liquid and solid mercury.

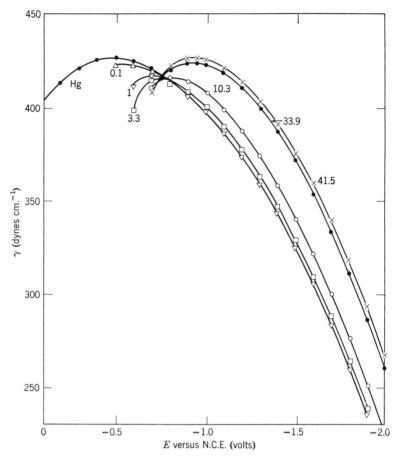

FIG. 6-2. Electrocapillary curves for thallium-amalgam of varying composition (in weight percent) in 0.5M sodium sulfate at 21°C [Frumkin and Gorodetzkaja (8)] (by permission of *Z. physik. Chem.*)

Formation of amalgams with metals which are highly soluble in mercury offers another possibility of changing some properties of the metallic phase while retaining its liquid state. Frumkin and Gorodetzkaja (8) reported electrocapillary curves for thallium-amalgam containing up to 41% thallium by weight and determined the relative surface excess of thallium. The point of zero charge shifts markedly toward negative potentials on increase of thallium concentration (Fig. 6-2). The validity of the Gouy-Chapman theory for this amalgam electrode in sodium fluoride solution (0.002, 0.01, 0.1M) was recently investigated by Boguslavskii and Damaskin (9) by the method of Sec. 3-2. The agreement between theory and experiment was excellent, and it was shown that the minimum in the capacity-potential curve in dilute solution coincides with the point of zero charge. Results are analogous to those of Fig. 3-5. Adsorption of uncharged substances at the thallium-amalgam electrode is briefly discussed in the recent review of Frumkin and Damaskin (10).

TABLE 6-1 Point of Zero Charge of Indium-Amalgams in $0.1M$ Perchloric Acid at $25°$ C[a]

Concentration of Indium, Mole Fraction	Point of Zero Charge,[b] Volts
0.644	−0.560
0.522	−0.540
0.500	−0.520
0.400	−0.460
0.300	−0.424
0.200	−0.392
0.163	−0.369
0.084	−0.317
0.039	−0.295
0.0092	−0.257
0.00094	−0.216
0.000094	−0.203
0.000047	−0.190
0	−0.165

[a] According to Butler and Makrides (12) from determination of the potential corresponding to zero-capacity current at a dropping amalgam electrode in the absence of an electrode reaction.

[b] Versus hydrogen electrode at atmospheric pressure in $0.1M$ perchloric acid.

Cadmium, indium, and copper amalgams have also been investigated as ideal polarized electrode (11, 12). Liquid amalgams containing up to 70 atom-percent indium can be prepared at room temperature. They display a shift of the point of zero charge up to −0.5 volt according to Butler and Makrides (12) (Table 6-1).

The interfacial tension of reversible amalgam-electrodes has not been studied, although it could be measured, for instance, by the method recently applied by Koenig, Wohlers, and Bandini (14) to the mercury-mercurous ion reversible electrode. Sluyters' method (15–17) of separating the faradaic impedance from the double-layer capacity could also be applied. de Levie's improvement (17a) of this method should also prove useful in such studies.

Two conclusions can be drawn from this work on liquid electrodes. (*a*) The structure of the diffuse double layer can be changed in a known fashion by variation of the amalgam composition; this possibility has been exploited to a limited extent in the correlation between double-layer structure and electrode kinetics (Chapter 9). (*b*) The considerable difference between the double-layer properties of liquid metals and such solid metals as platinum do not have their main origin in the solid state of the electrode. This conclusion is not unexpected.

6-2   Solid Electrode in Aqueous Solution

a. Point of Zero Charge

As we already indicated in Sec. 6-1, the study of electrodes other than mercury is focused on the compact double layer rather than the diffuse double layer. The experimental determination of properties of the double layer with solid electrodes has raised very serious difficulties which have been progressively overcome, although not entirely. Progress in this area has not been achieved as a result of the publication of one or a few major papers but rather by the painstaking gathering of experimental facts. Some well-established conclusions which are largely due to the Frumkin school can be drawn about the double layer at solid electrodes in aqueous solution, but they are of qualitative nature. Quantitative interpretation of the type developed for mercury is still lacking.

The same experimental data as for mercury are needed for solid electrodes: interfacial tension, point of zero charge, double-layer capacity, and amount of specifically adsorbed species. The problem is complicated with most solid electrodes in aqueous solution by formation of adsorbed oxygen and hydrogen. In this respect, it is very fortunate indeed that hydrogen is hardly adsorbed on mercury because otherwise our understanding of the double-layer structure would probably not have reached its present level. It is obviously not possible with solid electrodes to apply the electrocapillary electrometer method, but variations of interfacial tension can be deduced from the measurements of contact angles at a three-phase boundary, for example, for a gas bubble at the metal surface in the electrolyte. The initial work on this method was done by Möller (18) and was greatly extended by Frumkin. [See Part 3 of Smolders' papers (19) for detailed references to Frumkin's work.] The method was recently reexamined by Smolders (19, 20), but it has not been applied extensively. It is less accurate than the electrocapillary electrometer and it involves more serious experimental problems that one might gather from the apparent simplicity of its principle. First we examine results on the point of zero charge.

The available methods for the determination of the point of zero charge are mentioned or described in some detail by Ershler (21), Parsons (22), Vetter (23), and Frumkin (24). More recent papers (25–30) have dealt with the same topic. The most comprehensive list of points of zero charge was compiled by Frumkin (31). It is given in Table 6-2 with the datum for platinum revised by Balashova (32). The points of zero charge for solid metals are not as reliable as for mercury because of uncertainty in the interpretation of results for some of the methods. In particular, the assumption that the minimum in capacity-potential curves for dilute solution occurs at the point of zero charge does not seem valid. This assumption is correct for mercury (see Fig. 3-5) for a $z - z$ electrolyte, and it was thought for a while that the same criterion applied to solid metals (33, 34). Birintseva and Kabanov (35) concluded that this approach is not valid for platinum because of interference by oxygen and hydrogen adsorption even in the so-called double-layer region (see Sec. 6-2b). The present position was very aptly put by Frumkin (24).

It is seen in Table 6-2 that the point of zero charge depends markedly on the nature of the metal. This is to be expected since the work function varies from one metal to another. If there were no complications due to adsorption, we might expect a linear plot of the point of zero charge against work function (8, 36–38). Such a plot is shown in Fig. 6-3 for the E_z's of

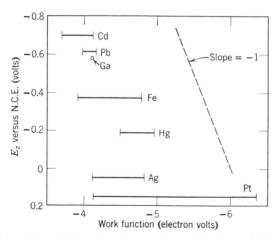

FIG. 6-3. Variation of the point of zero charge with the work function for various metals. Data on E_z from Frumkin (31) (Table 6-2). Bars indicate range of reported data, not their precision. Work function from Weisslar (39).

Table 6-2 and the work functions tabulated by Weisslar (39). Similar diagrams are given by Parsons (22) and Rüetschi and Delahay (37). However, as Parsons (22) and Frumkin (24) noted, ion specific adsorption and variations of the surface potential from one metal to another make such a correlation very uncertain. The dependence of the point of zero charge on pH for certain metals, which was investigated by Kheifets and Krasikov

TABLE 6-2   Point of Zero Charge for Various Metals in Aqueous Solution at Room Temperature[a]

Metal	Point of Zero Charge, Volts versus N.H.E.	Solution	Method
Cd	−0.90	0.005M KCl	Capacity minimum
Cd	−0.70	0.005M KCl	Hardness maximum
Tl	−0.82	0.001M KCl	Capacity minimum
Tl	−0.69	0.5M Na$_2$SO$_4$	Hardness maximum
Pb	−0.67	0.0005M H$_2$SO$_4$	Capacity minimum
Pb	−0.62	0.1M NaCl	Hardness maximum
Ga	−0.6	1M KCl + 0.1M HCl	Electrocapillary curve
Fe	−0.37	0.0005M H$_2$SO$_4$	Capacity minimum
Hg	−0.19	Various dilute solutions with little specific adsorption	Electrocapillary curve
Ag	0.05	0.1M KNO$_3$	Adsorption
Pt	0.15	0.05M Na$_2$SO$_4$	Adsorption
Te	0.6	0.05M Na$_2$SO$_4$	Hardness maximum

[a] From Frumkin (31) except for platinum for which E_z is taken from Balashova (32).

(40), points further toward the complex nature of data such as those of Table 6-2. Further comments on the point of zero charge are made incidentally in Secs. 6-6b and 6-6c.

A few words may be added about the so-called Billiter potential which has been considered in the past as the point of zero charge for solutions containing a reversible redox system. These potentials are very different from those obtained by more orthodox methods in the absence of a redox system. The explanation must be in the difference between the methods of measurement, for there is no reason to expect the presence of a redox couple to cause a major shift of the true point of zero charge. This point is clearly made by Frumkin (24, 31). Detailed references and a discussion of Billiter potentials can be found in Vetter's monograph (23).

b. Double-Layer Capacity

Capacities of solid electrodes have been measured with the study of the double layer as primary objective and also in conjunction with investigations of hydrogen and oxygen overvoltage and faradaic impedance measurements. No single extensive review has been published, although detailed comments and references can be found in Frumkin's reviews on electrode kinetics (24, 31, 41). The list of references at the end of the chapter is by no means exhaustive, but it indicates the magnitude of the effort. Capacity measurements which are incidental to faradaic impedance determinations are not included except for the hydrogen and oxygen electrodes. References are listed by metal: platinum (30, 42–68); iridium and rhodium (69, 70); lead (47, 54, 71–77); cadmium (77, 78); thallium (79); zinc (80, 81); nickel (82, 83); copper (61, 84); silver (61, 85); and gold (86). References for metals such as aluminum and tantalum, for which there are complications by formation of an anodic film, are not considered here.

A difficulty common to all solid metals is the experimental frequency dependence of the electrode impedance. Two cases must be distinguished according to whether the capacity being measured includes the capacitive component of the faradaic impedance for hydrogen ion discharge and oxygen production (formation of the corresponding films). Metals with high hydrogen overvoltage can be studied without interference by faradaic impedance. This is the case for cadmium, lead, thallium, and zinc according to Frumkin (41). Frequency dependence for these metals is considerably minimized for electrodes with a smooth surface, as obtained, for instance, by melting of a hanging metal drop in an inert atmosphere (47, 48, 51, 71, 87). Single crystals may also exhibit only minor frequency dependence as was shown by Leikis and Kabanov (73) and by Chuang-Hshin Cha and Iofa (81) (Figs. 6-4 and 6-5). These remarks also apply to metals such as platinum on which adsorbed films of hydrogen and oxygen are formed, but the frequency dependence corresponding to faradaic impedance is, of course, not eliminated, even with electrodes having a smooth surface.

A number of authors (47, 71, 54, 89) have related frequency dependence to microcracks at the surface of the electrode. Measurements with smooth electrodes lend strong support to this view, and recent work, especially by Ksenshek and Stender, Winsel, Euler, and de Levie on porous electrodes gives a quantitative interpretation of the effect, at least for simplified geometrical models of the electrode. [See references to earlier work in de Levie (89).] de Levie showed that an ideal polarized electrode composed of parallel tubes having a very small cross section area in

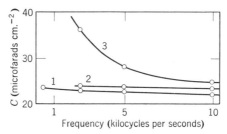

FIG. 6-4. Dependence of double-layer capacity on frequency for single crystal and polycrystalline zinc at −1.22 volts against the normal hydrogen electrode. Curve 1, single crystal in $1M$ potassium chloride; curve 2, same as curve 1 but in $0.2M$ potassium chloride; and curve 3, polycrystalline zinc in $1M$ potassium chloride [Chuang-Hshin Cha and Iofa (81)] (by permission of Consultants Bureau Enterprises).

comparison with their length exhibits an electrode impedance with a phase shift of $\pi/4$ as a result of distributed resistance and capacity much in the same way as for a transmission line. The measured capacity varies linearly with $1/\omega^{1/2}$ ($\omega = 2\pi f$, f being the frequency). Experiment confirmed this theoretical prediction. Such a dependence of capacity was indeed reported by Sarmousakis and Prager (58) for rough platinum electrodes. Electrode roughness cannot be interpreted by the model used for porous electrodes, but analysis of models closer to the actual electrode surface geometry have been developed (90). The small residual frequency

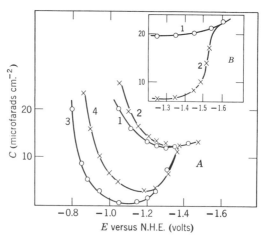

FIG. 6-5. Capacity-potential curves for single crystal of zinc at 10 kc. Diagram A: $0.5M$ potassium chloride (curve 1), $0.5M$ potassium iodide (curve 2), $0.5M$ potassium chloride + $0.00024M$ tetrabutylammonium chloride (curve 3), $0.5M$ potassium iodide + $0.00024M$ tetrabutylammonium iodide (curve 4). Diagram B: $1M$ potassium chloride (curve 1), $1M$ potassium chloride + $0.001M$ tetrabutylammonium chloride (curve 2) [Chuang-Hshin Cha and Iofa (81)] (by permission of Consultants Bureau Enterprises).

dependence that still prevails for "smooth" electrodes without known complication by faradaic impedance may possibly be caused by remaining surface imperfections, asymmetry of the electrode assembly, adsorption of uncharged substances present as traces, parasitic redox couples, etc.

Variations of the capacitive component of the electrode impedance with potential are shown in Fig. 6-6 for platinum, and the corresponding

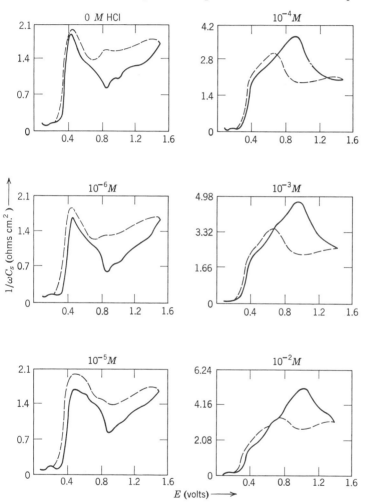

FIG. 6-6. Variations of the capacitive component (RC series circuit; $\omega = 2\pi f$) of the electrode impedance at 1000 c.p.s. with potential for platinum in $1M$ perchloric acid at 25°C. Concentration of hydrochloric acid as indicated. Potentials referred to hydrogen electrode at atmospheric pressure in the solution being tested. Solid curve, anodic sweep; dotted curve, cathodic sweep [Breiter (67)] (by permission of Pergamon).

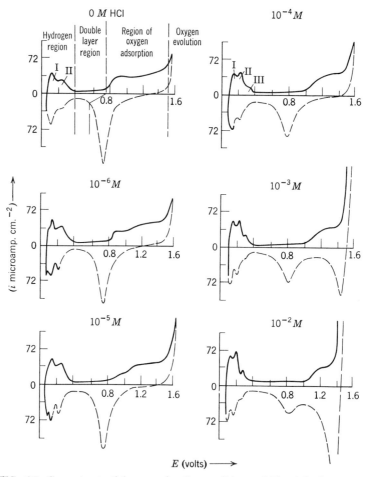

FIG. 6-7. Current-potential curves for the conditions of Fig. 6-6. Same notations. Rate of potential scanning: 30 millivolts sec.$^{-1}$ [Breiter (67)] (by permission of Pergamon).

current-potential curves are given in Fig. 6-7. These diagrams will be discussed in Sec. 6-2c and Chapter 10. Suffice it is to note here that three regions may be distinguished as indicated in Fig. 6-7, top left. In the so-called double-layer region we assume as a first approximation that there is no interference by hydrogen and oxygen adsorption provided the potential is made increasingly positive during capacity measurements (anodic sweep). There is considerable hysteresis in the cathodic sweep because the oxygen that was adsorbed at the more positive potentials is not readily reduced. The large current peak in Fig. 6-7 in the cathodic sweep corresponds to reduction of adsorbed oxygen. Capacity-potential curves for platinum are strongly pH-dependent (Figs. 6-8 and 6-9) (40, 63, 68). Such variations are attributed to the effect of pH on the capacitive component of faradaic impedance and are not primarily related to the double-layer structure (24, 63). This complication invalidates estimates of the point of zero charge (51, 57, 60, 61) of platinum in which the potential at the minimum of capacity-potential curves is taken as the point of zero charge, as noted by Frumkin (24) (cf. Sec. 6-2a).

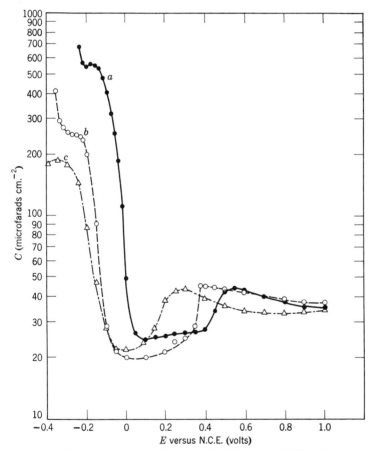

FIG. 6-8. Differential capacity of activated platinum at 25°C against potential in nitrate medium (acid and potassium salt) of varying pH at an ionic strength of approximately one. pH values: 0 (curve a); 2.1 (b); and 3 (c) [Banta and Hackerman (68)] (by permission of The Electrochemical Society).

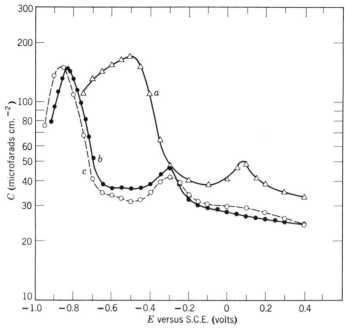

FIG. 6-9. Same diagram as in Fig. 6-8 but for pH 6.55 (curve a); 11.4 (b); and 12.2 (c) [Banta and Hackerman (68)] (by permission of The Electrochemical Society).

c. Specific Ionic Adsorption

The amount of specifically adsorbed ions for a single electrolyte can be determined by the method shown in Sec. 4-2 from the point of zero charge and the variations of capacity with potential. The method is only valid when one ionic species is specifically adsorbed and the electrode is an ideal polarized electrode. These restrictions prevent application to a number of solid metals such as platinum for which there is danger of simultaneous adsorption of cations and anions and complication by adsorption of hydrogen or oxygen. Several methods, which hopefully might be free of these restrictions, have been applied: capacity measurements, charging curves, radiotracer techniques, and shift of potential at open circuit following the addition of specifically adsorbed ions. Application has been made to a number of ions, and to chloride, bromide, and iodide in particular (42, 46, 51, 58, 60, 91–111, 114). Methodology will not be covered here, but some essential points and results will be indicated. Frumkin's articles (41, 41a) may be consulted for further details.

Capacity measurements were discussed in Sec. 6-2b, and the effect of chloride adsorption was shown in Fig. 6-6 and 6-7. Similar diagrams are given by Breiter (111) for bromide and chloride. [See also extensive references to previous work in (111).] There is competition between the adsorption of hydrogen (42, 46, 91–93, 97, 101–103, 107) and oxygen (95, 96, 98, 105, 109, 114). The capacity-potential curve in Fig. 6-6 changes markedly with hydrochloric acid concentration below $10^{-4}M$ but little above, and this concentration, according to Breiter (111), corresponds to near saturation. Related information is also obtained from charging curves [cf. Frumkin (41)].

Radiotracers techniques have been applied with success (100, 104, 109, 110, 112–114a), for they allow trace analysis in solution. Conventional methods, however, such as conductivity measurements, may also be applied provided they are sufficiently sensitive to allow determination of the adsorbed amount of ions from the change in bulk concentration. Much of the work was done by Balashova (100, 110, 112–114) and the various experimental factors such as electrode treatment were examined in detail by her (110). Figures 6-10 and 6-11 show the type of results obtained by this method. The pronounced decrease in the adsorbed sulfate ion at sufficiently cathodic and anodic potentials is caused by hydrogen and oxygen adsorption.

The effect of ionic specific adsorption can also be examined by following the electrode potential at open circuit after addition of the specifically adsorbed electrolyte. The method was worked out by Obrucheva (101, 115–117) and is briefly discussed by Frumkin (118). The drift of potential caused by spurious electrode reactions must be minimized, and the

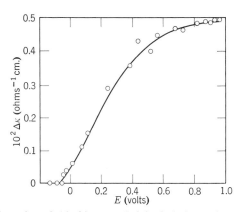

FIG. 6-10. Adsorption of chloride on a platinized platinum electrode in 0.01M hydrochloric acid as a function of potential. Potentials referred to hydrogen electrode at atmospheric pressure in solution. The change of conductivity $\Delta\kappa$ of the bulk solution resulting from adsorption is plotted along the ordinate axis [Balashova (110)] (by permission of Pergamon).

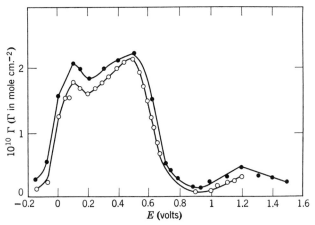

FIG. 6-11. Same plot as in Fig. 6-10 but for sulfate adsorption on platinum from 0.005M sulfuric acid. Tracer (●) and conductivity (○) measurements [Balashova (100)] (by permission of *Z. physik. Chem. (Leipzig)*).

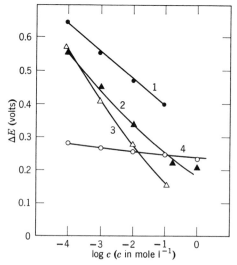

FIG. 6-12. Dependence of the shift of potential on initial concentration of adsorbed ion. Initial potential: 0.7 volt for curves 1, 2, and 3; 0.3 volt for curve 4. Electrolyte: 1M of potassium chloride (1); bromide (2, 4); and iodide (3). Potentials referred to hydrogen electrode at atmospheric pressure in 0.5M sulfuric acid [Frumkin (118)] (by permission of Wiley).

solution must be highly purified. Requirements are particularly stringent with smooth electrodes since trace impurities are much more effective than with electrodes covered with a spongy metal deposit of high area. The typical result of Fig. 6-12 shows the increasing effect of adsorption from chloride to iodide and also the effect of potential. Details are given by Frumkin (41).

d. Adsorption of Uncharged Substances

Study of adsorption of uncharged substances from capacity measurements for solid electrodes is briefly discussed by Frumkin and Damaskin (10). Only limited information has been obtained thus far, but it has been demonstrated that capacity peaks can be observed for solid metals as for mercury although they may not be as sharp as for this metal. Data for the adsorption of alcohols are available for lead (47), thallium (79), silver (85), and gold (86). A limited number of capacity measurements have been made in conjunction with the study of anodic oxidation of organic substances (cf., for example, 119, 120; see also Chapter 10).

More detailed information on adsorption was gathered from studies using radiotracer techniques. Only methods which allow radioactivity measurements with the metal in solution at a controlled potential are to be retained. A number of techniques, which are briefly reviewed by Dahms and Green (121), have been worked out (122–129). Results with gold are particularly encouraging. Coverage-potential curves (Fig. 6-13) have the same general shape as for mercury (121). Reasonably well-defined

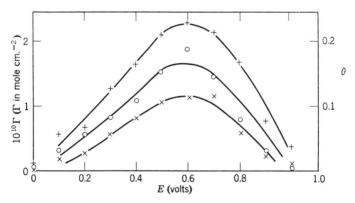

FIG. 6-13. Adsorption of benzene on gold from 0.5M sulfuric acid aqueous solution as a function of potential. Potentials referred to calomel electrode (potassium chloride concentration not specified by authors). Benzene concentrations: ×, 2 × 10⁻⁴M; ○, 5 × 10⁻⁴M; +, 10⁻³M [Dahms and Green (121)] (by permission of The Electrochemical Society).

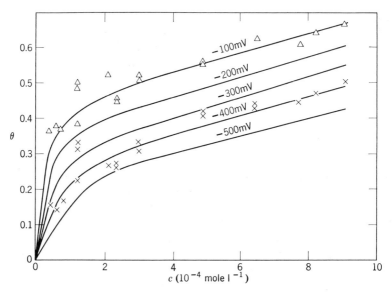

FIG. 6-14. Isotherm, at constant potential in the outer plane, for adsorption of thiourea on gold in aqueous solution of $0.25M$ sodium sulfate $+ 0.1M$ sulfuric acid. Typical scatter shown for the isotherms at -400 ($\times$) and -100 ($\triangle$) millivolts [Wroblowa and Green (129)] (by permission of Pergamon).

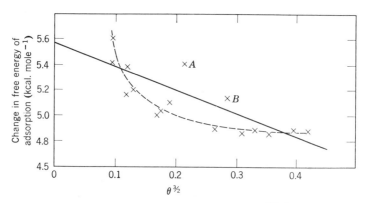

FIG. 6-15. Plot of standard free energy of adsorption with $\theta^{3/2}$ (θ, coverage) at a constant potential of -0.3 volt in the outer plane. Same case as in Fig. 6-14. See text for comments on dotted curve and points A and B. [Wroblowa and Green (129)] (by permission of Pergamon).

isotherms have been reported by Wroblowa and Green (129) (Fig. 6-14). These authors consider that the standard free energy for adsorption of thiourea on gold varies linearly with $\theta^{3/2}$ (Eqs. 5-6) for $0.1 \leqslant \theta \leqslant 0.4$. They traced the solid straight line in Fig. 6-15, but it seems that their results are better represented by the dotted curve if we omit points A and B which appear to be badly in error. Figures 13 to 15 are shown primarily to give an idea of the scattering of points to be expected by radio-tracer measurements and to point out that methodology and instrumentation have now reached a stage at which the same type of data can be obtained for solid electrodes as for mercury, although *with a somewhat lower accuracy*. Uncertainty in data may lead to inconclusive or possibly erroneous statements (Fig. 3-15), and caution seems in order in the use of such data to prove or disprove a point of theory.

The approach followed in the study of ionic adsorption (Sec. 6-2c), in which the adsorbed amount is deduced from variation of the bulk concentration, was also applied to uncharged substances. Conway, Barradas and Zavidzky (130, 131) studied adsorption of organic heterocyclic bases on nickel, copper, and silver and utilized spectrophotometry as an analytical tool to follow the variations of bulk concentration. Isotherms with only minor scattering of points were reported for pyridine, quinoline, and acridine. Electrode pretreatment had a marked effect on the adsorbed amount.

6-3 Nonaqueous Solvents

a. Mixtures of Water and Another Solvent

The thermodynamic study of adsorption on mercury in mixed solvents is of limited interest and is dealt with in only a few papers (132–138). Rigorous analysis of data from Eqs. 2-9 and 2-16 is hampered by the necessity of keeping constant the chemical potential of the electrolyte. This condition requires detailed measurements of activities in a series of mixed solvents. The type of results being obtained is illustrated by Fig. 6-16.

b. Nonaqueous Solvents at the Exclusion of Molten Salts

Almost all the work on the double layer in nonaqueous solvents has been done with mercury. It would appear, however, that nonaqueous solvents might be of interest for solid metals for which hydrogen adsorption interferes in aqueous solution. No new major advance in our understanding of the double layer has resulted thus far from studies with nonaqueous solvents (except molten salts), but there are a few points well worth noting. A number of references can be found in the review of Frumkin and

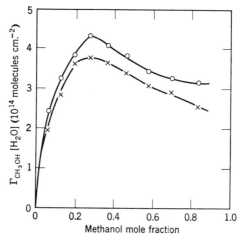

FIG. 6-16. Relative surface excess of methanol (with respect to water) for $0.01M$ hydrochloric acid in contact with mercury (crosses) and air (open circles) at 25°C. [Parsons and Devanathan (132)] (by permission of The Faraday Society).

Damaskin (10) and a few other papers may be added to their list: formic acid (no details, however) (139), formamide (140), adsorption of oleic, elaidic, and stearic acid in ethanol solution (141), and acetonitrile (142).

The Gouy-Chapman theory is verified in methanol as well as in water, as was shown by Grahame (143). Results for methanol are similar to those for water in the higher temperature range. The capacity of the compact double layer is smaller than for water, and the capacity-potential curve exhibits no hump (Fig. 6-17). Agreement between the Gouy-Chapman theory and experiment is extremely good for 0.1, 0.01, and $0.001M$ potassium fluoride in methanol. It is noteworthy that agreement for rather positive charges on the electrode is as good as we might wish (Fig. 6-18).

The hump that is often observed in aqueous solutions at not too high a temperature in the absence of strong specific adsorption (Sec. 4-5) is generally not observed with organic solvents. A hump, however, was observed by Damaskin and Povarov (144) with N-methylformamide and, just as for aqueous solution, it becomes less pronounced when the temperature is raised (Fig. 6-19). The opinion that the hump is only observed with water (145) must be revised in view of these findings. It is to be noted that capacities with N-methylformamide are lower than with water despite the higher dielectric constant ($\epsilon = 182.4$ at 25°C) for the former solvent. We cannot therefore correlate directly capacities with the bulk dielectric constant as has sometimes been attempted (140). This is clearly pointed out by Frumkin and Damaskin (10).

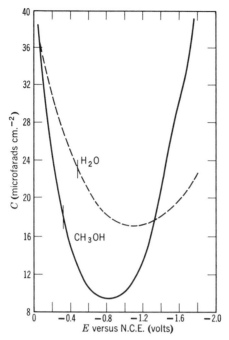

FIG. 6-17. Differential capacity of the compact double layer as a function of potential for mercury. Solid curve: $0.66M$ potassium fluoride in methanol at 25°C. Dotted line: $0.45M$ sodium fluoride in water at 88°C. Vertical lines show point of zero charge [Grahame (143)] (by permission of the Bunsengesellschaft).

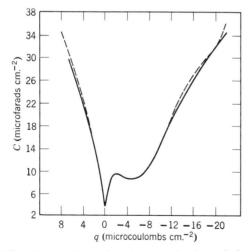

FIG. 6-18. Differential capacity against charge on the electrode for mercury in $0.001M$ potassium fluoride in methanol at 25°C. Solid curve, experimental capacities; dotted curve, calculated capacities [Grahame (143)] (by permission of the Bunsengesellschaft).

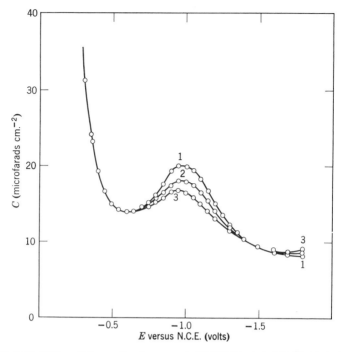

FIG. 6-19. Differential capacity of mercury in 0.1M potassium chloride against potential at 0°C (curve 1); 25°C (2); and 50°C (3). Potentials referred to normal calomel electrode in water with a bridge filled with saturated potassium chloride in water [Damaskin and Povarov (144)] (by permission of Consultants Bureau Enterprises).

6-4   Molten Salts

Study of the interface between metals and molten salts goes back to the early work of von Hevesy and Lorenz (146), but it is only more recently that systematic studies of electrocapillary curves (147–158) and double-layer capacities (159–168) have been carried out. The present status of the field is reviewed by Ukshe, Bukun, Leikis, and Frumkin (169) and is commented upon by Liu, Johnson, and Laitinen (170). With the exception of the work of Randles and White (160), which dealt with mercury in eutectic mixtures of low melting point (125–225°C), all other references pertain to investigations at relatively high temperatures (400°C and above). Technical difficulties have been largely overcome (169). Measurements with liquid metals are of particular interest since the difficulties associated with the use of solid electrodes are avoided. Double-layer capacities have been measured for the following liquid metals according to Ukshe, Bukun, Leikis, and Frumkin (169): aluminum, antimony, bismuth, cadmium,

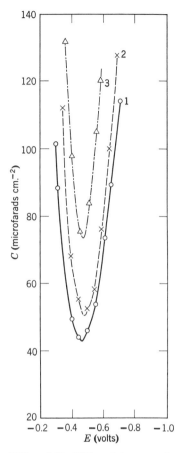

FIG. 6-20. Differential capacity versus potential for lead in sodium chloride at 820°C (curve 1); sodium bromide at 800°C (curve 2); and sodium iodide at 800°C (curve 3). Potentials referred to a lead-lead chloride (10 percent by weight) electrode in the melt [Ukshe, Bukun, Leikis, and Frumkin (169)] (by permission of Pergamon).

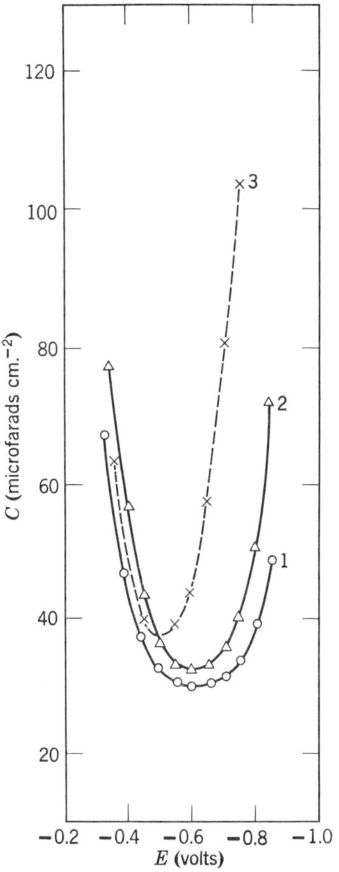

FIG. 6-21. Same type of data as in Fig. 6-20. Curve 1, potassium chloride; curve 2, potassium iodide; and curve 3, sodium chloride + potassium chloride (1:1). Temperature 800°C [Ukshe, Bukun, Leikis, and Frumkin (169)] (by permission of Pergamon).

gallium, indium, lead, silver, tellurium, thallium, and tin. Capacity-potential curves are nearly symmetrical (Figs. 6-20, 6-21) with respect to the minimum for most metals (except silver, thallium, and tin), and integration of these curves yield electrocapillary curves in good agreement with direct measurement of interfacial tension (Fig. 6-22). The minimum

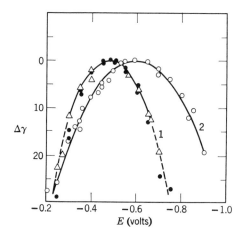

FIG. 6-22. Electrocapillary curves for lead in sodium chloride (curve 1) and potassium chloride (curve 2) melts at 820°C. Variations of interfacial tension plotted in ordinate. Points are experimental values; curves correspond to calculated interfacial tensions by integration of capacity-potential curves. Same reference electrode as in Fig. 6-20 [Ukshe, Bukun, Leikis, and Frumkin (169)] (by permission of Pergamon).

in capacity-potential curves agrees well with the maximum of electrocapillary curves. The increase of capacity on either side of the minimum may be interpreted as being caused by deformation of the melt structure.

The capacity depends markedly on the nature of the anion for lithium and sodium (Fig. 6-20) and not for potassium and cesium (Fig. 6-21). This is explained (169) by noting that the halide anions which were studied are bulkier than lithium and sodium cations, and consequently their mutual repulsion must be particularly significant. Anions and cations for potassium and cesium have ionic radii which are not as different as for lithium and sodium. The difference between the lithium-sodium and potassium-cesium groups also shows up in the temperature coefficient of the capacity at the minimum of the capacity-potential curve. This coefficient is 0.11 microfarad cm.$^{-2}$ per degree for the first group, whereas it is only 0.033 for the second group. These observations are most interesting and point toward the need for quantitative interpretation based on models.

REFERENCES

1. A. N. Frumkin and A. Gorodetzkaja, *Z. physik. Chem.*, **A136**, 215 (1928).
2. A. Murtazaev and A. Gorodetzkaja, *Acta Physicochim. U.R.S.S.*, **4**, 75 (1936).
3. D. C. Grahame, *Anal. Chem.*, **30**, 1736 (1958).
4. D. I. Leikis and E. S. Sevastyanov, *Doklady Akad. Nauk. S.S.S.R.*, **144**, 1320 (1962).

5. S. Karpachev, N. Ladygin, and V. Zykov, *Zhur. Fiz. Khim.*, **17**, 75 (1943).
6. A. V. Gorodetzkaja and M. A. Proskurnin, *ibid.*, **12**, 411, (1938).
7. V. L. Kheifets and B. S. Krasikov, *Doklady Akad. Nauk S.S.S.R.*, **94**, 517 (1954).
8. A. N. Frumkin and A. Gorodetzkaja, *Z. physik. Chem.*, **A136**, 451 (1928).
9. L. I. Boguslavskii and B. B. Damaskin, *Zhur. Fiz. Khim.*, **34**, 2099 (1960).
10. A. N. Frumkin and B. B. Damaskin, *Modern Aspects of Electrochemistry*, Vol. 3, J. O'M Bockris, editor, Butterworths, London, in press.
11. A. N. Frumkin and F. J. Cirves, *J. Phys. Chem.*, **34**, 74 (1930).
12. J. N. Butler and A. C. Makrides, *Trans. Faraday Soc.*, **60**, 1664 (1964),
13. S. A. Nikolaeva and U. V. Pal'm, *Zhur. Fiz. Khim.*, **33**, 91 (1959).
14. F. O. Koenig, H. C. Wohlers, and D. Bandini, paper presented at the Moscow C.I.T.C.E. meeting, 1963.
15. J. H. Sluyters, *Rec. trav. chim.*, **79**, 1092 (1960); **82**, 100 (1963).
16. J. H. Sluyters and J. J. C. Oomen, *ibid.*, **79**, 1101 (1960).
17. M. Rehbach and J. H. Sluyters, *ibid.*, **80**, 469 (1961); **81**, 301 (1962), **82**, 525, 535, 553 (1963).
17a. R. de Levie, *Electrochim. Acta*, in press.
18. H. G. Möller, *Z. physik. Chem.*, **A65**, 226 (1908).
19. C. A. Smolders and E. M. Duyvis, *Rec. trav. chim.*, **80**, 635 (1961).
20. C. A. Smolders, *ibid.*, **80**, 650, 699 (1961).
21. B. V. Ershler, *Uspekhi Khim.*, **21**, 237 (1952); *Chem. Abstr.*, **48**, 471 (1954).
22. R. Parsons, *Modern Aspects of Electrochemistry*, Vol. 1, J. O'M. Bockris, editor, Butterworths, London, 1954, pp. 103–179.
23. K. J. Vetter, *Elektrochemische Kinetik*, Springer, Berlin, 1961, pp. 81–91.
24. A. N. Frumkin, *J. Electrochem. Soc.*, **107**, 461 (1960).
25. Z. László, *Kolloid Z.*, **172**, 63 (1960).
26. D. N. Staicopolus, *J. Electrochem. Soc.*, **108**, 900 (1961).
27. B. Jakuszewski and Z. Kozlowski, *Roczniki Chem.*, **36**, 1873 (1962).
28. T. M. Green and H. Dahms, *J. Electrochem. Soc.*, **110**, 466 (1963).
29. T. N. Voropaena, B. V. Deryagin, and B. N. Kabanov, *Izvest. Akad. Nauk S.S.S.R. Otd. Khim. Nauk*, 257 (1963).
30. L. I. Antropov, *Ukrain. Khim. Zhur.*, **29**, 555 (1963).
31. A. N. Frumkin, *Z. Elektrochem.*, **59**, 807 (1955).
32. N. A. Balashova, *Doklady Akad. Nauk. S.S.S.R.*, **103**, 639 (1955).
33. T. I. Borisova, B. V. Ershler, and A. N. Frumkin, *Zhur. Fiz. Khim.* **22**, 925 (1948).
34. T. I. Borisova and B. V. Ershler, *ibid.*, **24**, 337 (1950).
35. T. P. Birintseva and B. N. Kabanov, *Doklady Akad. Nauk S.S.S.R.*, **132**, 868 (1960).
36. M. I. Temkin, *Izvest. Akad. Nauk S.S.S.R., Otd. Khim. Nauk*, 235 (1946).
37. P. Rüetschi and P. Delahay, *J. Chem. Phys.*, **23**, 697 (1955).
38. V. M. Novakovskii, E. A. Ukshe, and A. I. Levin, *Zhur. Fiz. Khim.*, **29**, 1847 (1955).
39. G. L. Weisslar, *Encyclopedia of Physics*, Vol. 21, S. Flügge, editor, Springer, Berlin, 1956, pp. 302–382.
40. V. L. Kheifets and B. S. Krasikov, *Zhur. Fiz. Khim.*, **31**, 1992 (1957).
41. A. N. Frumkin, *Advances in Electrochemistry and Electrochemical Engineering*, Vol. 3, P. Delahay, editor, Interscience, New York, 1963, pp. 287–391.
41a. A. N. Frumkin, *Electrochim. Acta*, **5**, 265 (1961).
42. B. V. Ershler, *Acta Physicochim. U.R.S.S.*, **7**, 327 (1937).
43. P. Dolin, B. V. Ershler, and A. N. Frumkin, *Zhur. Fiz. Khim.*, **14**, 907 (1940).

44. P. Dolin, B. V. Ershler, and A. N. Frumkin *Acta Physicochim. U.R.S.S.*, **13**, 779 (1940).
45. P. Dolin and B. V. Ershler, *Zhur. Fiz. Khim.*, **14**, 886 (1940).
46. P. Dolin and B. V. Ershler, *Acta Physicochim. U.R.S.S.*, **13**, 747 (1940).
47. T. I. Borisova, B. V. Ershler, and A. N. Frumkin, *Zhur. Fiz. Khim.*, **22**, 925 (1948).
48. T. I. Borisova and B. V. Ershler, *ibid.*, **24**, 337 (1950).
49. A. Eucken and B. Weblus, *Z. Elektrochem.*, **55**, 114 (1951).
50. S. Schuldiner, *J. Electrochem. Soc.*, **99**, 488 (1952).
51. W. D. Robertson, *ibid.*, **100**, 194 (1953).
52. V. L. Kheifets and B. S. Krasikov, *Doklady Akad. Nauk S.S.S.R.*, **94**, 101 (1954).
53. S. Schuldiner, *J. Electrochem. Soc.*, **101**, 426 (1954).
54. E. O. Ayazyan, *Doklady Akad. Nauk S.S.S.R.*, **100**, 473 (1955).
55. A. Rius, J. Llopis and F. Colom, *Proceedings of the International Committee on Electrochemical Thermodynamics and Kinetics*, 6th Meeting, Butterworths, London, 1955, pp. 280–288.
56. M. Breiter, H. Kammermaier, and C. A. Knorr, *Z. Elektrochem.*, **60**, 37 (1956).
57. V. L. Kheifets and B. S. Krasikov, *Doklady Akad. Nauk S.S.S.R.*, **109**, 586 (1956).
58. J. N. Sarmousakis and M. J. Prager, *J. Electrochem. Soc.*, **104**, 454 (1957).
59. J. Llopis and F. Colom, *Proceedings of the International Committee on Electrochemical Thermodynamics and Kinetics*, 8th Meeting, Butterworths, London, 1958, pp. 414–427.
60. P. V. Popat and N. Hackerman, *J. Phys. Chem.*, **62**, 1148 (1958).
61. J. J. McMullen and N. Hackerman, *J. Electrochem. Soc.*, **106**, 341 (1959).
62. B. N. Kabanov and T. P. Birintseva, *Doklady Akad. Nauk S.S.S.R.*, **131**, 132 (1960).
63. T. P. Birintseva and B. N. Kabanov, *ibid.*, **132**, 868 (1960).
64. H. A. Laitinen and C. G. Enke, *J. Electrochem. Soc.*, **107**, 773 (1960).
65. M. Breiter, *Transactions of the Symposium on Electrode Processes*, E. Yeager, editor, Wiley, New York, 1961, pp. 307–325.
66. M. Breiter, *J. Electrochem. Soc.*, **109**, 42, 425, 622 (1962).
67. M. Breiter, *Electrochim. Acta*, **8**, 925 (1963).
68. M. C. Banta and N. Hackerman, *J. Electrochem. Soc.*, **111**, 114 (1964).
69. M. Breiter, H. Kammermaier, and C. A. Knorr, *Z. Elektrochem.*, **60**, 119, 454 (1956).
70. K. Franke, C. A. Knorr, and M. Breiter, *ibid.*, **63**, 226 (1959).
71. T. I. Borisova and B. V. Ershler, *Zhur. Fiz., Khim.*, **24**, 337 (1950).
72. B. N. Kabanov, I. G. Kiseleva, and D. I. Leikis, *Doklady Akad. Nauk S.S.S.R.*, **99**, 805 (1954).
73. D. I. Leikis and B. N. Kabanov, *Trudy Inst. Fiz. Khim. Akad. Nauk S.S.S.R.*, **6**, 5 (1957); *Chem. Abstr.*, **53**, 918 (1959).
74. D. I. Leikis and E. K. Venstrem, *Doklady Akad. Nauk S.S.S.R.*, **112**, 97 (1957).
75. J. M. Kolotyrkin, *Proceedings of the International Committee on Electrochemical Thermodynamics and Kinetics*, 9th Meeting, Butterworths, London, 1959, pp. 406–419.
76. U. B. Pal'm and V. E. Past, *Doklady Akad. Nauk S.S.S.R.*, **146**, 1374 (1962).
77. J. M. Kolotyrkin and N. Y. Bune, *Zhur. Fiz. Khim.*, **29**, 435 (1955); *Doklady Akad. Nauk S.S.S.R.*, **100**, 295 (1955).
78. A. V. Pamfilov and V. S. Kuzub, *Ukrain. Khim. Zhur.*, **26**, 182 (1960).
79. T. I. Borisova and B. V. Ershler, *Zhur. Fiz. Khim.*, **24**, 337 (1950).
80. B. S. Krasikov and V. V. Sysoeva, *Doklady Akad. Nauk S.S.S.R.*, **114**, 826 (1957).

81. Chuang-Hshin Cha and Z. A. Iofa, *ibid.*, **131**, 137 (1960).
82. J. O'M. Bockris and E. C. Potter, *J. Chem. Phys.*, **20**, 614 (1952).
83. L. M. Elina, T. I. Borisova, and T. I. Zalkind, *Zhur. Fiz. Khim.*, **28**, 785 (1954).
84. J. O'M. Bockris and N. Pentland, *Trans. Faraday Soc.*, **48**, 833 (1952).
85. D. I. Leikis, *Doklady Akad. Nauk, S.S.S.R.*, **135**, 1429 (1960).
86. G. M. Schmid and N. Hackerman, *J. Electrochem. Soc.*, **110**, 440 (1963).
87. J. Clavilier, *Compt. rend.*, **257**, 3889 (1963).
88. V. V. Losev, *Doklady Akad. Nauk S.S.S.R.*, **88**, 499 (1953).
89. R. de Levie, "On Porous Electrodes in Electrolyte Solutions," Dissertation, University of Amsterdam, 1963; *Electrochim. Acta*, **9**, 1231 (1964).
90. R. de Levie, *Electrochim. Acta*, submitted.
91. A. Shlygin and A. N. Frumkin, *Acta Physicochim. U.R.S.S.*, **3**, 791 (1935).
92. A. Shlygin, A. N. Frumkin, and W. Medvedovskii, *ibid.*, **4**, 911 (1936).
93. A. N. Frumkin and A. Shlygin, *ibid.*, **5**, 819 (1936).
94. B. V. Ershler and M. Proskurnin, *ibid.*, **6**, 195 (1937).
95. A. Hickling, *Trans. Faraday Soc.*, **41**, 333 (1945).
96. B. V. Ershler, *Disc. Faraday Soc.*, **1**, 269 (1947).
97. E. Wicke and B. Weblus, *Z. Elektrochem.*, **56**, 169 (1952).
98. A. D. Obrucheva, *Zhur. Fiz. Khim.*, **26**, 1148 (1952).
99. W. Lorenz and H. Mühlberg, *Z. Elektrochem.*, **59**, 736 (1955).
100. N. A. Balashova, *Z. physik. Chem. (Leipzig)*, **207**, 340 (1957).
101. A. D. Obrucheva, *Zhur. Fiz. Khim.*, **32**, 2155 (1958).
102. T. P. Birintseva and B. N. Kabanov, *ibid.*, **33**, 844 (1959).
103. M. Breiter and B. Kennel, *Z. Elektrochem.*, **64**, 1180 (1960).
104. J. Richter and W. Lorenz, *Z. physik. Chem. (Leipzig)*, **217**, 136 (1961).
105. J. Llopis and A. Sancho, *J. Electrochem. Soc.*, **108**, 720 (1961).
106. V. E. Kazarinov and N. A. Balashova, *Doklady Akad. Nauk S.S.S.R.*, **134**, 864 (1960).
107. M. Breiter, *Electrochim. Acta.*, **7**, 25 (1962).
108. J. Llopis and M. Vazquez, *ibid.*, **6**, 167 177 (1962).
109. K. Schwabe, *ibid.*, **6**, 223 (1962).
110. N. A. Balashova, *ibid.*, **7**, 559 (1962).
111. M. Breiter, *ibid.*, **8**, 925 (1963).
112. N. A. Balashova, *Doklady Akad. Nauk S.S.S.R.*, **103**, 639 (1955).
113. N. A. Balashova, *Zhur. Fiz. Khim.*, **32**, 2266 (1958).
114. V. E. Kazarinov and N. A. Balashova, *Doklady Akad. Nauk S.S.S.R.*, **139**, 3, 641 (1961).
114a. N. A. Balashova and G. G. Zhmakin, *ibid.*, **143**, 358 (1962).
115. A. D. Obrucheva, *ibid.*, **120**, 1072 (1958).
116. A. D. Obrucheva, *ibid.*, **141**, 1413 (1961).
117. A. D. Obrucheva, *ibid.*, **142**, 859 (1962).
118. A. N. Frumkin, *Transactions of the Symposium on Electrode Processes*, E. Yeager, editor, Wiley, New York, 1961, pp. 1–12.
119. M. Breiter, *Electrochim. Acta*, **7**, 533 (1962).
120. M. Breiter, *ibid.*, **8**, 973 (1963).
121. H. Dahms and M. Green, *J. Electrochem. Soc.*, **110**, 1075 (1963).
122. F. Joliot, *J. chim. phys.*, **27**, 119 (1930).
123. W. H. Power and J. W. Heyd *Anal. Chem.*, **28**, 523 (1956).
124. H. D. Cook, *Rev. Sci. Instruments*, **27**, 1081 (1956).
125. I. A. Kafalas and H. C. Gatos, *Rev. Sci. Instruments*, **29**, 47 (1958).

126. E. A. Blomgren and J. O'M. Bockris, *Nature*, **186**, 305 (1960).
127. M. Green. D. A. J. Swinkels, and J. O'M. Bockris, *Rev. Sci. Instruments*, **33**, 18 (1962).
128. H. Dahms, M. Green, and J. Weber, *Nature*, **196**, 1310 (1962).
129. H. Wroblowa and M. Green, *Electrochim. Acta.*, **8**, 679 (1963).
130. B. E. Conway, R. G. Barradas, and T. Zavidzky, *J. Phys. Chem.*, **62**, 676 (1958).
131. R. G. Barradas and B. E. Conway, *J. Electroanal. Chem.*, **6**, 314 (1963).
132. R. Parsons and M. A. V. Devanathan, *Trans. Faraday Soc.*, **49**, 673 (1953).
133. R. S. Maizlish, I. P. Tverdovskii, and A. N. Frumkin, *Zhur. Fiz. Khim.*, **28**, 87 (1954).
134. A. A. Moussa, H. M. Sammour, and H. A. Ghaly, *Egypt. J. Chem.*, **1**, 165 (1958).
135. H. K. Zimmerman, *Bull. Soc. Chim. Beograd*, **23–24**, 1 (1959).
136. S. Ueda, F. Tsuji and A. Watanabe, *J. Electrochem. Soc. Japan*, **29**, E190, E192 (1961).
137. S. Minc and M. Brzostowska, *Roczniki Chem.*, **36**, 1901, 1909 (1962).
138. J. Dojlido and B. Behr, *ibid.*, **37**, 1043 (1963).
139. T. A. Pimfold and F. Selba, *J. Am. Chem. Soc.*, **78**, 2095 (1956).
140. S. Minc, J. Jastrzebska, and M. Brzostowska, *J. Electrochem. Soc.*, **108**, 1160 (1961).
141. G. A. Korchinskii, *Ukrain. Khim. Zhur.*, **28**, 473 (1962); *Chem. Abstr.*, **57**, 15832 (1962).
142. G. A. Korchinskii, *ibid.*, **28**, 693 (1962); *Chem. Abstr.*, **58**, 5067 (1963).
143. D. C. Grahame, *Z. Elektrochem.*, **59**, 740 (1955).
144. B. B. Damaskin and Yu. M. Povarov, *Doklady Akad. Nauk S.S.S.R.*, **140**, 394 (1961).
145. N. F. Mott and R. J. Watts-Tobin, *Electrochim. Acta*, **4**, 79 (1961).
146. G. von Hevesy and R. Lorenz, *Z. physik. Chem.*, **A74**, 443 (1910).
147. S. V. Karpachev and A. G. Stromberg, *ibid.*, **A176**, 182 (1936).
148. S. V. Karpachev and A. G. Stromberg, *Zhur. Fiz. Khim.*, **10**, 739 (1937).
149. S. V. Karpachev and A. G. Stromberg, *ibid.*, **13**, 183, 397, 1831 (1939).
150. S. V. Karpachev and A. G. Stromberg, *Acta Physicochim. U.R.S.S.*, **12**, 523 (1940).
151. S. V. Karpachev and A. G. Stromberg, *ibid.*, **16**, 331 (1942).
152. S. V. Karpachev and A. G. Stromberg, *Zhur. Fiz. Khim.*, **18**, 47, 234 (1944).
153. V. A. Kuznetsov, V. P. Kochergin, M. V. Tishchenko, and E. G. Pozdnysheva, *Doklady Akad. Nauk S.S.S.R.*, **92**, 1197 (1953).
154. V. A. Kuznetsov, V. V. Ashpur, and G. S. Poroshiva, *ibid.*, **101**, 301 (1955).
155. V. A. Kuznetsov, V. I. Aksenov, and M. P. Klevtsova, *ibid.*, **128**, 763 (1959).
156. V. A. Kuznetsov, T. D. Dyakova, and V. P. Mal'tseva, *Zhur. Fiz. Khim.*, **33**, 1551 (1959).
157. V. A. Kuznetsov, L. S. Zagainova, M. P. Klevtsova, and Z. A. Shevrina, *Nauk. Doklady vys. Shkoly, Khim. i Khim. Tekhnol.*, 268, 1959; *Chem. Abst.* **53**, 19505 (1959).
158. V. A. Kuznetsov, M. P. Klevtsova, L. S. Zagainova, L. S. Vaintraub, and T. A. Korobova, *Zhur. Fiz. Khim.*, **34**, 1345 (1960).
159. V. A. Kuznetsov and L. S. Zagaynova, *Zhur. Fiz. Khim.*, **35**, 1640 (1961).
160. J. E. B. Randles and W. White, *Z. Elektrochem.*, **59**, 666 (1955).
161. H. A. Laitinen and R. A. Osteryoung, *J. Electrochem. Soc.*, **102**, 598 (1955).
162. H. A. Laitinen and H. C. Gaur, *ibid.*, **104**, 730 (1957).
163. E. A. Ukshe, N. G. Bukun, and D. I. Leikis, *Doklady Akad. Nauk S.S.S.R.*, **135**, 1183 (1960).
164. H. A. Laitinen and D. K. Roe, *Coll. Czechoslov, Chem. Commun.*, **25**, 3065 (1960).

165. E. A. Ukshe, N. G. Bukun, and D. I. Leikis, *Zhur. Fiz. Khim.*, **36,** 2322 (1962).

166. O. V. Gorodis'kii, I. K. Delimarskii, and E. V. Panov, *Doklady Akad. Nauk S.S.S.R.*, **146,** 129 (1962).

167. E. A. Ukshe, N. G. Bukun, and D. I. Leikis, *Izvest. Akad. Nauk S.S.S.R., Otd. Khim. Nauk*, 31 (1963).

168. G. A. Martynov and B. V. Deryagin, *Doklady Akad. Nauk S.S.S.R.*, **152,** 140 (1963).

169. E. Ukshe, N. G. Bukun, D. I. Leikis, and A. N. Frumkin, *Electrochim. Acta*, **9,** 431 (1964).

170. C. H. Liu, K. E. Johnson, and H. A. Laitinen, *Molten Salt Chemistry*, M. Blander, editor, Interscience, New York, 1964, pp. 681–733.

PART TWO

ELECTRODE KINETICS

CHAPTER 7

Kinetics of Simple Electrode Processes
without Specific Adsorption or Chemisorption

7-1 Introduction

Electrode reactions are heterogeneous processes whose kinetics depends on the rate of charge transfer and mass transfer and possibly the rate of chemical reactions coupled with charge transfer. Charge transfer may involve one or several steps. Only one rate-determining step or the kinetics of two or more consecutive steps will be considered here. Chemical reactions associated with charge transfer may be too rapid to require kinetic treatment, but this simplification is often not possible. Coupled reactions may occur either solely at the surface of the electrode (hetero-geneous reactions) or in solution near the electrode (homogeneous reactions). They may precede or follow charge transfer or they may involve intermediate products in the over-all electrode reaction.

Because of the heterogeneous nature of electrode processes, their kinetics is profoundly affected by the double-layer structure and by adsorption of reactants, products, supporting electrolyte, and any additive. Control by mass transfer becomes increasingly predominant as the rate of the electrode reaction increases, and correction for mass transfer is often necessary.

Our study will progress with the increasing complexity of the electrode process. This chapter deals with simple processes whose rate-determining step is the over-all reaction in the absence of coupled chemical reaction and specific adsorption. Complex electrode processes are covered in Chapter 8. The influence of the double-layer structure is analyzed in

Chapter 9 in the absence of adsorption of reacting species. Processes with chemisorption or potential-dependent adsorption of reacting species are discussed in Chapters 10 and 11, respectively.

7-2 Current-Overvoltage Characteristic

a. Derivation

We consider the simple electrode process

$$O + ne = R \tag{1}$$

which involves two soluble species. Substance R may be soluble in solution or in a liquid electrode, for example, a metal in an amalgam. Reacting species and supporting electrolyte are assumed not to be specifically adsorbed (or chemisorbed). The rate-determining step is the same as the over-all reaction and consequently involves n electrons. No complication due to mass transfer is supposed to prevail, that is, the concentrations of O and R at the electrode are the same as in the bulk of the solution except, of course, for concentration gradients resulting from the double-layer structure.

The following derivation of the current-overvoltage characteristic is inspired by Parsons' treatment (1) but corresponds to a simpler case. Notation and approach are essentially those used by Mohilner and Delahay (1a) in a similar treatment with consideration of specific adsorption. The historical background will be given with the introduction of fundamental concepts. [See also Vetter's review (2).] A concise treatment of the essential ideas is available (3).

We distinguish the following states in the over-all reaction 1 on the assumption that R is soluble in the solution. The modification when R is soluble in a liquid electrode is trivial. Thus:

  I: O in the bulk of the solution outside the diffuse double layer and n electrons e in the electrode;
 II: O in the o'uter plane of closest approach and n electrons e in the electrode;
 ≠: the transition state;
III: R in the outer plane of closest approach;
IV: R in the bulk of the solution outside the diffuse double layer.

We now write the standard free energies corresponding to states I to IV and divide electrochemical potentials into chemical and inner potentials

(Sec. 1-3). [Electrochemical potentials were introduced by Van Ryssel-berghe (4) in electrode kinetics.] Thus

$$
\begin{aligned}
G_\mathrm{I}^0 &= \mu_\mathrm{O}{}^0 + n\mu_e{}^0 - nF\phi_\mathrm{M} \\
G_\mathrm{II}^0 &= \mu_\mathrm{O}{}^0 + n\mu_e{}^0 + zF\phi_2 - nF\phi_\mathrm{M} \\
G_\mathrm{III}^0 &= \mu_\mathrm{R}{}^0 + z'F\phi_2 \\
G_\mathrm{IV}^0 &= \mu_\mathrm{R}{}^0
\end{aligned}
\tag{2}
$$

where the μ^0's are the standard potentials; z and z' are the ionic valences, with sign, of O and R, respectively; ϕ_M is the inner potential of the electrode M, referred to the inner potential ϕ_s in the bulk of the solution outside the diffuse double layer; the potential ϕ_s is set at zero for the sake of convenience; and ϕ_2 is the potential in the outer plane of closest approach referred to the potential ϕ_s. It is assumed in the writing of G_II^0 and G_III^0 that $\mu_\mathrm{O}{}^0$ is the same in states I and II and $\mu_\mathrm{R}{}^0$ the same in states III and IV. This approximation, however, does not affect the result of the derivation.

Derivation of the rate of reaction 1 by the theory of absolute rates requires the value of the standard free energy of activation $\overrightarrow{\Delta G^0_{\neq}} = G^0_{\neq} - G_\mathrm{I}{}^0$ for the forward reaction to be known and $\overleftarrow{\Delta G^0_{\neq}} = G^0_{\neq} - G_\mathrm{IV}^0$ for the backward reaction to be known. [For the introduction of the absolute rate theory in electrode kinetics, see Eyring, Glasstone, and Laidler (5).] Calculation of $G^0_{\neq}$ would require a detailed model of the transition state, which is generally not available. This difficulty is avoided by assuming that the potential-dependent part of $G^0_{\neq} - G_\mathrm{II}^0$ is some fraction α of the potential-dependent part of $G_\mathrm{III}^0 - G_\mathrm{II}^0$. We thus introduce the *transfer coefficient* α by

$$
\begin{aligned}
(G^0_{\neq})_e - (G_\mathrm{II}^0)_e &= \alpha[(G_\mathrm{III}^0)_e - (G_\mathrm{II}^0)_e] \\
&= \alpha[(z' - z)F\phi_2 + nF\phi_\mathrm{M}] \\
&= \alpha nF(\phi_\mathrm{M} - \phi_2)
\end{aligned}
\tag{3}
$$

where the subscript e designates the potential-dependent part of the standard free energies. The last Eq. 3 is deduced from the preceding one by noting that $z' = z - n$. Equation 3 implies the reasonable assumption of a monotonic variation of the potential-dependent part of the standard free energy between states II and III. The introduction of α by Eq. 3, which leads to formulas describing experimental results, is not accepted by Van Rysselberghe (12). He considers that α must be defined in terms of the difference $G_\mathrm{III}^0 - G_\mathrm{II}^0$ and not in terms of the potential-dependent part of this difference. This matter is still open to further discussion.

The transfer coefficient was first introduced in electrode kinetics by Erdey-Gruz and Volmer in 1930 (6) for the particular case of hydrogen ion discharge. Butler (7) had considered somewhat earlier the influence of electrode potential on the rates of the forward and backward reactions. Audubert (8) alluded to this problem simultaneously with Butler, but did not develop the idea until later (9).

We now examine why the difference $(G_{III}^0)_e - (G_{II}^0)_e$ appears in Eq. 3 and not some other difference between the potential-dependent parts of the standard free energy of states I and III. The following intuitive arguments can be advanced: (a) it is the electrical field in the region between electrode and outer plane which affects the rate of the reaction; (b) the drop of potential between the bulk of the solution and the outer plane affects kinetics only indirectly in causing a variation of the concentrations of species O and R in the plane of closest approach. We select state II corresponding to the outer plane as what Frumkin (11) called the *pre-electrode state*. This approach allows us very conveniently to use double-layer theory to interpret the effect of double-layer structure on kinetics and is fairly well justified by its success in the analysis of experimental results. The ultimate reason for the writing of Eq. 3 is thus a pragmatic one, and a firmer basis is needed. It may be added that Erdey-Gruz and Volmer (6) did not go into this problem. They wrote, in terms of our formulation $(G_{IV}^0)_e - (G_I^0)_e$ instead of $(G_{III}^0)_e - (G_{II}^0)_e$ in Eq. 3, and thus did not consider the effect of the double layer.

We write by analogy with Eq. 3

$$(G_{\neq}^0)_e - (G_{III}^0)_e = (\alpha - 1)[(G_{III}^0)_e - (G_{II}^0)_e]$$
$$= (\alpha - 1)[(z' - z)F\phi_2 + nF\phi_M] \qquad (4)$$
$$= (\alpha - 1)nF(\phi_M - \phi_2)$$

The standard free energy of activation for the forward reaction $\overrightarrow{\Delta G_{\neq}^0}$ can now be decomposed into a chemical part $(\overrightarrow{\Delta G_{\neq}^0})_n$ and an electro-chemical part $(\overrightarrow{\Delta G_{\neq}^0})_e$. The latter is readily deduced from Eq. 3. Thus

$$\overrightarrow{\Delta G_{\neq}^0} = G_{\neq}^0 - G_I^0$$
$$= (\overrightarrow{\Delta G_{\neq}^0})_n + (\overrightarrow{\Delta G_{\neq}^0})_e$$
$$= (\overrightarrow{\Delta G_{\neq}^0})_n + (G_{\neq}^0)_e - (G_I^0)_e \qquad (5)$$
$$= (\overrightarrow{\Delta G_{\neq}^0})_n + [(G_{\neq}^0)_e - (G_{II}^0)_e] + [(G_{II}^0)_e - (G_I^0)_e]$$
$$= (\overrightarrow{\Delta G_{\neq}^0})_n + \alpha nF(\phi_M - \phi_2) + zF\phi_2$$

Similarly, the standard free energy of activation for the backward reaction is

$$
\begin{aligned}
\overleftarrow{\Delta G}{}^0_{\neq} &= G^0_{\neq} - G^0_{IV} \\
&= (\overleftarrow{\Delta G}{}^0_{\neq})_n + (\overleftarrow{\Delta G}{}^0_{\neq})_e \\
&= (\overleftarrow{\Delta G}{}^0_{\neq})_n + (G^0_{\neq})_e - (G^0_{IV})_e \\
&= (\overleftarrow{\Delta G}{}^0_{\neq})_n + [(G^0_{\neq})_e - (G^0_{III})_e] + [(G^0_{III})_e - (G^0_{IV})_e] \\
&= (\overleftarrow{\Delta G}{}^0_{\neq})_n + (\alpha - 1)nF(\phi_M - \phi_2) + z'F\phi_2
\end{aligned}
\tag{6}
$$

The current densities for the forward and backward reactions can now be written by applying the theory of absolute rates (5) for a transmission coefficient equal to unity. Thus

$$
\overrightarrow{i} = nF \frac{kT}{h} e^{-\overrightarrow{\Delta G}{}_{\neq}{}^0/RT} a_O
$$

$$
\overleftarrow{i} = nF \frac{kT}{h} e^{-\overleftarrow{\Delta G}{}_{\neq}{}^0/RT} a_R
\tag{7}
$$

where k is the Boltzmann constant, h the Planck constant, and the a's are the activities of O and R in the bulk of the solution outside the diffuse double layer. We shall simply refer to the "current density" as "current" in the future to simplify matters. We write Eq. 7 in an explicit form by introducing the standard free energies of activation from Eqs. 5 and 6. We have after introducing the parameter f used in Part One and noting that $z' = z - n$

$$
f = \frac{F}{RT}
\tag{8}
$$

$$
\overrightarrow{i} = nF \frac{kT}{h} e^{-(\overrightarrow{\Delta G}{}_{\neq}{}^0)_n/RT} e^{-\alpha n f \phi_M} e^{(\alpha n - z)f\phi_2} a_O
\tag{9}
$$

$$
\overleftarrow{i} = nF \frac{kT}{h} e^{-(\overleftarrow{\Delta G}{}_{\neq}{}^0)_n/RT} e^{(1-\alpha)n f \phi_M} e^{(\alpha n - z)f\phi_2} a_R
$$

The right-hand members of the rate Eqs. 7, 9, and 10 should really be divided by the activity coefficient of the activated complex. The latter may possibly be potential-dependent under certain conditions and may thus be significant. This point was not made by Parsons in his paper (1) but was called to the writer's attention by him (77).

The net current i

$$
i = \overrightarrow{i} - \overleftarrow{i}
\tag{10}
$$

is written by taking by convention a net reduction current as positive and a net oxidation current as negative. Thus a net *cathodic* current is positive and a net *anodic* current is negative. This widely adopted convention agrees with the writing of reaction 1 as a reduction which, in its turn, follows from adoption of the IUPAC Stockholm convention for electrode potentials (Sec. 1-3). The transfer coefficient α, introduced in Eq. 3, corresponds to the cathodic process and $1 - \alpha$ corresponds to the anodic process.

At the equilibrium potential $\phi_M{}^e$, the net current is equal to zero and $\overrightarrow{i} = \overleftarrow{i}$. We introduce the *true exchange current* $i_t{}^0$ which is equal to $\overrightarrow{i} = \overleftarrow{i}$ at $\phi_M{}^e$ for $\phi_2 = 0$, that is, in the absence of the double-layer effect. Equations 9 and 10 become

$$i = i_t{}^0 e^{(\alpha n - z)f\phi_2}[e^{-\alpha nf(\phi_M - \phi_M{}^e)} - e^{(1-\alpha)nf(\phi_M - \phi_M{}^e)}] \tag{11}$$

We define the *apparent exchange current* i^0 by

$$i^0 = i_t{}^0 e^{(\alpha n - z)f\phi_2} \tag{12}$$

and we introduce the *overvoltage* η

$$\eta = E - E^e = \phi_M - \phi_M{}^e$$

where the E's are the usual electrode potentials against some reference electrode, for example, the normal hydrogen electrode. Exchange currents in the literature are almost never corrected for the double-layer effect and, to simplify terminology and notations, we shall refer to them as "exchange currents" (i^0), it being understood that they are apparent values. Equations 11 and 12 yield

$$i = i^0(e^{-\alpha nf\eta} - e^{(1-\alpha)nf\eta}) \tag{13}$$

It must be recalled in the application of Eq. 13, that i^0 depends on ϕ_2 and consequently on E. Moreover, we must introduce in Eq. 12 the value of ϕ_2 at the potential E prevailing in measurements from which i^0 is deduced. If η does not exceed a few millivolts, ϕ_2 at E is nearly equal to ϕ_2 at E^e, but this is not the case at higher overvoltages. This point will be discussed in detail in Sec. 9-2, and we shall limit ourselves here to the discussion of Eq. 13 for the case in which ϕ_2 is held constant when the overvoltage varies. This condition is very approximately fulfilled, especially for low overvoltages, when the ionic concentration is *at least* $0.1M$ and the potential is not too close to the point of zero charge. The potential ϕ_2 varies then rather slowly with E (See Fig. 3-6), and i^0 can be regarded as independent of the overvoltage as a first approximation. This approximation must suffice for the time being for a number of processes (for example, those on solid electrodes) for which the double-layer correction cannot be made with any certainty.

The concept of exchange current was introduced by Butler (56) in 1936. Bowden and Agar (78) listed data on exchange current in a review as early as 1938. Early reference to the exchange current was also made in the papers by Eyring, Glasstone, and Laidler (5), Rojter, Juza, and Poluyan (13) and Dolin and Ershler (14). The latter authors coined the expression "exchange current." This choice was a very apt one because there is an exchange between the electrode and the solution which can easily be demonstrated, for instance, for a metal-amalgam metal-ion electrode by the labeling of the metal in one of the phases by a radiotracer. The tracer immediately appears in the other phase when the amalgam is put into contact with the metal-ion solution, provided the exchange current is not too low, although there is no net current flowing through the electrode-solution interface.

The concept of overvoltage was first introduced in electrode kinetics by Caspari (15). This author introduced the symbol "η" which has been widely used ever since. [See also the references he quotes to earlier work by Le Blanc (1891, 1893) and Nernst (1897).] The term "overpotential" is also used (16). η is the *charge-transfer overvoltage* according to Vetter's nomenclature (2, 17, 18). It is frequently called *activation overvoltage*, but this expression is not entirely unambiguous, as noted by Vetter, because partial control of an electrode process by a chemical reaction also corresponds to an "activation process."

b. Properties of the Current-Overvoltage Characteristic

A plot of i/i^0 against $nf\eta$ according to Eq. 13 is shown in Fig. 7-1 for different values of α (19). Current-voltage curves are asymmetrical

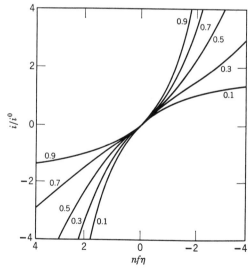

FIG. 7-1. Plot of i/i^0 against $nf\eta$ for different values of the transfer coefficient [Gerischer and Vielstich (19)] [(by permission of *Z. physik. Chem. (Frankfurt)*)].

with respect to the point $\eta = 0$ except for $\alpha = 0.5$. We have $i \gtrless 0$ for $\eta \lessgtr 0$, that is, the overvoltage is negative for a net cathodic process and positive for a net anodic process. When $|\eta| \ll 1/\alpha nf$ [or $|\eta| \ll 1/(1 - \alpha)nf$], the exponentials in Eq. 13 can be linearized, as was first pointed out by Butler (20). The current-overvoltage characteristic is then linear, that is,

$$i = -i^0 nf\eta \tag{14}$$

where the minus sign follows from Eq. 13 and ultimately from the convention of taking a net cathodic current as positive. This relationship which holds for overvoltages not exceeding a few millivolts (Table 7-1),

TABLE 7-1   Relative Error in Current Resulting from the Use of the Linear Approximation for the Current-Overvoltage Characteristic[a]

Overvoltage, millivolts	Relative Error for $n = 1$ at 25°C, percent	
	$\alpha = 0.5$	$\alpha = 0.2$
−20	−2.5	+23
−10	−0.76	+11.6
−5	−0.26	+6.0
−2	−0.13	+2.4
+2	−0.13	−2.4
+5	−0.26	−6
+10	−0.76	−11.6
+20	−2.5	−23

[a] Error affecting absolute value of current.

has been used extensively in the treatment of relaxation and perturbation methods for the study of fast electrode processes. Since the current-overvoltage characteristic of Eq. 14 is of the form of Ohm's law, we can define according to Vetter (17, 18) a *charge-transfer resistance*

$$-\left(\frac{\partial \eta}{\partial i}\right)_{i \to 0} = \frac{1}{nfi^0} \tag{15}$$

At high overvoltages, we have $|\eta| \gg 1/\alpha nf$ [or $|\eta| \gg 1/(1 - \alpha)nf$], and one of the exponentials in Eq. 13 can be dropped (Table 7-2). The familiar

TABLE 7-2   Relative Error in Current Resulting from the Use of the Tafel Relationship

Overvoltage, millivolts	Relative Error for $n = 1$ at $25°C$,[a] percent	
	$\alpha = 0.5$	$\alpha = 0.2$
-200	0.04	0.04
-100	2.1	2.1
-50	16.6	16.6
-20	84.6	84
$+20$	84.6	84
$+50$	16.6	16.6
$+100$	2.1	2.1
$+200$	0.04	0.04

[a] Relative error affecting absolute value of current. All errors are positive. Note that relative errors are essentially independent of α.

linear dependence of overvoltage on the logarithm of current, already discovered by Tafel in 1905 (21), follows:

$$\ln \frac{i}{i^0} = -\alpha nf\eta \qquad \text{(cathodic processes)}$$

$$\ln \frac{|i|}{i^0} = (1 - \alpha)nf\eta \qquad \text{(anodic processes)} \qquad (16)$$

These relationships hold when the overvoltage exceeds at least 0.1 volt. They are often written in the form and with the notations originally reported by Tafel

$$\eta = a \pm b \log |i| \qquad (17)$$

where the $\pm$ sign holds for anodic and cathodic processes, respectively, and the constants a and b are deduced from Eq. 16. Thus

$$a = \frac{1}{\alpha nf} \ln i^0 \qquad b = \frac{2.303}{\alpha nf} \qquad \text{(cathodic processes)}$$

$$a = -\frac{1}{(1 - \alpha)nf} \ln i^0 \qquad b = \frac{2.303}{(1 - \alpha)nf} \qquad \text{(anodic processes)} \qquad (18)$$

The two Tafel lines at high overvoltage, namely

$$\ln i = \ln i^0 - \alpha nf\eta \qquad \text{(cathodic processes)}$$

$$\ln |i| = \ln i^0 + (1 - \alpha)nf\eta \qquad \text{(anodic processes)} \qquad (19)$$

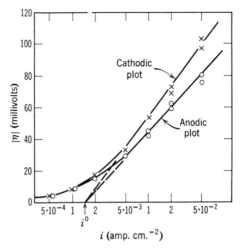

FIG. 7-2. Determination of the exchange current by intersection of the Tafel lines for high cathodic and anodic overvoltages for discharge of $0.005M$ Cd^{++} in $0.4M$ potassium sulfate on cadmium-amalgam at $20°C$. Note that somewhat higher overvoltages would have been desirable for Tafel plots (cf. Table 7-2) but measurements would have been more difficult since i^0 ($= 1.5$ milliamp cm^{-2}) is relatively high [Lorenz (22)] by permission of the Bunsengesellschaft).

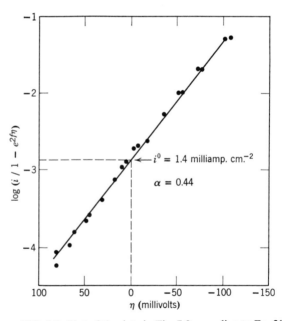

FIG. 7-3. Plot of the data in Fig. 7-2 according to Eq. 21.

intersect at the point having $\ln i^0$ as ordinate and $\eta = 0$ as abscissa [Fig. 7-2 according to Lorenz (22)]. The slope of the cathodic Tafel line yields α and that of the anodic line gives $1 - \alpha$. We can thus verify that the sum of the experimentally determined values of α and $1 - \alpha$ is equal to unity. The $\ln i$ versus η plots have the line $\eta = 0$ as asymptote. This type of plot can be applied to the determination of equilibrium potentials whenever the exchange current is so low that direct potentiometric measurements are not practical, but we must be certain that the over-all reaction is the rate-determining step before applying this method. This condition is often not fulfilled when exchange currents are low.

Another plot, which is valid regardless of the magnitude of the over-voltage, was introduced by Allen and Hickling (79). (Actually, they wrote a more complete equation with a stoichiometric number.) Equation 13 is rewritten in the form

$$\frac{i}{1 - e^{nf\eta}} = i^0 e^{-\alpha nf\eta} \tag{20}$$

Hence

$$\ln \frac{i}{1 - e^{nf\eta}} = \ln i^0 - \alpha nf\eta \tag{21}$$

where i is taken with its sign. The slope of the plot of Eq. 21 yields α and the intercept at $\eta = 0$ gives the exchange current (Fig. 7-3). There seems to be no reason why this type of diagram should not be preferred to Tafel plots since the low overvoltage limitation is removed.

It also follows from Eq. 13 that the ratio of the anodic component of the net current to the cathodic component is

$$\frac{e^{(1-\alpha)nf\eta}}{e^{-\alpha nf\eta}} = e^{nf\eta} \tag{22}$$

This relationship, which was pointed out by Horiuti and Ikusima (23), may be applied as a check of diagrams such as Fig. 7-2.

7-3 Exchange Current

a. Explicit Form

The true exchange current i_t^0 was already defined in conjunction with Eq. 11, and is given by Eq. 9 in which ϕ_M is set equal to the equilibrium potential ϕ_M^e and the exponential in ϕ_2 is dropped. Thus

$$i_t^0 = nF \frac{kT}{h} e^{-(\overrightarrow{\Delta G}_{\neq}^0)n/RT} e^{-\alpha nf\phi_M^e} a_O$$

$$= nF \frac{kT}{h} e^{-(\overleftarrow{\Delta G}_{\neq}^0)n/RT} e^{(1-\alpha)nf\phi_M^e} a_R \tag{23}$$

The equilibrium potential $\phi_M{}^e$ can be expressed by the Nernst equation

$$\phi_M{}^e = \phi_M{}^0 + \frac{1}{nf} \ln \frac{a_O}{a_R} \tag{24}$$

where $\phi_M{}^0$ corresponds to the standard potential for reaction 1. Equation 23 now becomes

$$i_t{}^0 = nFk_t{}^0 a_O^{1-\alpha} a_R{}^\alpha \tag{25}$$

where the *true standard rate constant* $k_t{}^0$ is

$$k_t{}^0 = \frac{kT}{h} e^{-(\overrightarrow{\Delta G \neq}{}^0)n/RT} e^{-\alpha n f \phi_M{}^0}$$
$$= \frac{kT}{h} e^{-(\overleftarrow{\Delta G \neq}{}^0)n/RT} e^{(1-\alpha)n f \phi_M{}^0} \tag{26}$$

We also define the *apparent standard rate constant* k^0, just as we introduced in Eq. 12 the apparent exchange current, by including the term in ϕ_2 of Eq. 12 in k^0. The constant k^0 was first introduced by Randles (24). Thus

$$k^0 = k_t{}^0 e^{(\alpha n - z)f\phi_2} \tag{27}$$

and consequently,

$$i^0 = nFk^0 a_0^{1-\alpha} a_R{}^\alpha \tag{28}$$

We seldom measure activities in electrode kinetics and Eq. 28 is thus written with concentrations rather than activities. The constant k^0 is generally defined accordingly.

The dependence of the exchange current on activities (concentrations) was first examined by Esin (24a) in 1940 for the Ti(IV)/Ti(III) couple and was systematically applied and extended by Vetter (17, 25, 26) and Gerischer (27–30). [For reviews see Vetter (2, 31a).] Lewartowicz followed independently the same approach (32) and so did Petrocelli (32a). The form of Eq. 28 in terms of k^0 was given by Berzins and Delahay (33). The significance of the constant $k_t{}^0$ has been discussed by Randles (24) in terms of potential energy curves.

Application of Eq. 28 has become common practice for a number of years, and values of k^0 have been compiled by Tanaka and Tamamushi (34) for a rather large number of reactions. Most data are quoted for k^0 and not for $k_t{}^0$, for the correction for the double layer involves some uncertainties (Chapter 9). It really does not matter much whether we quote k^0 or i^0 since these two parameters are related by Eq. 28. Values of k^0 give a more immediate indication how *inherently* fast an electrode process is since it is not necessary to consider concentrations as one must do when quoting i^0. It should be emphasized, however, that the use of k^0 is justified only when the hypotheses at the beginning of Sec. 7-2 are valid. When this is not the case, we may still be justified in computing an apparent exchange current by application of Eq. 13.

b. Determination of the Transfer Coefficient from the Dependence of the Exchange Current on Reactant Activities

It follows from Eq. 23, as written in terms of i^0 instead of i_t^0, that the plot of $\ln i^0$ against the equilibrium potential E^e at constant a_0 is linear and has the slope $-\alpha n f$. Conversely, the linear plot of $\ln i^0$ against E^e at constant a_R has the slope $(1 - \alpha)n f$ (Fig. 7-4). This method of determining the transfer coefficient was first used independently by Vetter (17, 25, 26), Gerischer (27–30), Lewartowicz (32), Petrocelli (32a), and Parsons (1).

Instead of plotting $\ln i^0$ against E^e, we can use the wholly equivalent procedure of plotting $\ln i^0$ against the logarithm of the activity of one reactant, the activity of the other reactant remaining constant (Fig. 7-5). We deduce directly from Eq. 28

$$\left(\frac{\partial \ln i^0}{\partial \ln a_O}\right)_{a_R} = 1 - \alpha$$
$$\left(\frac{\partial \ln i^0}{\partial \ln a_R}\right)_{a_O} = \alpha \tag{29}$$

This method for the determination of α is particularly useful in relaxation and perturbation methods in which overvoltages not exceeding a few millivolts often prevail (to simplify the mathematical treatment). The

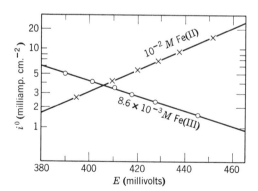

FIG. 7-4. Variations of the exchange current with the equilibrium potential for the Fe(III)/Fe(II) couple on platinum in $1M$ sulfuric acid at $25°C$. Potential referred to silver-silver chloride electrode in 1 molar potassium chloride [Gerischer (27)] (by permission of the Bunsengesellschaft).

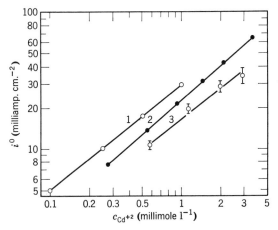

FIG. 7-5. Determination of the transfer coefficient for the cadmium-cadmium amalgam electrode in sodium sulfate ($1M$ for line 1; $0.5M$ for lines 2 and 3) at 25°C. Line 1, single-step galvanostatic method [Berzins and Delahay (33)]; line 2, faradaic impedance method [Gerischer (28)]; line 3, voltage-step method [Vielstich and Delahay (35)]. Values of α: 0.22, 0.17, and 0.25, respectively (by permission of the American Chemical Society).

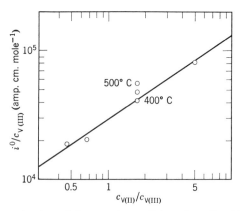

FIG. 7-6. Determination of the transfer coefficient from Eq. 30 for the V(III)/V(II) couple on platinum in potassium chloride-lithium chloride eutectic mixture in the 400 to 500°C range [Laitinen, Tischer, and Roe (36)] (by permission of The Electrochemical Society).

current-overvoltage relationship is then linear (Eq. 14), and α cannot be determined directly from it. At high overvoltages, α can be computed directly from the Tafel plot, and Eqs. 29 and 30 are of less immediate use. Application of Eq. 29 has become widespread. [See, for example, diagrams for molten salt systems similar to Fig. 7-5 in Laitinen, Tischer, and Roe (36).] It must be realized that plots such as Fig. 7-5 yield only an approximate transfer coefficient because $\phi_2 - \phi_2^e$ varies with E^e. The error is generally quite negligible unless E^e is near the point of zero charge and the supporting electrolyte concentration is quite low.

Application of Eq. 29 requires constancy of a_O or a_R, and it may be more convenient from an experimental point of view to apply the following relationship (36) deduced from Eq. 28:

$$\frac{d \ln i^0/a_O}{d \ln a_R/a_O} = \alpha \tag{30}$$

Thus both activities a_O and a_R can be varied simultaneously, and $\ln (i^0/a_O)$ is plotted against $\ln (a_R/a_O)$ (Fig. 7-6). This amounts to plotting $\ln (i^0/a_O)$ against the equilibrium potential (cf. Eq. 23).

c. Heat of Activation

The heat of activation, defined by (10, 24) $-k_t^0\, \partial \ln k_t^0/\partial(1/T)$, is an experimentally determinable quantity. It can also be defined by the same relation, as written in terms of the apparent standard constant, but it then includes a contribution from the diffuse double layer (10) (see Chapter 9). Heats of activation have been reported for a number of processes, but their availability has not contributed very significantly to the understanding of electrode kinetics. Values generally do not exceed 10 kcal mole^{-1}.

Instead of applying this definition we can determine the temperature coefficient $\partial \ln i/\partial T$ at constant overvoltage and reactant concentrations and deduce what Temkin (37) has called a "real heat of activation" (in comparison with the nonmeasurable "ideal heat of activation" which is defined at constant ϕ_M). Difficulties in following this approach have been discussed by Temkin (37) and Agar (38) (see also 38a and 38b).

7-4 Influence of Mass Transfer

The influence of mass transfer has not been considered thus far, and it was assumed that the activities in the pre-electrode state had only to be corrected for the double-layer structure. This simplification can be made for processes with a sufficiently low exchange current, but otherwise mass transfer must be considered. We shall first examine how the previous results must be modified without making any assumption about the details of mass transfer.

The difference between the activities a_O and a_R at the electrode surface, aside from any double-layer correction, and the bulk activities $a_O{}^s$ and $a_R{}^s$ has two consequences: (a) The activities a_O and a_R now appear in the expression of i^0 (Eq. 28); (b) there is, as originally noted by Nernst (46) and Brunner (47), a shift of equilibrium potential of

$$\frac{1}{nf} \ln \frac{a_O{}^s/a_O}{a_R{}^s/a_R}$$

Equation 13 thus becomes

$$i = i^0 \left[\frac{a_O}{a_O{}^s} e^{-\alpha nf\eta} - \frac{a_R}{a_R{}^s} e^{(1-\alpha)nf\eta} \right] \tag{31}$$

where i^0 *is written for the bulk activities $a_O{}^s$ and $a_R{}^s$*, and η is the total over-voltage, that is, $\eta = E - E^e$, E^e being the equilibrium potential corresponding to the bulk activities $a_O{}^s$ and $a_R{}^s$. The ratios $a_O/a_O{}^s$ and $a_R/a_R{}^s$ depend on the current, and their calculation requires quantitative treatment of mass transfer.

When $|\eta| \ll 1/\alpha nf$ [or $|\eta| \ll 1/(1 - \alpha)nf$], Eq. 31 becomes

$$i = i^0 \left(\frac{a_O}{a_O{}^s} - \frac{a_R}{a_R{}^s} - nf\eta \right) \tag{32}$$

Hence

$$-\left(\frac{\partial \eta}{\partial i} \right)_{i\to 0} = \frac{1}{nf} \left[-\frac{1}{a_O{}^s} \left(\frac{\partial a_O}{\partial i} \right)_{i\to 0} + \frac{1}{a_R{}^s} \left(\frac{\partial a_R}{\partial i} \right)_{i\to 0} + \frac{1}{i^0} \right] \tag{33}$$

where the first two terms between brackets correspond to the *mass-transfer resistance* and the last term corresponds to the charge-transfer resistance. Equation 32 has been extensively applied to the theory of relaxation and perturbation methods for fast electrode processes because its linear form simplifies the derivation of analytical solutions in diffusion problems.

Mass transfer processes will not be discussed here because this material belongs more properly to the treatment of methodology, but some general references will be quoted and an approximate treatment, based on the Nernst diffusion layer model, will be given. Rigorous hydrodynamic analysis for steady-state electrolysis is possible for a few cases in which electrode geometry is favorable. Reference is made to Levich's monograph (39) and particularly to his work on the rotating disk electrode described therein. [See also Riddiford's review (40) for this particular electrode.] Current-overvoltage characteristics have been derived for non-steady-state electrolysis for a number of methods of which polarography and, to a lesser extent, chronopotentiometry are the most important. Extensive reviews are available, for example, Refs. 41–43. [See also Heyrovská's survey of the polarographic literature (44).]

We now consider the explicit forms of Eqs. 31 and 32 which are readily derived from the Nernst model of the diffusion layer (46, 47). It is assumed in this model that the current is proportional to $a_O{}^s - a_O$ or to $a_R - a_R{}^s$, the proportionality constant being independent of the current. The latter assumption results in an approximation, as one can ascertain, for instance, by comparing the results that follow with the more rigorous theory in polarography, but the error is small. The ratio of activities in Eqs. 31 and 32 thus can be directly related to the cathodic ($i_c{}^l$) and anodic ($i_a{}^l$) *limiting currents* and to the current i. We prefer the expression "limiting current" to "diffusion current" because diffusion is not necessarily the sole mode of mass transfer and convection may have to be considered. Thus

$$\frac{a_O}{a_O{}^s} = 1 - \frac{i}{i_c{}^l}$$

$$\frac{a_R}{a_R{}^s} = 1 + \frac{i}{i_a{}^l}$$

$$(34)$$

There $i \gtrless 0$ for a net cathodic or anodic current, respectively; $i_c{}^l > 0$ and $i_a{}^l > 0$. Thus $a_O \gtrless a_O{}^s$ and $a_R \lessgtr a_R{}^s$ for $i \lessgtr 0$, respectively. Furthermore, $a_O = 0$ for $i = i_c{}^l$ and $a_R = 0$ for $i = i_a{}^l$. Equations 34 hold for steady-state and non-steady-state electrolysis. In the latter case, we can substitute for $i_c{}^l$ and $i_a{}^l$ explicit forms derived from the detailed solution of the mass-transfer problem. Combination of Eqs. 31 and 34 yields immediately the complete current-overvoltage curve. The first detailed calculations of this type were made by Heyrovsky and Ilkovic (48) in polarography. [See also Agar and Bowden (38a).] A number of authors (17, 18, 25, 31, 32, 51, 52) treated this problem afterward with varying degrees of complexity [See Gerischer's review (45) and Refs. 39–43.]

The influence of mass transfer is shown in Figs. 7-7 and 7-8. The current-overvoltage curve for $i^0/i^l \geqslant 10$ is nearly the same as the curve calculated on the assumption of equilibrium for charge transfer ($i^0 \to \infty$). It is then said that the electrode process is *reversible*. This rather poorly choosen term really means that the exchange current is so high that, for all practical purposes, the potential can be calculated by introducing in the Nernst equation the activities of Eq. 34. *Irreversible* processes have an exchange current which is too low for this procedure to be applied, and kinetics must be considered. It is seen that the distinction between reversibility and irreversibility is quite arbitrary and depends on the relative magnitude of the exchange and limiting currents. The expressions are convenient and are frequently used, especially in polarography. Their

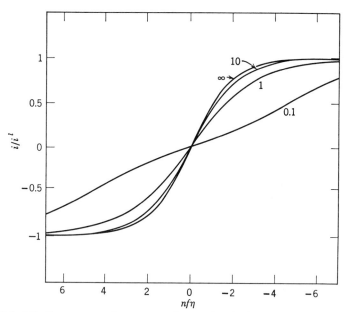

FIG. 7-7. Current-overvoltage curves for equal cathodic and anodic limiting currents for $\alpha = 0.5$ and for different ratios, i^0/i^l, of the exchange current to the limiting current [Gerischer (45)] (by permission of the Bunsengesellschaft).

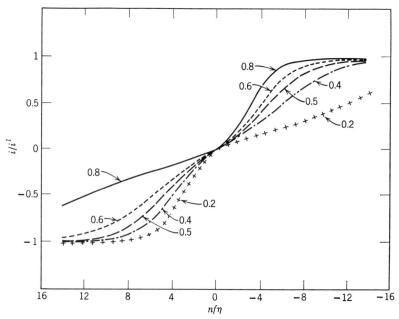

FIG. 7-8. Same plot as in Fig. 7-7 for $i^0/i^l = 0.1$ and for different values of the transfer coefficient α [Gerischer (45)] (by permission of the Bunsengesellschaft).

interpretation was clarified by the writer (41). The current-overvoltage characteristic for a reversible process, as obtained by the procedure just outlined, is

$$E = E^e + \frac{1}{nf} \ln \frac{i_a^l}{i_c^l} + \frac{1}{nf} \ln \frac{i_c^l - i}{i_a^l + i} \tag{35}$$

This familiar result of the polarographic theory need not be discussed any further here.

In the Tafel region we have (cf. with Eq. 16)

$$\ln \frac{i}{i^0} \frac{1}{1 - i/i_c^l} = -\alpha nf\eta \qquad \text{(cathodic processes, } i > 0, i_c^l > 0, \eta < 0) \tag{36}$$

$$\ln \frac{|i|}{i^0} \frac{1}{1 + i/i_a^l} = (1 - \alpha)nf\eta \qquad \text{(anodic processes, } i < 0, i_a^l > 0, \eta > 0)$$

or

$$\eta = \frac{1}{\alpha nf} \ln \frac{i^0}{i_c^l} + \frac{1}{\alpha nf} \ln \frac{1 - i/i_c^l}{i/i_c^l} \qquad \text{(cathodic processes)} \tag{37}$$

$$\eta = \frac{1}{(1 - \alpha)nf} \ln \frac{i_a^l}{i^0} + \frac{1}{(1 - \alpha)nf} \ln \frac{|i|/i_a^l}{1 - |i|/i_a^l} \qquad \text{(anodic processes)}$$

The plot of $|i|/i^l$ against η for cathodic and anodic processes has the same general shape as a reversible polarographic wave (cf. Eq. 35 with $i_a^l = 0$ or $i_c^l = 0$), but it is more drawn out because of the presence of the coefficient α or $1 - \alpha$ in Eq. 37. The half-wave potential $E_{1/2}$ depends on the ratio i^l/i^0 for a given process and thus varies with the rate of mass transfer, that is, $E_{1/2}$ becomes more cathodic for irreversible cathodic processes and more anodic for irreversible anodic processes when the rate of mass transfer increases. The plot of the logarithm term in Eq. 37 against η (or against potential) is linear and yields the value of the transfer coefficient.

The following equation, which is analogous to Eq. 21,

$$\ln \frac{i}{(1 - i/i_c^l) - (1 + i/i_a^l)e^{nf\eta}} = \ln i^0 - \alpha nf\eta \tag{38}$$

allows direct determination of i^0 and α regardless of the magnitude of the overvoltage.

At low overvoltages ($|\eta| \leqslant 5$ mv), Eq. 32 yields after combination with Eq. 34

$$i\left(\frac{1}{i^0} + \frac{1}{i_c^l} + \frac{1}{i_a^l}\right) = -nf\eta \tag{39}$$

Charge-transfer control is predominant when the conditions

$$\frac{1}{i^0} \gg \frac{1}{i_c^{\,l}} \quad \text{and} \quad \frac{1}{i^0} \gg \frac{1}{i_a^{\,l}}$$

are fulfilled. Thus there is essentially charge-transfer control for $i^0 \ll i^l$ and mass-transfer control for $i^0 \gg i^l$, where i^l represents the cathodic and anodic limiting currents. Hence the measurement of high exchange current densities requires high rate of mass transfer, that is, vigorous stirring in steady-state methods and high rates of diffusion in non-steady-state methods. Such high rates of diffusion are achieved by decreasing the time of measurement in relaxation or perturbation methods and by increasing the frequency in alternating current methods. The mass-transfer component of the quantity being measured is eliminated in these methods by some procedure which amounts to extrapolation to infinite limiting cathodic and anodic currents (cf., for example, 3, 45).

7-5   Mixed Potentials

Mixed potentials are observed at open circuit, for instance, when a metal is immersed in a corroding solution (for example, zinc-amalgam in acid solution). Zinc dissoves in this particular case and hydrogen is evolved. The potential at open circuit is determined by the kinetics of the two coupled electrode processes, as was shown by Wagner and Traud (53) in a classical paper. The essential idea was anticipated in earlier papers by

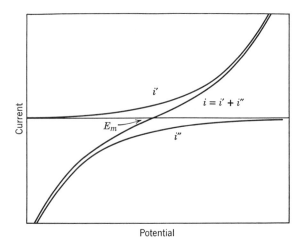

FIG. 7-9. Current-potential curves leading to a mixed potential [Wagner and Traud (53)] (by permission of the Bunsengesellschaft).

Frumkin (80) and Hammett and Lorch (81) on the kinetics of dissolution of sodium amalgam.

Wagner and Traud showed that the current-potential curve being measured is the algebraic sum of the current-potential curves for each process (Fig. 7-9). The algebra of the problem which can be somewhat cumbersome for more than two simultaneous processes has been worked out in considerable detail by Akimov (54). The subject is of paramount importance in metallic corrosion, but it need not concern us here. It may be added, however, that mixed potentials have to be considered for some electrodes with adsorbed films (for example, oxygen on platinum; cf. Chapter 10).

7-6   Theories of Charge-Transfer Processes

The derivation of the current-overvoltage characteristic in Sec. 7-2 followed a phenomenological approach. The result therefore does not depend on any particular model for the transition state, but deeper understanding is, of course, desirable, indeed essential, in the correlation of kinetic parameters with molecular structure. The first attempt to develop a molecular model for electrode kinetics was made by Horiuti and Polanyi (55) by the introduction of potential-energy diagrams in 1935 [See Temkin (37) for comments.] Such diagrams have often been used in introductory treatments to show the effect of electrode potential on kinetics, for they allow definition of the transfer coefficient by a graphical procedure. This construction is shown in Fig. 7-10 [from Parson's review (55a)] which

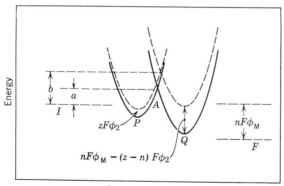

Reaction coordinate

FIG. 7-10. Energy-reaction coordinate diagram for an electrode process involving a n-electron reduction from the initial state I to the final state F via the pre-electrode states P and Q and the activated complex A. Energies of activation: a at the arbitrary zero of potential and b at potential ϕ_M ($b > a$ because $\phi_M > 0$ and reduction is retarded) [Parsons (55a)] (by permission of John Wiley).

is essentially the same as the original diagram of Horiuti and Polanyi. It is assumed that a variation of ϕ_M and ϕ_2 does not alter the shape of the energy versus reaction coordinate curves and causes only a vertical translation of these curves by a distance proportional to $nF\phi_M$ and $z'F\phi_2$, respectively. The transfer coefficient α is then equal to the ratio of the absolute value of the slope of the P-curve to the sum of the absolute values of the slopes of the P- and Q-curves at their intersection. Resonance rounds off the energy barrier, but this effect is generally neglected.

Detailed calculations have been made on diagrams such as Fig. 7-10 for hydrogen evolution [for example, Butler (56) and Parsons and Bockris (57)], and metal deposition [Conway and Bockris (58)], but the results are affected by uncertainty in the selection of numerical values of certain parameters. This approach has its place, but it is open to criticism as Hush (59) pointed out. [See also Volkenshtein (60), cited by Hush, for the parallel case of metal-gas adsorption.] It is useful, however, in pointing toward molecular structure considerations, for example, the heat of adsorption in hydrogen evolution (Chapter 10). [For the electron tunnel effect in charge transfer, cf., for example, Christov (60a).]

Two extreme cases can be distinguished, namely, electron transfer without major change in configuration and reactions involving the breaking of a bond. Considerable work has been done on the former type of charge transfer both for bulk redox reactions and electrode processes [Randles (24), Hush (59), Marcus (61–65), Gerischer (66), Levich, Dogonadze, and Chizmadhev (67–71)]. An excellent review by Marcus is available (82) and two other reviews should appear in the near future (72, 73). See also the collection of papers in Ref. 74 for charge transfer in solution. Processes leading to the breaking of a bond, such as hydrogen adsorption on a metal, still belong to future treatments. This difficult subject has a central position in electrode kinetics and in homogeneous charge-transfer processes, and current activity in this area indicates a novel orientation away from the more classical, descriptive aspects of electrode kinetics. These and future developments may well provide a sound basis for correlation of electrode kinetics with molecular structure. Two relevant reviews on the latter problem are also cited for processes involving inorganic (75) and organic (76) substances.

REFERENCES

1. R. Parsons, *Trans. Faraday Soc.*, **47**, 1332 (1951).
1a. D. M. Mohilner and P. Delahay, *J. Phys. Chem.*, **67**, 588 (1963).
2. K. J. Vetter, *Z. Elektrochem.*, **59**, 596 (1955).
3. P. Delahay, *Advances in Electrochemistry and Electrochemical Engineering*, Vol. 1, P. Delahay, editor, Interscience, New York, 1961, pp. 233–318.

4. P. Van Rysselberghe, *J. Chem. Phys.*, **17**, 1226 (1949).
5. H. Eyring, S. Glasstone, and K. J. Laidler, *J. Chem. Phys.*, **7**, 1053 (1939).
6. T. Erdey-Gruz and M. Volmer, *Z. physik. Chem.*, **150A**, 203 (1930).
7. J. A. V. Butler, *Trans. Faraday Soc.*, **19**, 729, 734 (1924).
8. R. Audubert, *J. chim. phys.*, **21**, 351 (1924).
9. R. Audubert, *J. Phys. Radium* (8), **3**, 81 (1942); *Disc. Faraday Soc.*, **1**, 72 (1947).
10. K. M. Joshi, W. Mehl, and R. Parsons, *Transactions of the Symposium on Electrode Processes*, E. Yeager, editor, Wiley, New York, 1961, pp. 249–263.
11. A. N. Frumkin, *Z. physik. Chem.*, **164A**, 121 (1933).
12. P. Van Rysselberghe, *Electrochim. Acta*, **8**, 583, 709 (1963); personal communication.
13. W. A. Rojter, W. A. Juza, and E. S. Poluyan, *Acta Physicochim. U.R.S.S.*, **10**, 389 (1939).
14. P. Dolin and B. V. Ershler, *ibid.*, **13**, 747 (1940).
15. W. A. Caspari, *Z. physik. Chem.*, **30**, 89 (1899).
16. G. Kortüm and J. O'M. Bockris, *Textbook of Electrochemistry*, Vol. 2, Elsevier, Amsterdam, 1951, p. 395.
17. K. J. Vetter, *Z. physik. Chem.*, **194**, 284 (1950).
18. K. J. Vetter, *Z. Elektrochem.*, **56**, 931 (1952).
19. H. Gerischer and W. Vielstich, *Z. physik. Chem. (Frankfurt)*, **3**, 16 (1955).
20. J. A. V. Butler, *Trans. Faraday Soc.*, **28**, 379 (1932).
21. J. Tafel, *Z. physik. Chem.*, **50**, 641 (1905).
22. W. Lorenz, *Z. Elektrochem.*, **58**, 912 (1954).
23. J. Horiuti and M. Ikusima, *Proc. Imp. Acad. (Tokyo)*, **15**, 39 (1939).
24. J. E. B. Randles, *Trans. Faraday Soc.*, **48**, 828 (1952).
24a. O. A. Esin, *Acta Physicochim. U.R.S.S.*, **13**, 429 (1940).
25. K. J. Vetter and G. Manecke, *Z. physik. Chem.*, **195**, 270, 337 (1950).
26. K. J. Vetter, *Z. Elektrochem.*, **55**, 121 (1951).
27. H. Gerischer, *ibid.*, **54**, 362, 366 (1950).
28. H. Gerischer, *ibid.*, **57**, 604 (1953).
29. H. Gerischer, *Z. physik. Chem.*, **202**, 292, 302 (1953).
30. H. Gerischer, *Z. physik. Chem. (Frankfurt)*, **2**, 79 (1954).
31. K. J. Vetter, Ref. 10, pp. 47–61.
31a. K. J. Vetter, *Elektrochemische Kinetik*, Springer, Berlin 1961.
32. E. Lewartowicz, *J. chim. phys.*, **49**, 557, 564, 573 (1952); **51**, 267 (1954).
32a. J. V. Petrocelli, *J. Electrochem. Soc.*, **98**, 187 (1951).
33. T. Berzins and P. Delahay, *J. Am. Chem. Soc.*, **77**, 6448 (1955).
34. N. Tanaka and R. Tamamushi, *Electrochim. Acta*, **9**, 963 (1964).
35. W. Vielstich and P. Delahay, *J. Am. Chem. Soc.*, **79**, 1874 (1957).
36. H. A. Laitinen, R. P. Tischer, and D. K. Roe, *J. Electrochem. Soc.*, **107**, 546 (1960).
37. M. I. Temkin, *Zhur. Fiz. Khim.*, **22**, 1081 (1948).
38. J. N. Agar, *Disc. Faraday Soc.*, **1**, 81 (1947).
38a. B. E. Conway and J. O'M. Bockris, *Can. J. Chem.*, **35**, 1124 (1957).
38b. B. I. Tomilov and M. A. Loshkarev, *Doklady Akad. Nauk S.S.S.R.*, **151**, 894 (1963).
39. V. G. Levich, *Physicochemical Hydrodynamics*, English translation by Scripta, Inc., Prentice-Hall, Englewood Cliffs, New Jersey, 1962.
40. A. C. Riddiford, *Advances in Electrochemistry*, Vol. 5, P. Delahay, editor, Interscience, New York, in preparation.
41. P. Delahay, *New Instrumental Methods in Electrochemistry*, Interscience, New York, 1954.

42. T. A. Kryukova, C. E. Sinyakova, and T. V. Aref'beva, *Polarographic Analysis*, Government Scientific and Technical Division of Chemical Literature, Moscow, 1959.
43. P. Zuman, editor, *Progress in Polarography*, 2 vols., Interscience, New York, 1962.
44. M. Heyrovská, Ref. 43, Vol. 1, pp. 1–19.
45. H. Gerischer, *Z. Elektrochem.*, **59**, 604 (1955).
45a. W. H. Reinmuth, *Anal. Chem.*, **36**, 211R (1964).
46. W. Nernst, *Z. physik. Chem.*, **47**, 52 (1904).
47. E. Brunner, *ibid.*, **47**, 54 (1904); **58**, 1 (1907).
48. J. Heyrovsky and D. Ilkovic, *Coll. Czechslov. Chem. Com.* **7**, 198 (1935).
48a. J. N. Agar and F. P. Bowden, *Proc. Roy. Soc.*, **169A**, 206 (1938).
49. O. A. Esin and M. Loshkarev, *Acta Physicochim. U.R.S.S.*, **10**, 513 (1939).
50. E. Lange and K. Nagel, *Z. Elektrochem.*, **53**, 21 (1949).
51. K. J. Vetter, *Z. physik. Chem.*, **196**, 360 (1951); **199**, 22 (1952).
52. K. J. Vetter, *Z. Elektrochem.*, **56**, 797 (1952).
53. C. Wagner and W. Traud, *ibid.*, **44**, 391 (1938).
54. G. V. Akimov, *Théorie et Méthodes d'Essai de la Corrosion des Métaux*, with supplements by N. D. Tomashov; French translation by S. Medvedieff, Dunod, Paris, 1957.
55. J. Horiuti and M. Polanyi, *Acta Physicochim. U.R.S.S.*, **2**, 505 (1935).
55a. R. Parsons, see Ref. 3, pp. 1–64.
56. J. A. V. Butler, *Proc. Roy. Soc.*, **157A**, 423 (1936).
57. R. Parsons and J. O'M. Bockris, *Trans. Faraday Soc.*, **46**, 914 (1951).
58. B. E. Conway and J. O'M. Bockris, *Electrochim. Acta*, **3**, 340 (1961).
59. N. S. Hush, *J. Chem. Phys.*, **28**, 962 (1958).
60. F. F. Volkenshtein, *Zhur. Fiz. Khim.*, **27**, 159 (1953).
60a. S. G. Christov, *Z. Elektrochem.*, **62**, 567 (1958); *Z. physik. Chem.* (*Leipzig*), **212**, 40 (1959).
61. R. A. Marcus, *J. Chem. Phys.*, **24**, 966, 979 (1956); **26**, 867, 872 (1957).
62. R. A. Marcus, *Trans. New York Acad. Sci.*, (2), **19**, 423 (1957).
63. R. A. Marcus, *Can. J. Chem.*, **37**, 155 (1959).
64. R. A. Marcus, *Disc. Faraday Soc.*, **29**, 21 (1960).
65. R. A. Marcus, Ref. 10, pp. 239–245.
66. H. Gerischer, *Z. physik. Chem.* (*Frankfurt*), **26**, 223, 325 (1960); **27**, 48 (1961).
67. V. G. Levich and R. R. Dogonadze, *Doklady Akad. Nauk S.S.S.R.*, **124**, 123 (1959); **133**, 158 (1960).
68. R. R. Dogonadze, *ibid.*, **142**, 1108 (1962).
69. V. G. Levich and R. R. Dogonadze, *Coll. Czechslov. Chem. Commun.*, **26**, 193 (1961).
70. R. R. Dogonadze and Yu. A. Chizmadzhev, *Doklady Akad. Nauk S.S.S.R.*, **144**, 1077 (1962); **145**, 849 (1962); **150**, 333 (1963).
71. V. G. Levich and R. R. Dogonadze, paper presented at the Moscow C.I.T.C.E. meeting, 1963.
72. K. J. Laidler, *Modern Aspects of Electrochemistry*, Vol. 3, J. O'M. Bockris, editor, Butterworths, London, in press.
73. V. G. Levich, *Advances in Electrochemistry and Electrochemical Engineering*, Vol. 5, P. Delahay, editor, Interscience, in preparation.
74. Collection of papers in *Disc. Faraday Soc.*, **29**, 261 (1960).
75. A. A. Vlček, *Progress in Organic Chemistry*, Vol. 5, F. A. Cotton, editor, Interscience, 1963, pp. 211–384.

76. P. J. Elving and B. Pullman, *Advances in Chemical Physics*, Vol. 3, I. Prigogine, editor, Interscience, New York, 1961, pp. 1–31.
77. R. Parsons, personal communication.
78. E. P. Bowden and J. N. Agar, *Ann. Reports Chem. Soc.*, **35**, 90–113 (1938).
79. P. L. Allen and A. Hickling, *Trans. Faraday Soc.*, **53**, 1626 (1957).
80. A. N. Frumkin, *Z. physik. Chem.*, **160**, 116 (1932).
81. L. P. Hammett and A. E. Lorch, *J. Am. Chem. Soc.*, **54**, 2128 (1932).
82. R. A. Marcus, *Ann. Rev. Phys. Chem.*, **15**, 155–196 (1964).

CHAPTER 8

Kinetics of Electrode Processes Involving More Than One Step

8-1 Two Consecutive Processes

Elucidation of the mechanism of electrode processes involving more than one step is often an arduous task because of the multiplicity of reaction paths. The various methods for the analysis of current-potential curves have limitations, for they often do not allow unambiguous assignment of mechanisms. Much progress has been achieved since 1950, but there is a definite need for techniques for the detection and, if possible, quantitative determination of intermediates at low concentration. We begin with processes involving two consecutive steps. The analysis of this simple case will give a hint of future difficulties.

We consider two consecutive one-electron charge transfer reactions involving soluble species

$$O + e = X \qquad (1a)$$

$$X + e = R \qquad (1b)$$

The current-overvoltage characteristic is readily derived by eliminating the activity of the intermediate X just as for consecutive reactions in chemical kinetics. The calculation was made by Vetter (1) for reactions 1 and was more recently extended by Hurd (2) to more than two consecutive steps. We apply Eq. 7-31, and include all double-layer effects in the apparent exchange currents i_a^0 and i_b^0 for the consecutive steps $1a$ and $1b$. Mass-transfer control is excluded. Since both reactions $1a$ and $1b$

contribute to exchange, we have

$$\frac{i}{2} = i_a^0 \left[e^{-\alpha_a f\eta} - \frac{a_X}{a_X^e} e^{(1-\alpha_a)f\eta} \right]$$

$$\frac{i}{2} = i_b^0 \left[\frac{a_X}{a_X^e} e^{-\alpha_b f\eta} - e^{(1-\alpha_b)f\eta} \right]$$

(2)

where α_a and α_b, which are generally different, correspond to steps $1a$ and $1b$, respectively; a_X is the activity of the intermediate X at the overvoltage

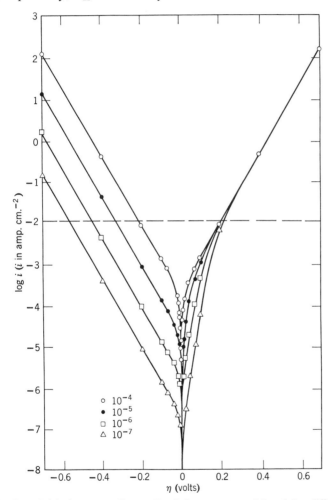

FIG. 8-1. Tafel plots according to Eq. 3 for $\alpha_a = \alpha_b = 0.5$ and for different values of the exchange current i_a^0 (in amperes per square centimeters) and for $i_b^0 = 10^{-4}$ amp. cm.$^{-2}$ [Hurd (2)] (by permission of The Electrochemical Society).

η and a_X^e is the activity of X at the equilibrium potential. Elimination of a_X/a_X^e from the two equations 2 yields

$$i = 2 \frac{e^{-(\alpha_a+\alpha_b)f\eta} - e^{(2-\alpha_a-\alpha_b)f\eta}}{\dfrac{1}{i_b^0} e^{(1-\alpha_a)f\eta} + \dfrac{1}{i_a^0} e^{-\alpha_b f\eta}} \tag{3}$$

Tafel plots (Fig. 8-1) at large cathodic overvoltages have a slope $-\alpha_a f$ and yield $2i_a^0$ by extrapolation to $\eta = 0$. Conversely, Tafel plots at large anodic overvoltages yield $(1 - \alpha_b)$ and $2i_b^0$. The sum of $\alpha_a + (1 - \alpha_b)$ is generally different from unity because $\alpha_a \neq \alpha_b$. If $i_a^0 \rightarrow \infty$, Tafel plots have the slopes $-(1 + \alpha_b)f$ and $(1 - \alpha_b)f$ in the cathodic and anodic ranges, respectively, and extrapolation to $\eta = 0$ yields $2i_b^0$. Conversely, the slopes are $-\alpha_a f$ and $(2 - \alpha_a)f$ for $i_b^0 \rightarrow \infty$, and the intercept at $\eta = 0$ is $2i_a^0$. Determination of the charge-transfer resistance at low overvoltages (cf. Eq. 7-15)

$$-\left(\frac{\partial \eta}{\partial i}\right)_{i\rightarrow 0} = \frac{1}{4f}\left(\frac{1}{i_a^0} + \frac{1}{i_b^0}\right) \tag{4}$$

provides a way of verifying the values of i_a^0 and i_b^0 determined from Tafel plots. Further details are given by Vetter (1) and especially by Hurd (2).

8-2   Elucidation of Mechanisms by Determination of Stoichiometric Numbers

Application of the foregoing method to processes involving more than two steps in series is possible, in principle, by the use of computers, as Hurd (2) suggested, but the uncertainty in the assignment of mechanism may be considerable. The difficulty will be fully appreciated by considering stoichiometric numbers v for electrode processes. This number was originally defined by Horiuti and Ikusima (4) for hydrogen overvoltage studies. The stoichiometric number for an electrode process involving a *single* rate-determining step is defined as the number of occurrences of the rate-determining step for the over-all reaction to occur once. For instance in the discharge of hydrogen ion we can a priori distinguish three reactions regardless of the likelihood of their actual occurrence, namely,

$$H^+ + e = H \tag{5a}$$

$$H^+ + H + e = H_2 \tag{5b}$$

$$H + H = H_2 \tag{5c}$$

Since the over-all reaction is $2H^+ + 2e = H_2$, the stoichiometric numbers for reactions 5a, 5b, and 5c are 2, 1, and 1, respectively, if we make the arbitrary assumption that only a single reaction is rate determining. We

infer from these simple considerations that the determination of stoichiometric numbers from experimental data provides a criterion for dis-
criminating between various possible mechanisms. Unfortunately, this
criterion is not necessarily unambiguous.

Horiuti (5) subsequently generalizes his definition of stoichiometric
numbers to encompass processes with multiple unit steps. Milner's
statement (6) of Horiuti's definition is particularly apt: "Any overall
reaction, then, must consist of a series of steps selected from the complete
set of possible unit steps; thus any reaction mechanism can be described

TABLE 8-1 Stoichiometric Numbers for
the Over-all Reaction $2H^+ + 2e = H_2$ with
the Steps of Eq. 5[a]

Stoichiometric	Mechanisms		
Number	A	B	C
ν_a	1	2	0
ν_b	1	0	2
ν_c	0	1	-1

[a] According to Milner (6). The table
lists the stoichiometric numbers for three
possible mechanisms A, B, and C.

completely by specifying the number of occurrences of each of the possible
unit steps for each occurrence of the over-all reaction." The combination
of all unit steps must, of course, lead to restrictive conditions which take
the form of linear equations. This question is discussed by Horiuti and
Nakamura (7) and especially by Milner (6). These considerations lead, for
instance, in the case of reaction 5, to the mechanisms of Table 8-1. The
number of possible mechanisms easily becomes staggering, as Milner
showed for the oxygen electrode. If we consider the intermediate species
OH, O, O_2H, and O_2H^- for the over-all reaction

$$O_2 + 2H_2O + 4e = 4OH$$

in alkaline solution, there are no less than eleven possible mechanisms
when we limit the number of steps by excluding two-electron transfers
and by assuming that O_2 evolution occurs only by the reaction $2O = O_2$.
Knowledge of the chemistry of the system and educated guesses often
narrow down the choice of mechanisms, but it must be recognized, as
Milner points out (6), that the multiplicity of mechanisms is an inherent
characteristic of complex electrode processes (or chemical reactions in
general).

Current-overvoltage characteristics including stoichiometric numbers have been considered by a number of authors and particularly by Horiuti and co-workers (4, 5, 7), Parsons (8), Oldham (9), Makrides (10), Mauser (11), Riddiford (12), and Mohilner (13). The papers by Mauser and Riddiford may be consulted for very general treatments, but the essential ideas are conveyed in a simpler fashion in Parson's classical paper of 1951 (8). Furthermore, application of the very general equations in Refs. 11 and 12 is often open to question because of complications arising from ion specific adsorption on solid electrodes (Chapter 10). Transposition of the following analysis to the general case considered by Mauser (11) and Riddiford (12) is not difficult except for more cumbersome algebra. The effect of the double-layer structure was considered but not treated in detail by Parsons in his original paper. Further details on this point are given by him in a recent review (14).

We consider for the sake of simplicity the same reaction as in Sec. 7-2, namely

$$O + ne = R \tag{6}$$

Substances O and R of ionic valence z and z', respectively are soluble and are not specifically adsorbed on the electrode. The supporting electrolyte is not specifically adsorbed either. Reaction 6 involves a single rate-determining step which must occur ν times for the over-all reaction to occur once. The derivation of the current-overvoltage characteristic in Sec. 7-2, can be readily transposed by noting that the rate-determining step now involves n/ν electrons. Thus

$$i = i_t^0 e^{(1/\nu)(\alpha n - z)f\phi_2}[e^{-(1/\nu)\alpha nf\eta} - e^{(1/\nu)(1-\alpha)nf\eta}] \tag{7}$$

or, after introduction of the apparent exchange current,

$$i = i^0[e^{-(1/\nu)\alpha nf\eta} - e^{(1/\nu)(1-\alpha)nf\eta}] \tag{8}$$

Furthermore,

$$i_t^0 = \frac{1}{\nu} nF k_t^0 a_O^{(1-\alpha)/\nu} a_R^{\alpha/\nu} \tag{9}$$

$$i^0 = \frac{1}{\nu} nF k^0 a_O^{(1-\alpha)/\nu} a_R^{\alpha/\nu} \tag{10}$$

$$k^0 = k_t^0 e^{(1/\nu)(\alpha n - z)f\phi_2} \tag{11}$$

Three kinetic parameters k^0 (or i^0), α, and ν must be determined. Tafel plots or plots corresponding to Eq. 7-21 yield i^0 and α/ν or $(1 - \alpha)/\nu$. The study of the variation of i^0 with a_O (or a_R) leads to either $(1 - \alpha)/\nu = p$ or $\alpha/\nu = q$, p and q being, respectively the slopes of the plots of $\ln i^0$ against $\ln a_O$ (at constant a_R) and $\ln i^0$ against $\ln a_R$ (at constant a_O).

The ratio v/i^0 is determined from the charge transfer resistance at low overvoltage (cf. Eq. 7-15)

$$-\left(\frac{\partial \eta}{\partial i}\right)_{i \to 0} = \frac{v}{nfi^0} \tag{12}$$

Hence all kinetic parameters can be determined. Change in mechanism from low to high overvoltage, however, hampers the application of this method. Application has been limited mostly to the hydrogen, oxygen, and halogen electrodes (cf. Chapter 10).

Mass transfer is easily corrected for by transposition of the approach of Sec. 7-4 to this treatment.

8-3   Elucidation of Mechanisms by Determination of Reaction Orders

a. Single Charge-Transfer Reaction

The determination of reaction orders in chemical kinetics is a time-honored method which only quite recently was transposed to electrode kinetics. Vetter was the foremost advocate of application to electrode kinetics (1, 17–32), but a number of authors independently advanced ideas similar, or at least related, to those of Vetter: Esin (33), Gerischer (34–38), Lewartowicz (39), Parsons (8), and Petrocelli (40, 41). Bockris and Potter (42, 43) applied the method of reaction orders to hydrogen over-voltage. Application by others has followed since these early contributions. A review of the essential points (15) and a thorough treatment (16) by Vetter are available.

Complex electrode reactions involve one or several charge-transfer reactions which may be coupled with a number of chemical reactions (cf., for example, Table 8-1). The charge-transfer reactions may involve species which do not necessarily appear in the over-all reaction. Analysis can be very involved, and we shall limit ourselves to processes with one or two charge-transfer reactions. We shall first assume that the species involved in the charge-transfer reactions are in equilibrium with the species appearing in the overall reaction, but we shall lift this restriction in the next section. We begin with processes with a single charge-transfer reaction.

The overall reaction is

$$p_1 O_1 + p_2 O_2 + \cdots + ne = s_1 R_1 + s_2 R_2 + \cdots \tag{13}$$

with the following single charge-transfer reaction

$$X + ne = Y \tag{14}$$

We assume that the charge-transfer reaction involves the same number of electrons as the over-all reaction. We write, by applying Eq. 7-9 to reaction 14

$$\overrightarrow{i} = \overrightarrow{k} a_X e^{-\alpha n f \phi_M}$$
$$\overleftarrow{i} = \overleftarrow{k} a_Y e^{(1-\alpha)n f \phi_M} \tag{15}$$

where $\overrightarrow{k}$ and $\overleftarrow{k}$ group the various terms, given in explicit form in Eq. 7-9 but not needed here. Because *we assume equilibrium* between X and the species O_j and between Y and species R_j,

$$a_X = K_1 \Pi a_{O_j}^{p_j'}$$
$$a_Y = K_2 \Pi a_{R_j}^{s_j'} \tag{16}$$

where p_j' and a_j' are the *reaction orders* with respect to species O_j and R_j, respectively. The coefficients p_j' and s_j' may be the same as the p_j and s_j of Eq. 13 or they may be different. At the equilibrium potential ϕ_M^e, $\overrightarrow{i} = \overleftarrow{i} = i^0$, i^0 being the apparent exchange current. Thus

$$i^0 = \overrightarrow{k} K_1 \Pi a_{O_j}^{p_j'} e^{-\alpha n f \phi_M^e}$$
$$= \overleftarrow{k} K_2 \Pi a_{R_j}^{s_j'} e^{(1-\alpha)n f \phi_M^e} \tag{17}$$

The reaction order for a particular species j is determined from the variation of i^0 with the activity (concentration) of this species, all other activities remaining constant.

By writing the Nernst equation for the over-all reaction 13

$$\phi_M^e = \phi_M^0 + \frac{1}{nf} \ln \frac{\Pi a_{O_j}^{p_j}}{\Pi a_{R_j}^{s_j}} \tag{18}$$

we easily derive, after returning to conventional electrode potentials,

$$\left(\frac{\partial \ln i^0}{\partial E^e}\right)_{a_{O_k \neq j}, a_{R_j}} = nf \left(\frac{p_j'}{p_j} - \alpha\right)$$
$$\left(\frac{\partial \ln i^0}{\partial E^e}\right)_{a_{O_j}, a_{R_k \neq j}} = nf \left[(1 - \alpha) - \frac{s_j'}{s_j}\right] \tag{19}$$

An alternate but wholly equivalent result is derived by noting, according to Eqs. 17 and 18, that i^0 is proportional to

$$a_{O_j}^{p_j' - \alpha p_j} a_{R_j}^{\alpha s_j}$$

or to

$$a_{O_j}^{(1-\alpha)p_j} a_{R_j}^{s_j' - (1-\alpha)s_j}$$

Hence

$$\left(\frac{\partial \ln i^0}{\partial \ln a_{O_j}}\right)_{a_{O_{k\neq j}},\,{}^a R_j} = p_j{}' - \alpha p_j$$

$$\left(\frac{\partial \ln i^0}{\partial \ln a_{R_j}}\right)_{a_{O_j},\,{}^a R_{k\neq j}} = s_j{}' - (1 - \alpha)s_j \tag{20}$$

b. Typical Applications

Three applications will be discussed for processes in which electrode coverage by strongly adsorbed reactants or products need not be considered in detail (Chapter 10); redox systems involving soluble species, discharge of metal ion complexes, and hydrogen ion discharge on mercury. We begin with the Mn(IV)/Mn(III) couple on platinum [Vetter and Manecke (20)] as a typical example of a redox couple whose kinetics is more involved than one might infer from the deceiving simplicity of the over-all reaction. It is seen from the Tafel plots of Figs. 8-2 and 8-3 that the cathodic current for essentially pure charge-transfer control in the Tafel

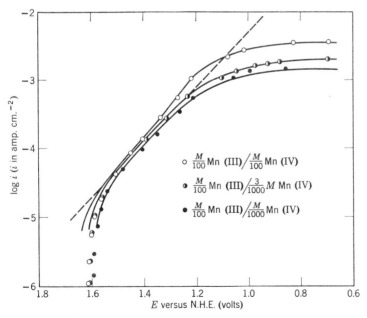

FIG. 8-2. Cathodic Tafel plots for the Mn(IV)/Mn(III) couple on platinum in 7.5M sulfuric acid at 25°C in stirred solution. Varying concentration of Mn(IV) and constant concentration of Mn(III). The dashed line is the Tafel plot after mass transfer correction. [Vetter and Manecke (20)] (by permission of *Z. physik. Chem.*).

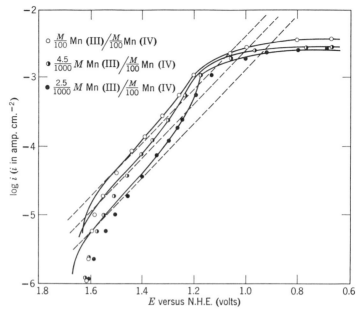

FIG. 8-3. Same plot as in Fig. 8-2 but for a constant concentration of Mn(IV) and a varying concentration of Mn(III) [Vetter and Manecke (20)] (by permission of *Z. physik. Chem.*).

range is practically independent of the Mn(IV) concentration, but it is proportional to Mn(III). The charge-transfer reaction thus is of zero and first order, respectively with respect to Mn(IV) and Mn(III) although the over-all reaction is the reduction of Mn(IV) to Mn(III). These findings lead to the mechanism

$$Mn(III) + e = Mn(II)$$

$$\frac{Mn(II) + Mn(IV) = 2Mn(III)}{Mn(IV) + e = Mn(III)}$$

Thus, Mn(III) is reduced to Mn(II), which reacts with Mn(IV) in a disproportionation reaction to give 2Mn(III). The charge-transfer reaction for the Mn(III)/Mn(II) couple is identical with the over-all reaction as was demonstrated by Vetter and Manecke (20). The cathodic current (with pure charge transfer) is proportional to the concentration of Mn(III) and independent of the Mn(II) concentration (Fig. 8-4).

Similarly, the charge-transfer reaction for the Ce(IV)/Ce(III) and Fe(III)/Fe(II) couples on platinum are identical with the over-all reaction

[(Gerischer (34)]. The same conclusion holds for the Ti(IV)/Ti(III) and Ti(III)/Ti(II) couples on mercury in sulfuric acid [Esin (33)] as well as for a few other redox couples and a number of amalgam electrodes. [For a review, cf. Vetter (15, 16).]

Application of the method of reaction orders to the discharge of metal ion complexes proved particularly fruitful in answering the long-standing question of a possible dissociation prior to charge transfer. The matter was debated for many years and was finally settled largely by determination of reaction orders. [See Parry and Lyons (44) for a detailed account of the historical background.] The discharge of cadmium on cadmium-amalgam in cyanide medium offers an excellent application [Gerischer (38)]. Variations of the exchange current with the Cd(II) concentration at constant amalgam and cyanide concentrations allowed the determination of the transfer coefficient (Eq. 20). The resulting α was also verified from the dependence of the exchange current on the amalgam concentration for fixed Cd(II) and cyanide concentrations. The reaction order with respect to cyanide was then determined from the log i^0 versus log c_{CN^-} plot at constant Cd(II) and amalgam concentrations by application of Eq. 20.

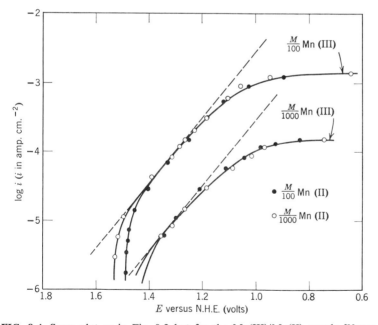

FIG. 8-4. Same plot as in Fig. 8-2 but for the Mn(III)/Mn(II) couple [Vetter and Manecke (20)] (by permission of *Z. physik. Chem.*).

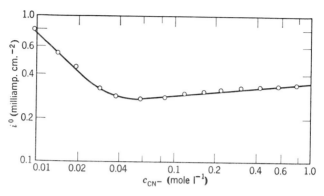

FIG. 8-5. Log-log plot of i^0 against c_{CN^-} for discharge of Cd(II) on cadmium-amalgam at 25°C. Sodium chloride was added to maintain the total concentration of supporting electrolyte at $5M$. Data obtained by faradaic impedance [Gerischer (38)] (by permission of the Bunsengesellschaft).

This plot (Fig. 8-5) is composed of two linear segments which can be interpreted by the following mechanisms:

$$Cd(CN)_4^{--} = Cd(CN)_2 + 2CN^-$$
$$Cd(CN)_2 + 2e = Cd(Hg) + 2CN^-$$

for $c_{CN^-} < 0.02M$, and

$$Cd(CN)_4^{--} = Cd(CN)_3^- + CN^-$$
$$Cd(CN)_3^- + 2e = Cd(Hg) + 3CN^-$$

for $c_{CN^-} > 0.06M$. Reduction involves both mechanisms in the 0.02–0.06M CN$^-$ range (approximate limits).

The total concentration of supporting electrolyte (sodium cyanide plus sodium chloride) was constant and very high (5 normal) in these studies for a reason, fully explained in Chapter 9, which will be briefly stated: Increase of the sodium chloride concentration accelerates the forward and backward chemical reactions associated with the charge-transfer reaction; equilibrium for these reactions is practically achieved in the measurement of i^0 and the determination of reaction orders by the preceding method is feasible. A few other cases of discharge of complex ions have been investigated [Vetter (15,16)].

The third application of the reaction order method we discuss pertains to the effect of pH on hydrogen evolution on mercury. The kinetics of this process on mercury is free of the complication resulting from hydrogen chemisorption (Chapter 10), and interpretation is quite straightforward. The pH effect is shown in Fig. 8-6, which was prepared by Vetter (15, 45) from measurements by different authors (46–49). Measurements in

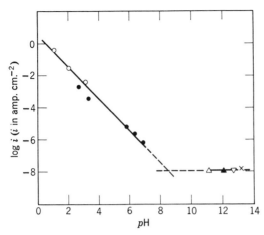

FIG. 8-6. Variation of the logarithm of current with pH for hydrogen evolution on mercury at -1.4 volts against the normal hydrogen electrode. Measurements: ($\bigcirc$) Bagotskii (46); ($\bullet$) Bagotskii and Yablova (47); ($\times$) Kaptsan and Iofa (48); ($\triangle$ $\blacktriangle$ $\triangledown$) Bockris and Watson (49) [Vetter (15)] (by permission of John Wiley).

alkaline medium are less reliable than in acid solution, as Frumkin noted (50), because of spurious catalytic action of traces of impurities. At any rate, Fig. 8-6 shows conclusively that the cathodic current is proportional to the concentration of hydrogen ion in the acid range and consequently reduction of hydrogen ions is the charge-transfer reaction. By contrast, the current in fairly strong alkaline medium is independent of pH, and direct reduction of water is the predominant charge-transfer mechanism. This conclusion is in agreement with previous calculations (51) which indicated that dissociation of water in alkaline solution is too slow to account for experimentally observed current densities by a mechanism involving dissociation of water and subsequent reduction of hydrogen ion. Study of double-layer effects on the kinetics of this reaction led to the same conclusion (Chapter 9).

c. Two Consecutive Charge-Transfer Reactions

Extension of the foregoing treatment to processes with several charge-transfer reactions is possible, in principle, but we shall limit ourselves to two consecutive charge-transfer reactions. It was shown in Sec. 8-1 that the Tafel plots at large cathodic overvoltages for the two consecutive reactions of Eq. 1 have a slope of $-\alpha_a f$ and an intercept $2i_a^0$ at $\eta = 0$. Hence the current at large cathodic overvoltages is proportional to the activity (concentration) of species O. Conversely, the current at large

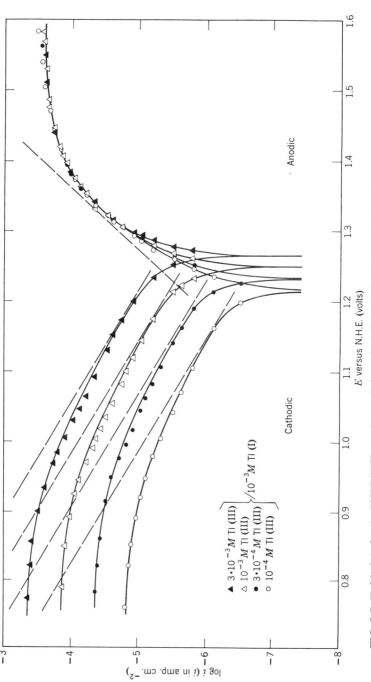

FIG. 8-7. Tafel plots for the Tl(III)/Tl(I) couple on platinum in $0.5M$ sulfuric acid at 25°C in stirred solution. Variable Tl(III) concentration and constant Tl(I) concentration. Dashed lines correspond to Eq. 3 as written for large cathodic or anodic overvoltages [Vetter and Thiemke (32)] (by permission of the Bunsengesellschaft).

anodic overvoltages is proportional to the activity of species R. These conclusions are borne out for the Tl(III)/Tl(I) couple (Figs. 8-7 and 8-8), and we conclude that reduction and oxidation are of the first order with respect to Tl(III) and Tl(I), respectively [Vetter and Thiemke (32)]. These observations would be in agreement with either a single two-electron transfer or two consecutive one-electron transfers, but the former mechanism is ruled out by two other features of the Tafel plots: the exchange current obtained by extrapolation to $\eta = 0$ from the cathodic and anodic sides are not the same; furthermore, the sum of $\alpha_a + (1 - \alpha_b)$ is different from unity. (See discussion of Eq. 3.) Conditions for application of the latter criterion are quite marginal Figs. 8-7 and 8-8), but the argument concerning the exchange current is convincing, especially since $i_a{}^0$ and $i_b{}^0$ obey Eq. 4. The over-all reaction thus involves two consecutive charge-transfer mechanisms, namely Tl(III) + e = Tl(II) and Tl(II) + e = Tl(I).

A similar conclusion was reached by Vetter (16) for the Sn(IV)/Sn(II) couple on mercury in hydrochloric acid medium on the basis of the data of Esin and Loshkarev (52).

Vetter (23) also studied the kinetics of the quinone-hydroquinone couple on platinum and accounted for his experimental results by mechanisms involving two one-electron steps in series. His conclusions, however, were seriously challenged by Loshkarev and Tomilov (72, 73), who concluded that a two-electron transfer prevails in general.

8-4   Coupling of Charge Transfer with Chemical Reactions Not at Equilibrium

It was assumed in Sec. 8-3 that any chemical reaction coupled with charge transfer is at equilibrium. This simplification is justified for certain processes, but it is necessary in some cases to take into account the kinetics of the chemical reactions coupled with charge transfer. We consider here the interplay between homogeneous (volume) chemical reaction and mass transfer and reserve heterogeneous (surface) reactions for Chapter 10. The subject will be introduced by considering a particularly instructive example, namely, the nitric-nitrous acids redox couple [Vetter (17–19, 22, 31)]. The cathodic limiting current depends not only on the concentration of nitric acid, as one would expect, but also on the concentration of nitrous acid (Fig. 8-9). It is inferred that nitrous acid is involved in some chemical reaction preceding charge transfer. Reaction order studies point toward the reaction

$$HNO_3 + NHO_2 = N_2O_4 + H_2O \qquad (21a)$$

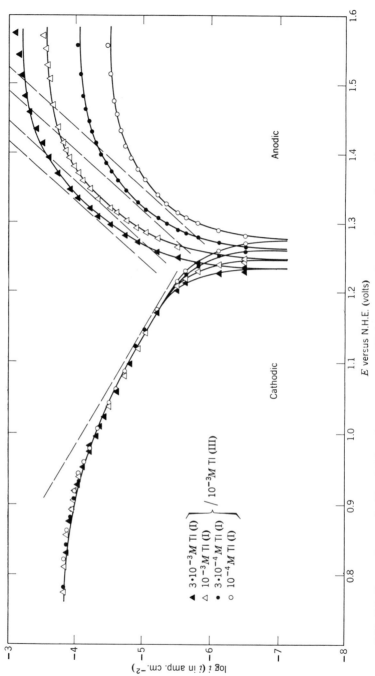

FIG. 8-8. Same plots as in Fig. 8-7 but for a constant Tl(III) concentration and a varying Tl(I) concentration [Vetter and Thiemke (32)] (by permission of the Bunsengesselschaft).

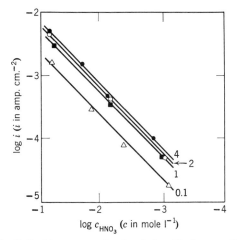

FIG. 8-9. Cathodic limiting current for the nitric acid-nitrous acid couple on platinum at 25°C in stirred solution as a function of nitrous acid concentration. Lines correspond to different values of the product $c_{H^+}c_{NO_3^-}$ in units (mole l^{-1})^2 [Vetter (22)] (by permission of the Bunsengesellschaft).

or (HNO_2 is weaker than HNO_3)

$$NO_3^- + HNO_2 = N_2O_4 + OH^- \tag{21b}$$

Direct reduction of N_2O_4, according to Vetter, is not as likely as the reduction of NO_2, and consequently the inverse dimerization

$$N_2O_4 = 2NO_2 \tag{21c}$$

precedes the charge-transfer reaction

$$NO_2 + e = NO_2^- \tag{21d}$$

The latter is followed by recombination of nitrite with hydrogen ion because nitrous acid is relatively weak. Thus

$$NO_2^- + H^+ = HNO_2 \tag{21e}$$

Reaction 21a (or 21b) is a slow chemical step and reaction 21d is a slow charge-transfer reaction. All other reactions are rapid. This mechanism is certainly not the only possible one in view of the comments in Sec. 8-2, but it fits all the facts and it is reasonable from a chemical viewpoint.

Processes with coupled chemical reaction were discussed by Eucken (53) as early as 1908, but it is only since the polarographic studies of Brdička and Koutecký and their colleagues in Prague and the development of other electrochemical methods that active interest was displayed. Much of this work has centered on the use of electrochemical methods as a tool for the kinetic of purely chemical reactions. The development of nonelectrochemical relaxation and perturbation methods by Eigen and co-workers since 1954 has somewhat deprived polarography and related methods from their once almost unique position in such studies, but the contribution of the Prague group to electrode kinetics nevertheless remains of considerable importance. Interpretation based on the diffusion layer model is available (16, 54), but detailed analysis of mass transfer is more fruitful. The key references cited in Sec. 7-4 may be consulted for further details. [See also Koutecky and Koryta (55) for polarography and Delahay (56) and Reinmuth (56a) for relaxation and perturbation methods for fast electrode processes.]

8-5   Detection and Determination of Intermediates

The methods of analysis of data in the previous sections contributed greatly to the elucidation of mechanisms, but experimental confirmation by detection and, if possible, quantitative determination of intermediates is still desirable or mandatory for complex processes. The problem is particularly arduous with intermediates of very low concentration.

Some success has been achieved by using the polarographic method with rapid scanning or stepwise variation of potential in the forward and backward direction. An intermediate produced by a cathodic process can then be detected, under favorable circumstances, during anodic scanning. This principle has been applied in a variety of ways, but discussion of this material belongs to methodology (see Sec. 7-4 for references).

Techniques in which intermediates are rapidly removed from the electrode by vigorous stirring and are then examined independently by some electrochemical (or spectroscopic) method should prove useful. One of these techniques, the rotating disk-ring electrode, has already been fully developed but has not yet been extensively applied. The intermediate is generated on the rotating disk electrode (cf. Sec. 7-4) and is reduced or oxidized on the electrically insulated surrounding ring electrode. The potentials of the disk and the ring can be adjusted independently. The principle of this technique was reported by Frumkin and Nekrasov (57), and the theory was worked out by Ivanov and Levich (58). A few applications (the reduction of oxygen, copper (II), and the oxidation of N-methyl aromatic amines) have been described (59–63).

Electron paramagnetic resonance (EPR) which is a sensitive technique for the detection and determination of radicals, has potentialities in electrode kinetics, especially in processes involving organic substances. Sensitivity in electrochemical studies is smaller than in measurements in the bulk of a solution because radicals must be transferred (diffusion, convection) to a sufficient distance away from the electrode to be detected. Only relatively stable radicals can therefore be studied by this method. The first application was made independently by Maki and Geske (64, 65) and by Galkin, Shamfarov, and Stefanishina (66). A number of laboratories, and particularly the one of Adams (67-70) are now actively engaged in this type of study, but most of the work seems to be oriented toward using electrolysis as a tool for generation of radicals. Application of EPR in conjunction with a variety of purely electrochemical techniques may prove fruitful (cf. Adams's work). EPR studies of the polarographic reduction of nitrobenzene were recently reviewed (71). See also Adams' review (74).

This brief outline of techniques for the study of intermediates is only indicative of what has been done, and other methods also have their application (for example, radiotracers; cf. Chapter 10). Altogether, there is room for much progress.

REFERENCES

1. K. J. Vetter, *Z. Naturforsch.*, **7a**, 328 (1952); see correction, *ibid.*, **8a**, 823 (1953).
2. R. M. Hurd, *J. Electrochem. Soc.*, **109**, 327 (1962).
3. K. J. Vetter, *Z. Elektrochem.*, **56**, 797 (1952).
4. J. Horiuti and M. Ikusima, *Proc. Imperial Acad. Tokyo*, **15**, 39 (1939).
5. J. Horiuti, *J. Research Inst. Catalysis, Hokkaido Univ.*, **1**, 8 (1948).
6. P. C. Milner, *J. Electrochem. Soc.*, **111**, 228 (1964).
7. J. Horiuti and T. Nakamura, *Z. physik. Chem. (Frankfurt)*, **11**, 358 (1957).
8. R. Parsons, *Trans. Faraday Soc.*, **47**, 1332 (1951).
9. K. B. Oldham, *J. Am. Chem. Soc.*, **77**, 4697 (1955).
10. A. C. Makrides, *J. Electrochem. Soc.*, **104**, 677 (1957).
11. H. Mauser, *Z. Elektrochem.*, **62**, 419 (1958).
12. A. C. Riddiford, *J. Chem. Soc.*, 1175, (1960).
13. D. M. Mohilner, *J. Phys. Chem.*, **68**, 632 (1964).
14. R. Parsons, *Advances in Electrochemistry and Electrochemical Engineering*, Vol. 1, P. Delahay, editor, Interscience, New York, 1961, pp. 1–64.
15. K. J. Vetter, *Transactions of the Symposium on Electrode Processes*, E. Yeager, editor, Wiley, New York, 1961, pp. 47–61.
16. K. J. Vetter, *Elektrochemische Kinetik*, Springer, Berlin, 1961.
17. K. J. Vetter, *Z. anorg. Chem.*, **260**, 242 (1949).
18. K. J. Vetter, *Z. physik. Chem.*, **194**, 199 (1950).
19. K. J. Vetter, *ibid.*, **194**, 284 (1950).
20. K. J. Vetter and G. Manecke, *ibid.*, **195**, 270, 337 (1950).
21. K. J. Vetter, *ibid.*, **196**, 360 (1951).
22. K. J. Vetter, *Z. Elektrochem.*, **55**, 121 (1951).
23. K. J. Vetter, *ibid.*, **56**, 797 (1952).
24. K. J. Vetter, *ibid.*, **56**, 931 (1952).
25. K. J. Vetter, *Z. physik. Chem.*, **199**, 22 (1952).
26. K. J. Vetter, *ibid.*, **199**, 285 (1952).
27. K. J. Vetter, *Z. Elektrochem.*, **59**, 435 (1955).
28. K. J. Vetter, *ibid.*, **59**, 596 (1955).
29. K. J. Vetter, and D. Otto, *ibid.*, **60**, 1072 (1956).
30. K. J. Vetter and J. Bardeleben, *ibid.*, **61**, 135 (1957).
31. K. J. Vetter, *ibid.*, **63**, 1189 (1959).
32. K. J. Vetter and G. Thiemke, *ibid.*, **64**, 805 (1960).

33. O. A. Esin, *Acta Physicochim. U.R.S.S.*, **13**, 429 (1940).
34. H. Gerischer, *Z. Elektrochem.*, **54**, 362, 366 (1950).
35. H. Gerischer, *ibid.*, **55**, 98 (1951).
36. H. Gerischer, *Z. physik. Chem.*, **198**, 286 (1951).
37. H. Gerischer, *ibid.*, **202**, 292, 302 (1953).
38. H. Gerischer, *Z. Elektrochem.*, **57**, 604 (1953).
39. E. Lewartowicz, *J. chim. phys.*, **49**, 557, 564, 573 (1952); **51**, 267 (1954).
40. J. V. Petrocelli, *J. Electrochem. Soc.*, **98**, 187, 291 (1951).
41. J. V. Petrocelli and A. A. Paolucci, *ibid.*, **98**, 291 (1951).
42. J. O'M. Bockris and E. C. Potter, *ibid.*, **99**, 169 (1952).
43. J. O'M. Bockris and E. C. Potter, *J. Chem. Phys.*, **20**, 614 (1952).
44. R. W. Parry and E. H. Lyons, *The Chemistry of the Coordination Compounds*, J. C. Bailar, editor, Reinhold, New York, 1956, pp. 625–671.
45. K. J. Vetter, *Angew. Chem.*, **73**, 277 (1961).
46. V. S. Bagotskii, *Doklady Akad. Nauk S.S.S.R.*, **58**, 1387 (1947).
47. V. S. Bagotskii and I. Yablokova, *Zhur. Fiz. Khim.*, **23**, 413 (1949).
48. O. Kaptsan and Z. A. Iofa, *ibid.*, **26**, 193, 201 (1952).
49. J. O'M. Bockris and R. G. H. Watson, *J. chim. phys.*, **49**, C 70 (1952).
50. A. N. Frumkin, ref. 14, pp. 65–121
51. P. Delahay, *J. Am. Chem. Soc.*, **74**, 3497 (1952).
52. O. A. Esin and M. Loshkarev, *Acta Physicochim. U.R.S.S.*, **10**, 513 (1939).
53. A. Eucken, *Z. physik. Chem.*, **64**, 562 (1908).
54. H. Gerischer and K. J. Vetter, *ibid.*, **197**, 92 (1951).
55. J. Koutecký and J. Koryta, *Electrochim. Acta*, **3**, 318 (1961).
56. P. Delahay, Ref. 14, pp. 233–318.
56a. W. H. Reinmuth, *Anal. Chem.*, **36**, 211 R (1964).
57. A. N. Frumkin and L. N. Nekrasov, *Doklady Akad. Nauk S.S.S.R.*, **126**, 115 (1959).
58. Yu. B. Ivanov and V. G. Levich, *ibid.*, **126**, 1029 (1959).
59. A. N. Frumkin, L. N. Nekrasov, V. G. Levich and Yu. B. Ivanov, *J. Electroanal. Chem.*, **1**, 84 (1959).
60. L. N. Nekrasov and B. P. Berezina, *Doklady Akad. Nauk S.S.S.R.*, **142**, 855 (1962).
61. Z. Galus, C. Olson, H. Y. Lee, and R. N. Adams, *Anal. Chem.*, **34**, 164 (1962).
62. Z. Galus and R. N. Adams, *J. Am. Chem. Soc.*, **84**, 2061 (1962); *J. Phys. Chem.*, **67**, 862 (1963).
63. L. N. Nekrasov and L. Myuller, *Doklady Akad. Nauk S.S.S.R.*, **149**, 1107 (1963); *Electrochim. Acta*, **9**, 1015 (1964).
64. A. H. Maki and D. H. Geske, *J. Chem. Phys.*, **30**, 1356 (1959).
65. D. H. Geske and A. H. Maki, *J. Am. Chem. Soc.*, **82**, 2671 (1960); **83**, 1852 (1961).
66. A. A. Galkin, Y. L. Shamfarov and A. V. Stefanishina, *Zhur. Eksptl. i Teoret. Fiz.*, **32**, 1581 (1957).
67. L. H. Piette, P. Ludwig, and R. N. Adams, *Anal. Chem.*, **34**, 916 (1962).
68. H. Y. Lee and R. N. Adams, *ibid.*, **34**, 1587 (1962).
69. T. Kitagawa, T. P. Layloff, and R. N. Adams, *ibid.*, **35**, 1086 (1963).
70. T. Miller, B. Lamb, and R. N. Adams, *J. Electroanal. Chem.*, **6**, 326 (1963).
71. T. Kitagawa, *Rev. Polarography (Japan)*, **12**, 11 (1964).
72. M. A. Loshkarev and B. I. Tomilov, *Zhur. Fiz. Khim.*, **34**, 1753 (1960); **36**, 132 (1962).
73. B. I. Tomilov and M. A. Loshkarev, *ibid.*, **36**, 1902 (1962).
74. R. N. Adams, *J. Electroanal. Chem.*, **8**, 151–162 (1964).

CHAPTER 9

Correlation between Electrode Kinetics and Double-Layer Structure in the Absence of Significant Specific Adsorption of Reactants and Products

9-1 Introduction

The double-layer structure was taken into account in a formal way in the derivation of the current-overvoltage characteristic in Sec. 7-2 (Eq. 7-12) but was not treated any further. The double-layer term was simply lumped together with the true exchange current, and the product of these two quantities was called the apparent exchange current i^0. This simplification can generally be made in the deduction of reaction mechanisms from current-overvoltage characteristics provided a large excess of supporting electrolyte is present (Chapter 8). Double-layer effects, however, are very significant, as was already pointed out in Sec. 7-2. Their quantitative study is limited at the present to electrode processes for which a fairly adequate understanding of the double-layer structure has been reached, that is, for liquid electrodes and mostly the mercury electrode. We do not mean to imply, however, that such studies should not be pursued with solid electrodes, even with the present rather qualitative understanding of their double-layer behavior. Much valuable information has indeed been obtained on solid electrodes by this approach (Chapter 10).

The simplest conditions for interpretation are achieved in the absence of specific adsorption of the supporting electrolyte, reactants, and products. Such ideal conditions never prevail in all rigor, although they are approached for a number of processes on mercury at markedly negative potentials with respect to the point of zero charge. Specific adsorption on mercury, under these conditions, is negligible for anions and only minor

197

for a number of cations, and the quantitative correlation between kinetics and double-layer structure is then rather successful. More complex cases must also be considered: specific adsorption of supporting electrolyte, adsorption of some organic additive (uncharged or ionic), and processes with coupled chemical reactions. Processes with chemisorption are analyzed in Chapter 10. The essential ideas will be discussed first, and interpretation of experimental results, which often requires consideration of a variety of effects, will follow.

The whole field rests on Frumkin's fundamental paper (1) of 1933 in which he correlated the double-layer structure to the rate of discharge of hydrogen ions. This major contribution to electrode kinetics followed the work of Erdey-Gruz and Volmer (1930) in which this electrode process was treated for control by the rate of charge transfer (cf. Chapter 7). Frumkin's initial paper provided an explanation of the earlier observation of Herasymenko and Šlendyk (2) on the influence of multivalent cations on the polarographic behavior of hydrogen ion. Early studies of double-layer effects in kinetics were limited to hydrogen ion discharge, but their scope became wider with the investigation of the reduction of anions after the initial observation by Krjukova (3) of seemingly abnormal polaro-graphic behavior. Thus began a series of systematic investigations which have been reviewed periodically by Frumkin (4–6) and subsequently by Parsons (7). Work in this area was almost exclusively carried out by the Frumkin school until 1958, at which date interest became widespread [Gierst (8, 9), Delahay and co-workers (10); see also the related approach of Reinmuth, Rogers, and Hummelstedt (11)].

9-2   Processes without Specific Adsorption of Supporting Electrolyte

In the absence of specific adsorption of reactants, products, and sup-porting electrolyte, Eq. 7-12 holds. Thus

$$i = i_t^0 e^{(\alpha n - z)f\phi_2}[e^{-\alpha nf\eta} - e^{(1-\alpha)nf\eta}] \tag{1}$$

The term in ϕ_2 in this equation appears for two reasons: the concentration of the discharged species in the pre-electrode state (Sec. 7-2) is different from the bulk concentration; and the "effective" potential is not E but $E - \phi_2$. These two corrections were clearly stated by Frumkin in his initial paper (1). The quantities i and η in Eq. 1 are determined by experi-ment, whereas the potential ϕ_2 is not measurable for electrodes.

Two methods of analyzing experimental data by Eq. 1 can thus be followed: (a) ϕ_2 is calculated from double-layer theory, generally by assuming that the pre-electrode state can be identified with the outer plane of closest approach, and the predictions of Eq. 1 are compared with experiment; (b) the reverse procedure is followed, that is, ϕ_2 is calculated directly from kinetic data and is compared with calculated values of ϕ_2. The former method is most frequently applied, but it involves the major assumption of identifiying the pre-electrode state with the state corresponding to the outer plane of closest approach. An additional complication arises from the very frequent use of a supporting electrolyte, for in principle, several planes of closest approach should be considered for mixed electrolytes (Sec. 3-5).

Two other problems must also be faced, which, however, do not bring any further complication. First, calculation of ϕ_2 is considerably simplified when equilibrium is supposed to prevail in the double layer, that is, when there is no current flowing. This is, of course, not the case in electrode kinetics, but it turns out, as we shall indicate in Sec. 9-5, that the double-layer structure is hardly altered by current flow except at very high current. Second, the possibility of interplay between the diffuse double layer and the diffusion layer must be recognized for processes with mixed control by mass transfer and charge transfer. This problem is related to the preceding one. Fortunately, no difficulty arises because the diffuse double layer is much thinner by several orders of magnitude than the diffusion layer, even in relaxation and perturbation methods at the limit of their present possibilities. Mass transfer may thus be corrected for without consideration of the double-layer structure, and the equations of Sec. 7-4 can be applied directly.

The implications of Eq. 1 are:

(a) The change of overvoltage $\Delta\eta$ resulting from a variation $\Delta\phi_2$ is at constant current

$$\Delta\eta = \left(1 - \frac{z}{\alpha n}\right)\Delta\phi_2 \tag{2}$$

where the ionic valence z of the species being reduced is taken with its sign. The quantities $\Delta\eta$ and $\Delta\phi_2$ have the same sign for $z/\alpha n < 1$ and have opposite signs for $z/\alpha n > 1$. Hence the shift of η has always the same sign as $\Delta\phi_2$ in the reduction of anions and the opposite sign of $\Delta\phi_2$ in reduction of cations ($z \geqslant n$ and $0 < \alpha < 1$). Application of Eq. 2 requires the value of the transfer coefficient α. This beings about a difficulty because Tafel plots yield only an apparent value of α which can differ appreciably from the true value (see the following). A plot corresponding to Eq. 2 is shown in Fig. 9-1 for the reduction of chromate in alkaline solution (16). This process offers an excellent example of a large double-layer correction (Sec. 9-7b). The half-wave potential, plotted in abscissa in Fig. 9-1,

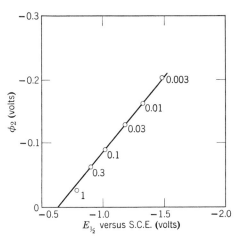

FIG. 9-1. Relationship between the half-wave potential $E_{1/2}$ and ϕ_2 for the polarographic reduction of $2 \times 10^{-4}M$ sodium chromate on mercury at 25°C for different sodium hydroxide concentrations (in moles per liter) [Tondeur, Dombret and Gierst (16)] (by permission of Elsevier).

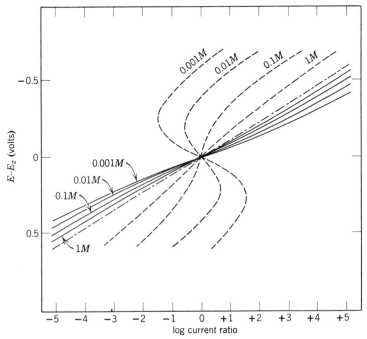

FIG. 9-2. Calculated Tafel plots for the process $O + e = R$ ($\alpha = 0.5$) on mercury in presence of sodium fluoride at 25°C. Values of ϕ_2 are taken from Fig. 3-7. Reduction of monovalent cation (solid curves) or anion (dotted curves). The dotted and dashed line corresponds to $\phi_2 = 0$ over the whole range of potentials. The logarithm of the ratio of the current at potential E to the current at E_z is plotted in abscissa [Joshi, Mehl and Parsons (7, 12)] (by permission of John Wiley).

corresponds to one-half of the diffusion current and is a potential at constant current (and essentially for a constant mass-transfer correction).

(b) Tafel plots are not linear and have the following varying slopes:

$$-\alpha n f + (\alpha n - z)f\frac{\partial\phi_2}{\partial\eta} \qquad \text{(cathodic range)}$$

$$(1 - \alpha)nf + (\alpha n - z)f\frac{\partial\phi_2}{\partial\eta} \qquad \text{(anodic range)}$$

The same remark applies to the plot corresponding to Eq. 7-21. The term in $\partial\phi_2/\partial\eta$ is often fairly constant (cf. Fig. 3-6) over the relatively limited over-voltage range generally investigated, and the apparent transfer coefficient is thus constant. Tafel plots may appear quite linear, but the apparent transfer coefficient, deduced from their slope, can be significantly different from the true transfer coefficient even at high supporting electrolyte concentrations (Fig. 9-2). Pronounced distortion with a minimum in the current-potential curve may also be observed, for example, in the reduction of anions (Sec. 9-7a).

(c) Equation 1 can be written in the form

$$i\,\frac{e^{zf\phi_2}}{1 - e^{-nf\eta}} = i_t^0 e^{\alpha n f(\phi_2 - \eta)} \tag{3}$$

from which it follows that a plot of the logarithm of the term on the left-hand side against $\phi_2 - \eta$ (or $\phi_2 - E$) is linear and has the slope αnf. The transfer coefficient is thus obtained (and not the apparent transfer coefficient as for Eq. 7-21). Equation 3 is applicable to any overvoltage but takes the following simpler form in the Tafel range

$$ie^{zf\phi_2} = i_t^0 e^{\alpha n f(\phi_2 - \eta)} \qquad \text{(cathodic range)}$$
$$ie^{f(z\phi_2 - n\eta)} = i_t^0 e^{\alpha n f(\phi_2 - \eta)} \qquad \text{(anodic range)} \tag{4}$$

A plot of the logarithm of the left-hand side of Eq. 4 against $\phi_2 - \eta$ is linear and has the slope αnf. All experimental points fall along a single line (Fig. 9-3) when Eq. 4 is verified despite wide variation in overvoltage (0.2 volt for the extreme concentrations of Al^{+3} in Fig. 9-3). The use of such *corrected Tafel plots* was advocated by Asada, Delahay, and Sundaram (13).

(d) Tafel plots at constant potential ϕ_2 can be drawn by a graphical method [Gierst (9)], which is illustrated in Fig. 9-4 for the reduction of peroxydisulfate according to Petrii and Frumkin (14, 15). The usual Tafel plot is drawn in the upper half of the diagram, and the variations of ϕ_2 with

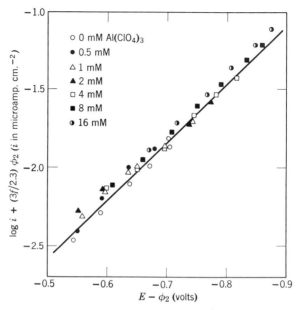

FIG. 9-3. Corrected Tafel plot for the reduction 1 mM Ga^{+3} in 20 mM perchloric acid on mercury at 25°C for a varying concentration of aluminum perchlorate. Potentials referred to a hydrogen electrode at atmospheric pressure in the solution being studied [Asada, Delahay, and Sundaram (13)] (by permission of the American Chemical Society).

E are plotted in the lower half for different concentrations of supporting electrolyte. In this particular case, current-potential curves exhibit a pronounced maximum which is discussed in Sec. 9-7a. The intercepts of the horizontal line for a selected value of ϕ_2 with the ϕ_2 versus E curves are determined for each concentration of supporting electrolyte and the corresponding points on the Tafel plots are determined. The resulting Tafel plots at constant ϕ_2 are linear and parallel when Eq. 1 holds with constant α and ϕ_2. This simple situation does not prevail for Fig. 9-4 (Sec. 9-7a). The dependence of E on ϕ_2 at constant current is also readily obtained from this diagram (curve MN). Considerable departure from the linear relationship predicted by Eq. 2 is observed in this particular instance.

(e) A plot of $\ln i$ against ϕ_2 at constant overvoltage is linear according to Eq. 1 and has the slope $(\alpha n - z)f$. Gierst initially thought (8, 9) that this plot allows the determination of the ionic valence of the discharged species even when it is different from the charge of the ionic species in the bulk of the solution. This is not the case, however, as was pointed out by Frumkin, Petrii, and Nikolaeva-Fedorovich (14, 15, 17). The double-layer correction

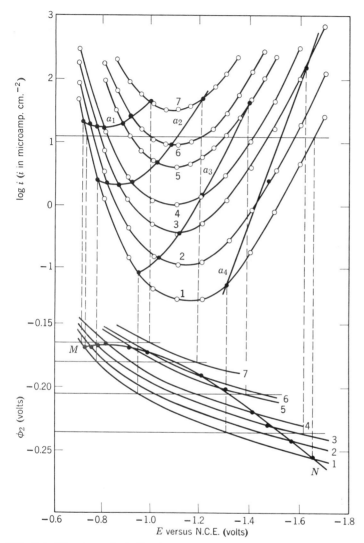

FIG. 9-4. Gierst's method (9) of drawing Tafel plots (curves a_1, a_2, a_3, and a_4) at constant potential ϕ_2, as applied to the reduction of $5 \times 10^{-4} M$ sodium peroxydisulfate on mercury. Sodium fluoride concentrations in moles per liter: 3×10^{-3} (curve 1); 5×10^{-3} (2); 7×10^{-3} (3); 10^{-2} (4); 1.5×10^{-2} (5); 2×10^{-2} (6), and 3×10^{-2} (7). Open circles are experimental points; solid circles in upper half of diagram correspond to Tafel plots for the four constant potentials ϕ_2. The curve MN on the lower half of the diagram represents variations of E with ϕ_2 at constant current. Currents are corrected for mass transfer [Petrii and Frumkin (14, 15)] (by permission of Pergamon).

in Eq. 1 indeed presupposes that the work done to bring species i from the bulk of the solution to the outer plane of closest approach is $zF\phi_2$, where the ionic valence z is supposed to be constant and equal to its value in the bulk of the solution. A detailed argument is given by Frumkin et al. (15).

(f) The apparent exchange current i^0 is related to the true exchange current i_t^0 by

$$i^0 = i_t^0 e^{(\alpha n - z)f\phi_2} \tag{5}$$

and a plot of $\ln i^0$ against ϕ_2 is linear and has the slope $(\alpha n - z)f$. Equation 5 seems to be valid for the reduction of zinc ion on zinc amalgam (18), for an essentially constant value of i_t^0 is obtained by its application (Table 9-1).

TABLE 9-1   Variations of Apparent Exchange Current with ϕ_2 for the Reduction of Zn^{++} on $Zn(Hg)$ at $25°C^{a,b}$

Electrolyte, mole l^{-1}	ϕ_2, millivolts	i^0, milliampere cm.$^{-2}$	i_t^0, milliampere cm.$^{-2}$
0.025M Mg(ClO$_4$)$_2$	−63.0	12.0	0.40
0.05	−56.8	9.0	0.43
0.125	−46.3	4.7	0.37
0.25	−41.1	2.7	0.38
0.025M Ba(ClO$_4$)$_2$	−60.8	9.1	0.33
0.05	−52.7	5.7	0.39
0.125	−42.8	3.2	0.31
0.250	−36.0	2.1	0.39

[a] For $c_{Zn(II)} = 2$ millimole l^{-1}, $c_{Zn(Hg)} = 0.048$ mole l^{-1}. i_t^0 computed for $\alpha = 0.30$.

[b] According to Aramata and Delahay (18).

This general relationship is particularly useful in relaxation and perturbation methods for fast electrode processes.

By recalling the explicit form of i_t^0 given by Eq. 7-25, we deduce

$$\left(\frac{\partial \ln i^0}{\partial \ln a_O}\right)_{a_R} = 1 - \alpha + \left(\alpha - \frac{z}{n}\right)\frac{\partial \phi_2}{\partial E^e}$$
$$\left(\frac{\partial \ln i^0}{\partial \ln a_R}\right)_{a_O} = \alpha - \left(\alpha - \frac{z}{n}\right)\frac{\partial \phi_2}{\partial E^e} \tag{6}$$

Comparison of Eq. 6 with Eq. 7-29 shows that the latter equation gives an apparent transfer coefficient which may differ significantly from the correct value. Reaction orders are affected in a similar way.

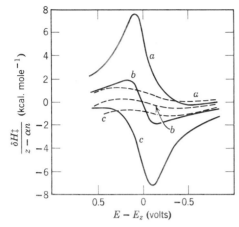

FIG. 9-5. Double-layer contribution, expressed as $\delta H^{\neq}/(z - \alpha n)$, to the heat of activation of the same reaction as in Fig. 9-2 and for the ϕ_2-values of Fig. 3-7. Sodium fluoride concentration: $0.001M$ (solid curves) and $1M$ (dotted curves). Temperature coefficient of the equilibrium potential: $+116$ volt degree (curves a); 0 (curves b); and -116 volt degree (curves c) [Joshi, Mehl, and Parsons (12)] (by permission of John Wiley).

(g) The heat of activation (Sec. 7-3c), which is determined from the variations of the apparent exchange current with temperature, includes a double-layer contribution

$$\delta H^{\neq} = -(\alpha n - z)f\left[\frac{\partial(\phi_2/T)}{\partial(1/T)}\right]_{\eta=0} \tag{7}$$

The equilibrium potential E^e varies with temperature, and $\delta H^{\neq}$ may be decomposed into two components corresponding to the variations of ϕ_2 with T and of E^e with respect to the point of zero charge. Detailed calculations, which follow directly from the theory of the diffuse double layer, are given by Joshi, Mehl, and Parsons (7, 12). They concluded (Fig. 9-5) that the double-layer contribution to the heat of activation can be very significant, especially since observed heats are often below 10 kcal. mole^{-1}.

9-3 Processes with Specific Adsorption
of the Supporting Electrolyte

We shall assume that only one ionic species of the supporting electrolyte is specifically adsorbed and that reactants and products are not specifically adsorbed. Treatment for specific adsorption is more uncertain than in the absence of specific adsorption because details of the double-layer structure are not fully understood. At least two effects must be considered: (a) Partial coverage of the electrode by specifically adsorbed ions which causes the current, at constant overvoltage, to decrease because of increase in the actual current density for the uncovered part of the electrode. (*b*) Variation of the potential ϕ_2 caused by specific adsorption. Anion specific adsorption causes ϕ_2 to be less positive, and cation specific adsorption has the opposite effect on ϕ_2 (Fig. 4-8). The resulting effect on the rate of an electrode process is readily deduced from Eq. 2. Thus the reduction rate of a non-specifically adsorbed anion, at a given potential, is decreased by addition of specifically adsorbed anions and increased by the presence of specifically adsorbed cations. The opposite conclusion holds for reduction of nonspecifically adsorbed cations. As the potential varies toward the region of desorption, ϕ_2 approaches values prevailing without

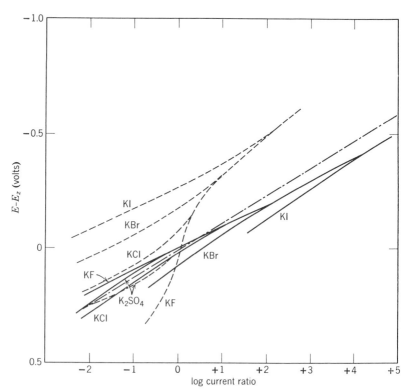

FIG. 9-6. Calculated Tafel plots for the reaction $O + e = R$ at 25°C for $\alpha = 0.5$ and for the values of ϕ_2 determined by Grahame and Soderberg (19) for different $0.1M$ supporting electrolytes. Reduction of monovalent cation (solid curves) or anion (dotted curves). The dotted and dashed line corresponds to $\phi_2 = 0$. The logarithm of the ratio of the current at potential E to the current at E_z is plotted in abscissa [Joshi, Mehl, and Parsons (12)] (by permission of John Wiley).

specific adsorption, and Tafel plots are distorted accordingly. The effect is illustrated in Fig. 9-6 in which coverage by the specifically adsorbed anions is not taken into account. The double-layer contribution to the heat of activation in specific adsorption can be analyzed in the same way as in Fig. 9-5 [Joshi, Mehl, and Parsons (7, 12)].

The selection of the potential in the pre-electrode state when there is specific adsorption of the supporting electrolyte is far from settled. This problem was analyzed by Breiter, Kleinerman, and Delahay (10), who advocated comparison of $\Delta\eta$ experimental shifts with the change of potential in the inner ($\Delta\phi_1$) and outer ($\Delta\phi_2$) planes. Values of ϕ_1 and ϕ_2 are only known tentatively for chloride and iodide (Sec. 4-4b), but further studies along this line might prove useful. It was found in the reduction of nitromethane in iodide medium that $\Delta\eta$ agrees fairly well with $\Delta\phi_1$ but not at all with $\Delta\phi_2$. Adsorption of nitromethane at the prevailing potentials is minor, but undoubtedly it complicates matters. Agreement between $\Delta\eta$ and $\Delta\phi_1$ becomes excellent when the variation of pH in the outer plane of closest approach is taken into account as noted by the writer (20). [The latter effect was pointed out independently by Mairanovskii (21), who considered the problem further (Sec. 11-3).]

These comments also apply to processes with adsorption of an organic additive. Thus two corrections can be considered for variation of coverage and potential in the pre-electrode state with the bulk concentration of additive. Details are given in Sec. 9-10 dealing with experimental results.

9-4 Processes with a Coupled Chemical Reaction

Consider a charge-transfer reation $O + ne = R$ preceded by the chemical reaction

$$X = O + Y \tag{8}$$

where O is reduced and X and Y are not. Reduction of O causes reaction 8 to proceed from left to right, and the over-all rate depends on the kinetics of charge transfer, mass transfer, and the chemical reaction. These processes have been studied extensively in polarography and chrono-potentiometry and are encountered in a number of cases, for example, the discharge of metal ion complexes (Secs. 8-3 and 8-4). Double-layer-effects were discussed independently by Gierst (8, 9) and the writer and co-workers (10). Further details were given by Gierst and Hurwitz (22), and theories were worked out by Matsuda (23) and, for less general conditions, by Hurwitz (24). The essential ideas can be conveyed by simple considerations (8-10), and details of theory will not be covered here.

The magnitude of the double-layer effect for reaction 8 depends on the relative thickness of the reaction layer (δ) and the diffuse double layer

$(1/\kappa)$ (Sec. 3-3). The concept of reaction layer thickness is introduced in the theory of polarography (Sec. 7-4) and need not be discussed here. Suffice it is to know that δ characterizes the distance from the electrode for which reaction 8 is not at equilibrium. Two limiting cases will be considered: $\delta \ll 1/\kappa$ and $\delta \gg 1/\kappa$. The former case corresponds to very fast reactions which are almost limited to the electrode surface. The rate of reaction 8 for $\delta \ll 1/\kappa$ is

$$\frac{dc_O}{dt} = k_f c_X - k_b c_O c_Y \tag{9}$$

where the k's are rate constants and the c's are the prevailing concentrations at the electrode surface. Since $\delta \ll 1/\kappa$ we may take as a rough approximation the concentrations in the outer plane by making the assumption of no specific adsorption of X, O, and Y. Thus

$$\frac{dc_O}{dt} = k_f c_X^s e^{-z'f\phi_2} - k_b c_O^s e^{-zf\phi_2} c_Y^s e^{-z''f\phi_2}$$

where z', z, and z'' are the ionic valence of X, O, and Y, respectively, and the c^s's are the concentrations outside the diffuse double layer. Since $z' = z + z''$

$$\frac{dc_O}{dt} = e^{-z'f\phi_2}(k_f c_X^s - k_b c_O^s c_Y^s) \tag{10}$$

that is, the rate of reaction 8 varies with $e^{-z'f\phi_2}$.

In the opposite case in which $\delta \gg 1/\kappa$, the concentrations in Eq. 9 are essentially those prevailing outside the diffuse double layer, and the rate of reaction 8 is independent of ϕ_2, as a first approximation. Examples are given in Sec. 9-8.

9-5   Nonequilibrium Double Layer

Double-layer effects in kinetics can generally be interpreted by assuming that there is no perturbation of the double-layer structure by the flow of current. Analysis without this restriction is worthwhile, for it leads to the condition which must prevail to warrant calculations based on an equilibrium double layer. The problem was initially attacked by Levich (25) and was later reexamined by him (26). Further work on this and the related question of superposition of the concentration gradients due to the double-layer structure and mass transfer was done by other investigators (8, 9, 27–34). A simple analysis of this difficult problem is given by Parsons (7). The conclusions were indicated in Sec. 9-2, and it turns out that no difficulty is encountered, even at the high current densitites prevailing in the study of fast electrode processes.

9-6   Comparison of Theory and Experiment: Reduction of Cations

A definite pattern has progressively emerged in the study of double layer-effects in electrode kinetics when reactants and products are not specifically adsorbed to any significant extent.

Conditions are first selected with minor specific adsorption of the supporting electrolyte, and the influence of the nature of the cation of the supporting electrolyte is systematically investigated, particularly for the alkali metals and tetra-alkylammonium ions. Study of the influence of the anion of the supporting electrolyte follows. Inference is then made about the effects of specific adsorption, ionic association in solution, etc.

Conclusions are best substantiated by considering a broad series of experiments with different systems, and progress on the details of double-layer effects has been rather slow once the major effect was well established and verified. We shall divide the examination of experimental results into four parts covering, respectively, the reduction of cations (this section), anions (Sec. 9-7), neutral substances (Sec. 9-9), and processes with coupled chemical reactions (Sec. 9-8). The influence of organic uncharged or ionic additives and the case of solid electrodes essentially free of chemisorption are discussed in Secs. 9-10 and 9-11, respectively.

a. Hydrogen Ion

Reduction of hydrogen ion on mercury played a prominent part in the early verification of the Frumkin theory. Work on this particular reaction was reviewed in detail by Frumkin (6), and only the essential points will be covered here. In the absence of supporting electrolyte, the discharge rate in not too concentrated solution of acid at a constant potential (versus some fixed reference electrode) is independent of the acid concentration (35). This follows immediately from Eq. 2 in which $\Delta\phi_2$ can be equated to $(1/f)\Delta \ln c_{H^+}$ as the reaction occurs, even at low current, at potentials markedly negative with respect to the point of zero charge [cf. Eq. 3-15 and Fig. 3-7]. Furthermore, $\alpha \approx 0.5$ in this particular case and

$$\Delta\eta \approx -(1/f) \Delta \ln c_{H^+}$$

This variation of η is exactly compensated by the change in equilibrium potential $\Delta E^e \approx (1/f)\Delta \ln c_{H^+}$, and consequently the current at constant E is essentially independent of the acid concentration. This conclusion was verified experimentally (36–40).

Studies in the absence of supporting electrolyte have the disadvantage of a simultaneous variation of two factors controlling the current, namely, the concentration of reactant and the potential ϕ_2. Subsequent work has therefore been done with an excess of supporting electrolyte because ϕ_2 can then be varied at constant reactant concentration. This procedure also allows the study of the influence of specific adsorption. Frumkin examined double-layer effects under these conditions (41, 42) and Bagotskii and Yablokova (43, 44) showed that experiment was in good agreement with theory. Earlier measurements by Levina and Zarinskii (45) with lanthanum chloride as supporting electrolyte had led tentatively to the same conclusion [see (6) for details].

Specific ionic effects and particularly cation specific adsorption must be considered in a detailed interpretation. The results of Maznichenko, Damaskin, and Iofa (46) in Table 9-2 are revealing in this respect. The

TABLE 9-2   Correlation between $\Delta\eta$ and $\Delta\phi_2$ for Hydrogen Ion Discharge on Mercury in Presence of Alkali Chloride for $i = 10^{-4}$ amp. cm.$^{-2}$ at 22°C[a]

Salt	HCl Concentration, mole l^{-1}	MCl Concentration, mole l^{-1}	$\Delta\eta$ Experimental,[b] millivolts	$\Delta\eta$ Calculated,[c] millivolts	$\Delta\phi_2$ Calculated,[d] millivolts
LiCl	0.001	0.001	−12	−	17.6
KCl	0.001	0.001	−16	−16	16.8
CsCl	0.001	0.001	−30	−	15.8
LiCl	0.001	0.01	−36	−	56.2
KCl	0.001	0.01	−47	−55	55.2
CsCl	0.001	0.01	−73	−	53.3
LiCl	0.001	0.033	−58	−	84.7
KCl	0.001	0.033	−69	−81	82.9
CsCl	0.001	0.033	−95	−	78.3
LiCl	0.01	0.1	−35	−	58.6
KCl	0.01	0.1	−47	−55	56.5
CsCl	0.01	0.1	−72	−	53.7
LiCl	0.01	0.33	−58	−	82
KCl	0.01	0.33	−69	−81	81.5
CsCl	0.01	0.33	−95	−	78.2
LiCl	0.01	1	−70	−	104.4
KCl	0.01	1	−80	−106	104.1
CsCl	0.01	1	−105	−	101

[a] According to Maznichenko, Damaskin, and Iofa (46).

[b] From pure acid to acid with MCl.

[c] From Eq. 2 with $\alpha = 0.527$.

[d] From capacity data and the Gouy-Chapman theory (Sec. 3-3). $\Delta\phi_2$ is the change of ϕ_2 for the pure acid to the acid with MCl.

shift of overvoltage $\Delta\eta$ from pure hydrochloric acid to mixtures of the acid and an alkali metal chloride increases in absolute value from lithium to cesium. Furthermore, $|\Delta\eta| < |\Delta\phi_2|$ for lithium and $|\Delta\eta| > |\Delta\phi_2|$ for cesium. Frumkin, Petrii, and Nikolaeva-Fedorovich reported without details (15) that the full data on which Table 9-2 is based and the earlier data of Bagotskii (38) give linear-corrected Tafel plots (Eq. 4). These plots are independent of electrolyte concentration for a given supporting electrolyte. Cation specific adsorption undoubtedly accounts in part for the results of Table 9-2, and particularly for cesium (Sec. 4-2). Departure from the Gouy-Chapman theory for the more concentrated solutions is undoubtedly another cause of discrepancy between experiment and theory. The Gouy-Chapman theory predicts values of $|\phi_2|$ which are substantially too high in the 0.01 to $1M$ range, as noted in Sec. 3-6, and consequently the calculated $\Delta\phi_2$'s in Table 9-2 are too large. The correction is indeed in the right direction, and recalculation of $\Delta\phi_2$'s from newer theories of the double layer would be interesting. Changes of properties of the solvation water might have to be considered when the supporting electrolyte contains a highly hydrated ion such as Li^+ or an ion with no primary hydration water such as Cs^+ (cf. Table 4-2). The imperfections of the Gouy-Chapman theory at high electrode charge, which are not revealed by capacity measurements (Sec. 3-2), become quite apparent in studies of this type. Finally, identification of the pre-electrode state with the state in the outer plane may account for part of the discrepancy in Table 9-2.

Anion specific adsorption causes pronounced distortion of the Tafel plots for hydrogen ion discharge on mercury as was shown in the early work of Iofa (47) and in the more recent study of Tsa Chuang-Hsin and Iofa (48). The Tafel plots in Fig. 9-7 become identical for the different halides at sufficiently high overvoltages because specific adsorption is then

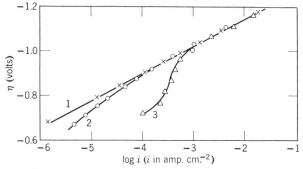

FIG. 9-7. Tafel plots for $1M$ hydrochloric with potassium halide: $2M$ chloride (curve 1); $2M$ bromide (2); and $2M$ iodide (3) [Tsa Chuang-Hshin and Iofa (48)] (by permission of Consultants Bureau Enterprises).

quite negligible. Specific adsorption of bromide and especially iodide, at lower overvoltages, causes a decrease of overvoltage. Thus ϕ_2 at a given potential E is more negative for iodide than for chloride (cf. Fig. 4-8) because of specific adsorption, and $|\eta|$ is lowered (Eq. 2). Quantitative interpretation is still tentative and has been argued between Parsons (49) and Frumkin (50). Specific adsorption must also be considered in the hydrogen ion discharge in concentrated acid solutions, but interpretation is complicated by variation of the activity coefficient of hydrogen ion [Frumkin (6) for a detailed discussion].

Discharge of hydrogen ion on amalgams has been studied in some detail (6) and often requires consideration of specific adsorption. Variation of the amalgam concentration provides a way of changing ϕ_2 at constant potential, whereas the electrolyte composition remains unchanged.

b. Zinc, Gallium, and Indium

Correlation between the double-layer structure and cation discharge on mercury has been studied in detail for a few metals. A wealth of information on the effect of supporting electrolyte on the kinetics of discharge is available in polarography and particulary in studies of fast electrode processes by relaxation and other methods [cf. the compilation of kinetic data by Tanaka and Tamamushi (51)]. Study of the influence of anion specific adsorption is often complicated by formation of complexes.

Discharge of zinc ion on zinc-amalgam was studied in detail by Koryta (52) by classical polarography. Aramata and Delahay (18) recently reported some results on this system obtained by the galvanostatic method. In addition to the references cited by Koryta, the recent relevant work by Losev and Molodov (53, 54) and Hush and Blackledge (55, 56) may be consulted. Koryta found fairly good agreement between measured apparent standard rate constants k^0 and values of k^0 calculated from the Gouy-Chapman theory for discharge in 0.1 to $1M$ potassium nitrate. The parameter k^0 decreases with increasing supporting electrolyte concentration as we would expect from Eq. 5. (ϕ_2 becomes less negative.) The rate constant k^0 also decreases in the sequence lithium to cesium much in the same way as for hydrogen ion discharge (Sec. 9-6a). Aramata and Delahay (18) found good agreement with the Frumkin correction in magnesium or barium perchlorate (Table 9-1), but discrepancies were quite considerable in sodium or aluminum perchlorate. This was attributed to differences in the ionic radii of zinc ion and the cation of the supporting electrolyte [cf. Sec. 3-5 on mixed electrolytes]. An explanation partially based on the difference of the ionic valences for zinc ion and the cation of the supporting electrolyte (13) was not ruled out.

The discharge of gallium ion on mercury was studied by Asada, Delahay, and Sundaram (13) in perchloric acid medium. Gallium (III) exists mostly as tripositive ions in this medium, and double layer effects were very pronounced because of the high value of z. The discharge is markedly irreversible and occurs at negative potentials with respect to E_z. Increase of the supporting electrolyte thus results in a higher overvoltage (Eq. 2). Good corrected Tafel plots were obtained (Fig. 9-3) with aluminum perchlorate as supporting electrolyte, but agreement was poor for magnesium perchlorate and even worse for sodium perchlorate. These discrepancies were ascribed by Asada et al. to the difference in the ionic valences of Ga(III) and Mg(II) or Na(I), but the authors also indicated the possibility of other explanations. Difference in ionic sizes and the necessity of considering two planes of closest approach for Ga(III) and the cation of the supporting electrolyte may well come into play (Sec. 3-5). An experiment allowing unambiguous interpretation is still lacking, although systematic investigation with supporting electrolytes of varying ionic radius and ionic valence might provide fairly definitive clues.

Double-layer effects in the polarographic reduction of indium were described qualitatively by Brainina (57) and were subsequently interpreted quantitatively by Stromberg and Brainina (58).

c. Europium(III)/(II)

Study of this redox couple is particularly interesting because the standard potential in perchloric acid is close to the point of zero charge ($E^0 \approx -0.15$ volt versus E_z), and double-layer effects can be examined on both sides of E_z. Preliminary results were discussed by Gierst (9), and a detailed investigation was subsequently reported by Gierst and Cornelissen (59). The latter authors list previous references on qualitative observations of double-layer effects for this system. Variation of the supporting electrolyte concentrations has opposite effects on each side of the point of zero charge (Fig. 9-8). All current-potential curves converge at E_z since $\phi_2 = 0$ at that potential, and consequently the current is independent of the supporting electrolyte concentration (Eq. 2). Tafel plots *for the forward reaction* [Eu(III) + e $\rightarrow$ Eu(II)] converge on that point (cf. with Fig. 9-2), but are linear and parallel after correction for the double-layer effect (Fig. 9-9). The plot of the logarithm of the rate of the forward reaction, at constant E, against ϕ_2 is linear and yields $z = 2.8 \pm 0.3$ for the Eu(III) ion. Quantitative interpretation for $E - E_z > 0$ was not carried out in detail in Ref. 59 because of specific adsorption of perchlorate ion, but could have been attempted by calculation of ϕ_2 by the method of Sec. 4-4a.

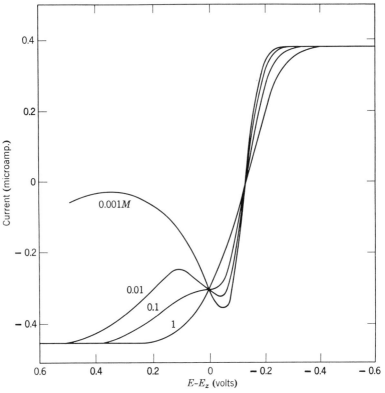

FIG. 9-8. Polarograms for $10^{-4}M$ Eu(III) + $10^{-4}M$ Eu(II) in perchloric acid of varying concentration at 25°C [Gierst and Cornelissen (9, 59)] (by permission of the Czechoslovak Academy of Sciences).

Gierst and Cornelissen (59) also examined qualitatively the influence of several specifically adsorbed anions. Increasing specific adsorption renders ϕ_2, at a given E, less positive and thus accelerate the oxidation of Eu(II) to Eu(III) (Fig. 9-10). Formation of complexes with some of the anions in Fig. 9-10 probably complicates quantitative interpretation.

d. Nickel(II) and Iron(II)

The polarographic behavior of Ni(II) in concentrated sodium perchlorate solution offers a good example of double-layer effects on a process with charge transfer preceded by a chemical reaction. (This, however, is not the first process of this type for which double-layer effects were studied; see discharge of cadmium cyanide in Sec. 9-8.) Initial work was reported

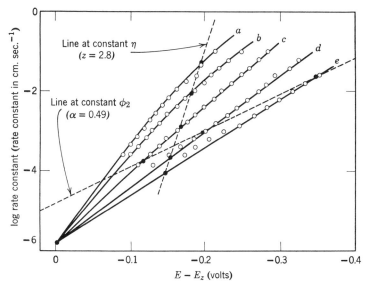

FIG. 9-9. Tafel plots, after correction for mass transfer, for the reduction at 25°C of $10^{-3}M$ Eu(III) in $10^{-3}M$ perchloric acid plus sodium perchlorate at the following molar concentrations: 0.03 (curve a); 0.06 (b); 0.1 (c); 0.3 (d); and 1 (e). The logarithm of the rate constant (including the effect of potential) for the forward reaction [Eu(III) + e → Eu(II)] is plotted in ordinate [Gierst and Cornelissen (9, 59)] (by permission of the Czechoslovak Academy of Sciences).

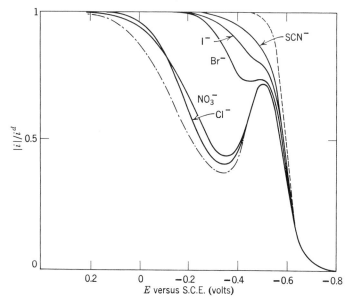

FIG. 9-10. Polarograms for the anodic oxidation of $2 \times 10^{-3}M$ Eu(II) in $3 \times 10^{-3}M$ perchloric acid (dotted and dashed curve) plus $5 \times 10^{-4}M$ of the sodium salt for various anions. The dashed curve corresponds to a reversible process [Gierst and Cornelissen (59)] (by permission of the Czechoslovak Academy of Sciences).

215

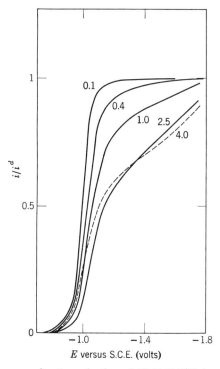

FIG. 9-11. Polarograms for the reduction of $10^{-2}M$ Ni(II) in sodium perchlorate of varying concentration (in moles per liter) [Dandoy and Gierst (60)] (by permission of Elsevier).

by Gierst (9) and was later expanded by Dandoy and Gierst (60) by classical polarography and chronopotentiometry. Ni(II) polarograms are considerably distorted at high sodium perchlorate concentrations (Fig. 9-11). This distortion had been previously interpreted as evidence for a two-step reduction of Ni(II), but this interpretation was disproved by Gierst. A distortion similar to that observed for the higher concentrations of sodium perchlorate is also found when the supporting electrolyte is $0.1M$ La(III). The distortion in $2M$ chloride solution of the alkali halide increases from lithium to cesium. These and other observations led Dandoy and Gierst to conclude that charge transfer is preceded by a relatively slow dehydration step. Quantitative data involving ϕ_2 variation are given by these authors, but calculation of ϕ_2 from the Gouy-Chapman theory is very uncertain at such high concentrations.

Discharge of Fe(II) on mercury also involves a dehydration step preceding charge transfer [Ivanov and Iofa (61, 62)], and the discharge rate is pH dependent.

9-7   Comparison of Theory and Experiment: Reduction of Anions

a. Peroxydisulfate, Ferricyanide, and Various Complexes of the Platinum Metal Group

These rather different anions are grouped here for the study of their reduction was carried out more or less simultaneously and they occupied for a number of years a central position in the study of double-layer effects in electrode kinetics (9, 14, 15, 17, 63–83) after the initial work of Krjukova (3). Progress up to 1955 was reviewed in detail by Frumkin (4) [also Refs. 5, 15, and 73], and Parsons stressed the essential points (7). We shall not concern ourselves with special problems related to polarographic maxima or with the periodic current variations that can be observed under certain conditions. [See Gokhstein (83) for pertinent literature.]

Current-potential curves for the reduction of peroxydisulfate, ferricyanide, and a number of complexes of the platinum (IV) and (II) group [$PtCl_4^{-2}$, $PtCl_6^{-2}$, $IrCl_6^{-2}$, $RhCl_6^{-2}$, $Pt(NH_3)_2Cl_2$] exhibit a pronounced minimum in the limiting current range in dilute supporting electrolyte solutions. The minimum generally disappears when the supporting electrolyte concentration is raised, and the normal potential-independent limiting current is observed. This is not always the case, however, and the minimum may remain even at high electrolyte concentrations, for example, with $PtCl_4^{--}$ in $1M$ potassium chloride (68). The correlation of this apparently abnormal behavior of anions with the double-layer structure was clearly recognized by Frumkin and Florianovich (63) in 1951 and was stated quantitatively by them with allowance for mass transfer (68). Interpretation was substantiated by a series of observations on the influence of the nature of the electrode and supporting electrolyte (cf. Ref. 4 for a review). An alternate explanation which was suggested (69) for *some* of the anions studied by Frumkin and co-workers does not appear very plausible (70).

Tafel plots for the reduction of peroxydisulfate were given in Fig. 9-4. Corrected Tafel plots are shown in Fig. 9-12 for peroxydisulfate in presence of different alkali metal chlorides and in Fig. 9-13 for ferricyanide. All points for a given electrolyte of varying concentration fall on a single curve in Figs. 9-12 and 9-13, but the plots are not linear, except for cesium chloride in Fig. 9-12 and for all electrolytes at the more negative values of $E - \phi_2$ in all cases. The plots are nearly parallel at sufficiently negative values of $E - \phi_2$ and yield $\alpha = 0.30$ for Fig. 9-12 and $\alpha = 0.16$, 0.17, and 0.19, respectively, for lines 1 to 3 in Fig. 9-13.

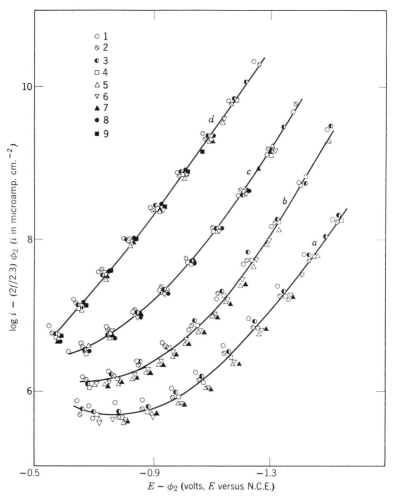

FIG. 9-12. Corrected Tafel plots for the polarographic reduction of $5 \times 10^{-4}M$ peroxydisulfate ion on mercury in the alkali halide solutions listed below. Current corrected for mass transfer. Composition and concentration of supporting electrolyte (in millimoles per liter): Curve a (lithium chloride + sodium chloride in the ratio 10:1): 10 (points 1), 15 (2), 20 (3), 30 (4), 40 (5), 50 (6), 70 (7). Curve b (sodium fluoride): 3 (points 1), 5 (2), 7 (3), 10 (4), 15 (5), 20 (6), and 30 (7). Curve c (potassium chloride): 2 (points 1), 3 (2), 4 (3), 5 (4), 6 (5), 7 (6), 8 (7), and 10 (8). Curve d (cesium chloride): 0 (points 1), 0.5 (2), 1 (3), 1.5 (4), 2 (5), 2.5 (6), 3 (7), 4 (8), and 5 (9). Peroxydisulfate was present as the sodium salt for curves a and b, potassium salt for curve c, and cesium salt for curve d [Frumkin and Petrii (14, 15)] (by permission of Pergamon).

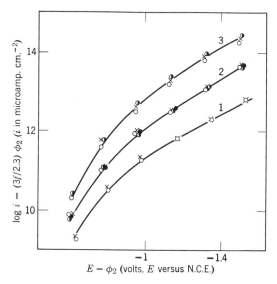

FIG. 9-13. Corrected Tafel for the reduction of $10^{-3}M$ ferricyanide on the dropping mercury electrode. Current corrected for mass transfer. Curve 1: lithium ferricyanide in $10^{-3}M$ ($\times$) and $3 \times 10^{-3}M$ ($\bigcirc$) lithium chloride. Curve 2: potassium ferricyanide without supporting electrolyte ($\bigcirc$) and with $5 \times 10^{-4}M$ ($\times$), $10^{-3}M$ ($\circleddash$), $1.5 \times 10^{-3}M$ ($\bullet$) potassium chloride. Curve 3: cesium ferricyanide without supporting electrolyte ($\bigcirc$) and with $3 \times 10^{-4}M$ ($\times$) and 5×10^{-4} M($\bullet$) cesium chloride [Frumkin, Petrii, and Nikolaeva-Fedorovich (15)] (by permission of Pergamon).

Cation specific adsorption accounts for the increase in rate, at a given potential, in Figs. 9-12 and 9-13, but it certainly is not a complete explanation. Imperfections of the Gouy-Chapman theory in the calculation of ϕ_2 can be invoked, but it should be noted that solutions are quite dilute and the charge on the electrode not exceeding negative. We would not expect too large an error in ϕ_2 under these conditions, although it must be recognized that the range of potentials in Figs. 9-12 and 9-13 is much larger than in most studies of double-layer effects in kinetics. This may result in a magnification of the discrepancy between theory and experiment which is not detected with other systems.

Frumkin et al. (15) also examined the influence of a difference in the plane of closest approach for the discharged species and the cation of the supporting electrolyte. They calculated the potential ϕ_x at a distance x from the plane of closest approach on the solution side by application of the Gouy-Chapman theory (Eq. 3-16) and found that the resulting corrected Tafel plots for peroxydisulfate (Fig. 9-14) are not very sensitive to the distance x unless it is absurdly large. A similar conclusion was

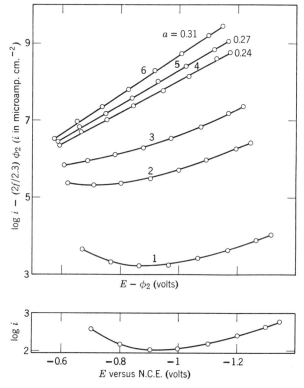

FIG. 9-14. *Bottom*: Tafel plot for the reduction of $5 \times 10^{-4}M$ cesium peroxydisulfate in $2 \times 10^{-3}M$ cesium chloride on the dropping mercury electrode. *Top*: corrected Tafel plots for the same system. Current corrected for mass transfer. Values of x in angströms for ϕ_x (see text): 55.4 (curve 1); 11.08 (2); 5.54 (3); 1.108 (4); 0.554 (5); and 0 (6). The transfer coefficient is indicated for curves 4 to 6 [Frumkin, Petrii, and Nikolaeva-Fedorovich (15)] (by permission of Pergamon).

reached for ferricyanide reduction. This calculation is only tentative, for it is based on the usual Gouy-Chapman theory, and a more detailed calculation in which the existence of two planes of closest approach is recognized at the onset might give a different result (see Sec. 3-5).

It may be concluded that the double-layer correction in this case holds as a first approximation. Consideration of cation specific adsorption accounts qualitatively for the increase in the rate of charge transfer in the sequence from lithium to cesium. It may not be an easy matter to settle further fine points because unambiguous experiments in support of speculation appear difficult to devise.

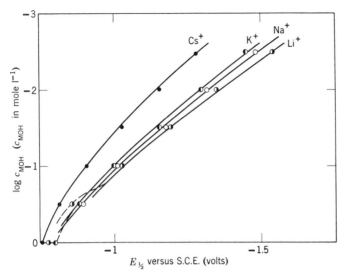

FIG. 9-15. Influence of supporting electrolyte in the polarographic reduction of $2 \times 10^{-4}M$ chromate in alkali metal hydroxide at 25°C [Tondeur, Dombret, and Gierst (16)] (by permission of Elsevier).

b. Chromate

Double-layer effects in the polarographic reduction of chromate ion in alkaline medium are striking because of the ionic valence -2 of this ion. Initial data were given by Gierst (9) and a very detailed study was reported by Tondeur, Dombret, and Gierst (16). The shift of the half-wave potential in sodium hydroxide is of the order of 0.8 volt when the supporting electrolyte concentration varies from 0.003 to $1M$ (Fig. 9-1). This shift is caused by variation of ϕ_2 since the rate-determining step is pH independent. The Frumkin correction holds very well over this wide range of potentials. The rate of reduction increases significantly in hydroxide medium from lithium to cesium (Fig. 9-15).

The polarographic wave is preceded by a small or hardly noticeable prewave in hydroxide medium which becomes very pronounced at lower pH's (Fig. 9-16). This prewave was reported by Green and Walkley (84) who concluded that it corresponds to the recombination reaction

$$CrO_4^{-2} + H^+ = HCrO_4^{-} \tag{11}$$

where $HCrO_4^{-}$ is reduced at less negative potentials than CrO_4^{-2}. These authors suggested that the maximum exhibited by the prewave was due to

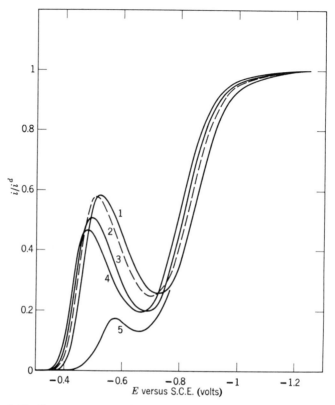

FIG. 9-16. Chromate prewave for 2×10^{-4} sodium chromate in phosphate buffers. Composition of buffer: $0.218M$ $Na_3PO_4 + 0.173M$ Na_2HPO_4 (curve 1); $0.109M$ $Na_3PO_4 + 0.0865M$ $Na_2HPO_4 + 0.5M$ NaF (2); $0.0654M$ $Na_3PO_4 + 0.0519M$ $Na_2HPO_4 + 0.7M$ NaF (3); $0.0218M$ $Na_3PO_4 + 0.0173M$ $Na_2HPO_4 + 0.9M$ NaF (4); $0.33M$ Na_3PO_4 [Tondeur, Dombret, and Gierst (16)] (by permission of Elsevier).

double-layer effects. Tondeur et al. (16) confirmed these conclusions and examined the double-layer effect quantitatively. They found the expected pH dependence on the rate and observed that the prewave height increases when the potential ϕ_2 becomes less negative. This observation agrees with the analysis of Sec. 9-4: the net rate of reaction 11 for production of $HCrO_4^-$ is indeed proportional to $e^{f\phi_2}$, as a first approximation. Cation specific adsorption therefore increases the height of the prewave (Fig. 9-17), and anion specific adsorption has the opposite effect (Fig. 9-18). This study offers an excellent example of the elucidation of reaction mechanisms by a systematic variation of the double-layer structure. Much valuable information can be gathered by this method despite present uncertainty about the finer points of the Frumkin correction.

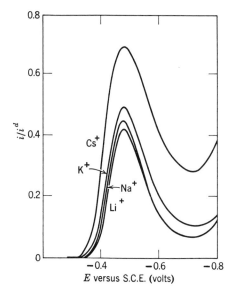

FIG. 9-17. Influence of the nature of the cation on the prewave for reduction of 2×10^{-4} sodium chromate in $0.1M$ alkali metal hydroxide at $25°C$ [Tondeur, Dombret, and Gierst (16)] (by permission of Elsevier).

c. Bromate and Iodate

Double-layer effects in the polarographic reduction of these anions in alkaline medium were initially reported by Gierst, (8, 9) and by Breiter, Kleinerman, and Delahay (10). The Frumkin correction was found to hold quite well especially when ϕ_2 was varied by adding potassium chloride. The less satisfactory agreement for potassium sulfate (10) was subsequently ascribed by Delahay and Aramata (85) to ion pair formation in the *bulk of the solution*. This effect is distinct from ion pair formation solely in the double layer which was considered by Frumkin (5, 78, 79, 82) and Reinmuth (87) to account for some of the features of anion reduction. Ionic association in the double layer is inferred from kinetic measurements, whereas ionic association in the bulk of the solution rests on a different experimental basis (conductivity, etc.). Even so, Delahay and Aramata (85) cite the words of caution of Robinson and Stokes (88) about evidence and quantitative data for ionic association in *aqueous* solution. Corrected Tafel plots, after correction for ion pair formation in solution (that is, introduction of the corrected ionic concentrations in Eq. 3-9), are nearly the same (Fig. 9-19) without and with 0.4 normal potassium salts (chloride, sulfate, and ferrocyanide). Corrected Tafel lines without consideration of

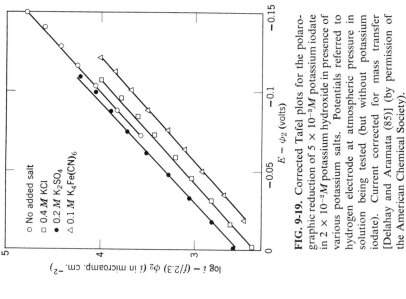

FIG. 9-19. Corrected Tafel plots for the polarographic reduction of $5 \times 10^{-3} M$ potassium iodate in $2 \times 10^{-2} M$ potassium hydroxide in presence of various potassium salts. Potentials referred to hydrogen electrode at atmospheric pressure in solution being tested (but without potassium iodate). Current corrected for mass transfer [Delahay and Aramata (85)] (by permission of the American Chemical Society).

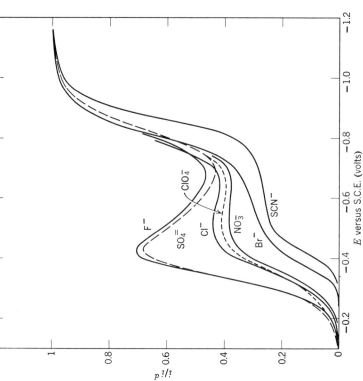

FIG. 9-18. Influence of anion specific adsorption on the prewave for the reduction of $2 \times 10^{-4} M$ sodium chromate in $0.9 M$ solution of the sodium salts of various anions at 25°C [Tondeur, Dombret, and Gierst (16)] (by permission of Elsevier).

ionic association are displaced by 0, −0.02, and −0.014 volt with respect to the lines in Fig. 9-19 for chloride, sulfate, and ferrocyanide, respectively. The remaining discrepancy may possibly result from the use of values of $|\phi_2|$ which are too high in agreement with the trend predicted by recent theories of the diffuse double layer (Sec. 3-6). It was further noted by Delahay and Aramata (85) that ionic association results in dissociation of the ion pair $K^+IO_3^-$ prior to charge transfer. The resulting complication is probably minor because ion pair formation is not strong for potassium iodate (pK = −0.25). The possibility of ionic association in the bulk of the solution must be recognized in analyzing the *details* of double-layer effects in electrode kinetics, and recalculation of some of the published data might be desirable.

The influence of the nature of the cation was investigated by Aramata and Delahay (86) and by Gierst (89). The usual sequence from lithium to cesium is disrupted, when the concentration of supporting electrolyte is varied (Fig. 9-20). Specific adsorption of cesium does increase the rate as expected but so does lithium, especially at low concentrations of

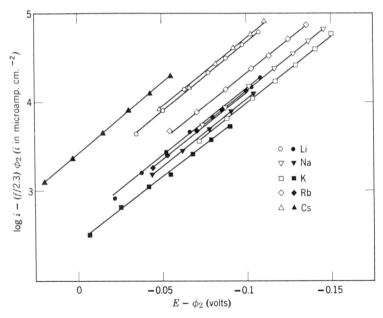

FIG. 9-20. Corrected Tafel plots for the polarographic reduction of $5 \times 10^{-3}M$ iodate in $2 \times 10^{-2}M$ hydroxide (open symbols) and in 2×10^{-2} hydroxide plus $0.1M$ chloride (solid symbols; except for potassium chloride which was $0.4M$) of the alkali metal. Same reference electrode as in Fig. 9-19 [Aramata and Delahay (86)] (by permission of the American Chemical Society).

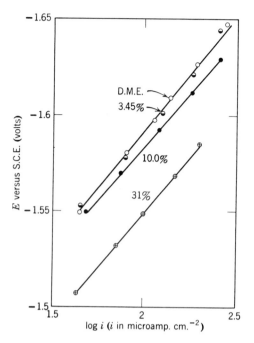

FIG. 9-21. Tafel plot for the reduction of $5 \times 10^{-3}M$ sodium bromate in $5 \times 10^{-2}M$ sodium hydroxide and $10^{-1}M$ sodium chloride on dropping mercury and dropping thallium-amalgam (composition in weight percent) electrodes at 30°C. Current corrected for mass transfer [Delahay and Kleinerman (91)] (by permission of the American Chemical Society).

supporting electrolyte. The cause for this peculiar behavior, which was also observed by Gierst (89), is not clear.

Reduction of iodate on a thallium amalgam of varying composition was investigated by Delahay and Kleinerman (90). [For an earlier study of peroxydisulfate reduction on this amalgam, see Kalish and Frumkin (66); for more recent results, see (15).] The potential ϕ_2 becomes less negative upon addition of thallium (Secs. 4-2 and 4-4a) and the rate increases. The Frumkin correction holds quite well. Similar results were obtained for the reduction of bromate (Fig. 9-21). (See also Refs. 92–94 for bromate reduction.)

Double-layer effects have been examined in the reduction of a few other anions: chromicyanide (91, 95), anion complexes of U(VI) (89, 96), and periodate (89). The abundant literature on the polarography of nitrate, in which double-layer effects are quite pronounced, may also be considered.

9-8 Comparison of Theory and Experiment:
Processes with a Coupled Chemical Reaction

These processes were discussed in Sec. 9-4, and examples were encountered in the reduction of Ni(II) and chromate. Discussion will be limited to the discharge of cadmium cyanide and Hg(II) cyanide.

The reduction of $Cd(CN)_4^{--}$ occurs via the formation of $Cd(CN)_3^-$ and, in more dilute cyanide solution, via $Cd(CN)_2$ as conclusively shown by Gerischer (Sec. 8-3b). He had to work with highly concentrated supporting electrolyte (5 molar) to obtain faradaic impedance data that could be interpreted by assuming equilibrium for the reaction preceding charge transfer. Gerischer subsequently determined the rate constant for dissociation of $Cd(CN)_4^{--}$ by chronopotentiometry (98) and the potentiostatic method (102).

The double-layer effect in the reduction of $Cd(CN)_4^{--}$ was recognized in 1954 by Siekierskii (99), who assumed direct reduction without prior dissociation and considered this case to be analogous to the reduction of peroxydisulfate. Koryta (101) also considered briefly double-layer effects. A detailed interpretation was given independently by Gierst (8, 9) and by Breiter, Kleinerman, and Delahay (10). The dissociation rate of $Cd(CN)_4^{--}$, according to the highly simplified Eq. 10, is proportional to $e^{2f\phi_2}$. Since the reaction occurs in the range in which $E - E_z < 0$, addition of a supporting electrolyte such as sodium chloride increases the dissociation rate. It turns out that the rate is sufficiently high in $5M$ supporting electrolyte for equilibrium to be virtually reached at the frequencies used by Gerischer in his faradaic impedance measurements.

The proportionality of the apparent rate constant for dissociation into $Cd(CN)_3^-$ to the factor $e^{2f\phi_2}$ was verified by Breiter et al. (10) for Gierst's earlier chronopotentiometric data (97). Gierst (8, 9) also verified this relationship on the basis of polarographic data. Similar considerations also apply to the reduction of $Hg(CN)_4^{--}$ (9, 100, 103). Reduction of $Cd(CN)_4^{--}$ on thallium-amalgam has also been studied (91).

9-9 Comparison of Theory and Experiment:
Uncharged Substances

Potential-dependent adsorption must generally be considered in the kinetics of uncharged reacting species as we shall see in Chapter 11, and the discussion of double-layer effects for these substances is given in that chapter (Sec. 11-3). Discussion is limited here to a reaction, the reduction of oxygen to hydrogen peroxide on mercury, for which adsorption can presumably be neglected. It has been known since the early days of polarography that oxygen is reduced to water with intermediate formation of hydrogen peroxide. The reaction is highly irreversible in acid and neutral media, and the half-wave potential is pH independent. The reaction is reversible under polarographic conditions in sufficiently alkaline solution, and the half-wave potential is pH dependent. The kinetics on mercury was studied in detail by Bagotskii and Yablokova (104). Since $z = 0$ for oxygen, $\Delta\eta = \Delta\phi_2$ (Eq. 2) when the reaction is totally irreversible. Hence addition of a specifically adsorbed anion, which renders ϕ_2 less positive, causes a shift of half-wave potential as large as -0.1 volt (for bromide). A quantitative and extensive study of double-layer effects in the polarographic reduction of oxygen was recently reported by Kůta and Koryta (104a).

Kolthoff and Jordan (105) suggested that in presence of an excess of hydrogen peroxide oxygen is regenerated by reaction of O_2^-, produced by the addition of an electron to O_2, with hydrogen peroxide. An exaltation of the first oxygen wave would then be observed. The possibility of this alternate mechanism prompted Cornelissen and Gierst (106) to report in a brief note the effect of supporting electrolytes for which ϕ_2 is sufficiently positive at potentials corresponding to the first oxygen wave. Exaltation of the first oxygen wave without any bulk concentration of hydrogen peroxide was indeed observed and explained by the increase of O_2^- concentration in the outer plane caused by the positive ϕ_2 values. However, these findings were attributed by Kolthoff and Izutsu (107) to stirring of the solution and to traces of volatile impurities in tetra-alkylammonium salts. These authors also disputed the earlier interpretation of Kolthoff and Jordan (105). Another effect, the salting-out of oxygen in the double layer, must also be considered according to Gierst (89), but his results are as yet unpublished.

9-10 Electrode Processes in Presence of an Organic Additive

a. Organic Ions

It was briefly pointed out in Sec. 9-3 that two effects of specifically adsorbed inorganic ions, the variations of ϕ_2 and coverage with electrolyte concentration, must also be taken into account for organic adsorbates. It may be added that analysis of data based on these two effects is not wholly adequate, especially at high coverage. Interpretation of data obtained with the dropping mercury electrode is often further complicated by variation of coverage during drop life as a result of slow adsorption with diffusion control (Sec. 5-8). We now examine the effect of organic ions and uncharged substances. The influence of mass transfer is considered in Sec. 9-10c.

Tetra-alkylammonium ions have played a prominent part (12, 47, 52, 59, 72, 73, 76, 108–121) in studies of the effect of organic ions on electrode kinetics, although organic anions have also been investigated (cf., for example, Ref. 122 and polarographic investigations). Influence on hydrogen ion discharge on mercury and some characteristics of adsorption of tetra-alkylammonium ions on mercury are reviewed by Frumkin (6). These cations are adsorbed in the same way as organic uncharged substances (cf. Chapter 5), all the more so when the number of carbon atoms increases. They are desorbed at markedly negative potentials despite their positive charge. Mass transfer need not be considered in fairly concentrated solution, just as for inorganic salts, but it causes coverage variation on the dropping mercury electrode at low concentrations (cf. Sec. 9-10c). Adsorption renders ϕ_2 less negative and lowers the reduction rate of cations (H^+, Zn^{+2}, etc.); conversely, the reduction rate of anions ($S_2O_8^{-2}$, CrO_4^{-2}, etc.) is increased (cf. Eq. 2). On the other hand, the increase of coverage with concentration of tetra-alkylammonium ions inhibits charge transfer, and there is an interplay between variations of ϕ_2 and coverage (121). Further complication arises from ion pair formation in the bulk of the solution with a number of anions [Zykov (117), Gierst et al. (121)].

The over-all effect on electrode kinetics thus depends on several factors whose relative importance can only be determined by a systematic investigation of several tetra-alkylammonium cations with varying organic character in presence of anions having different properties toward specific adsorption and ion pair formation. The paper of Gierst, Tondeur, Cornelissen, and Lamy (121) is a good example of such a systematic study. (See also the literature survey in Ref. 121.) Gierst et al. (121) examined the influence of tetra-alkylammonium cations on kinetics without and with another supporting electrolyte. The competitive effects of the variations of ϕ_2 and coverage in the reduction of chromate are quite evident in Fig. 9-22 for tetraproplyammonium and especially tetraethylammonium ions. The influence of ϕ_2 variations is predominant at low concentrations, whereas increasing electrode coverage more than compensates for the ϕ_2-effect at high concentrations. The rate of discharge thus exhibits a maximum. Only the descending branch of the curve in Fig. 9-22 could be observed for tetrabutylammonium ions because of the very effective blocking action of this ion. Tetramethylammonium ion only accelerates slightly the rate of reduction. Similar observations were made for the reduction of iodate; a maximum was also observed with tetraethylammonium ion; the increase in rate with tetramethylammonium ion was more pronounced than for chromate.

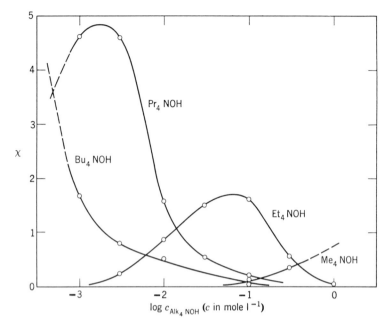

FIG. 9-22. Variations of the rate of polarographic reduction of $2 \times 10^{-4}M$ chromate in different tetra-alkylammonium hydroxides of varying concentration (in moles per liter) at 25°C. Rates were corrected for mass transfer and were measured at -0.75 volt (versus S.C.E.) on main wave of chromate (no interference by the prewave). The dimensionless parameter χ plotted in ordinate is proportional to the rate of discharge and is given by $(\tfrac{12}{7})^{1/2}\vec{k}t^{1/2}D^{-1/2}$ where t is the drop time, D is the diffusion coefficient of chromate, and the rate of chromate reduction is equal to the product of $\vec{k}$ by the chromate concentration corrected for mass transfer. Abbreviations: Me (methyl), Et (ethyl), Pr (propyl), Bu (butyl) [Gierst, Tondeur, Cornelissen, and Lamy (121)] (by permission of the authors).

Addition of another supporting electrolyte to tetra-alkylammonium hydroxide causes a shift of the chromate wave which depends strongly on the nature of the anions (Fig. 9-23). The following sequence was found for increasing effects: PO_4^{-3}, CO_3^{-2}, SO_4^{-2}, OH^-, F^-, $CH_3CO_2^-$, Cl^-, CN^-, BrO_3^-, NO_3^-, Br^-, ClO_3^-, I^-, SCN^-, and ClO_4^-. This sequence is very different from the one for anion specific adsorption in the absence of tetra-alkylammonium ion, F^-, OH^-, CO_3^{-2}, SO_4^{-2}, ClO_4^-, NO_3^-, Cl^-, Br^-, SCN^-, and I^-. Similar observations were also made by Gierst et al. for the discharge of zinc ion, the Eu(III/II) system, the reduction of iodate, and a few other electrode processes. They concluded that simultaneous adsorption of the tetra-alkylammonium cation and the inorganic anion cannot *solely* account for the results and that ion association is important.

They cite as evidence the disparities between these two sequences of ions and particularly the pronounced effects of ions which do not undergo strong specific adsorption (BrO_3^-, NO_3^-, ClO_3^-, and ClO_4^-). Furthermore, the first anion sequence closely resembles those for lowering of interfacial tension at a solution-air interface and for the efficiency of tetra-alkylammonium anion exchange resins.

Ionic association in solution probably accounts for the difficulties experienced by Joshi, Mehl, and Parsons (12) in the interpretation of the kinetics of the V(III/II) couple on mercury in presence of tetra-alkylammonium salts. The electrocapillary data of Devanathan and Fernando (120) on these salts might also have to be reexamined in the light of the findings of Gierst and co-workers.

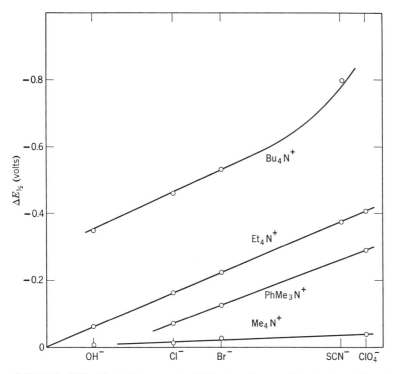

FIG. 9-23. Shift of the half-wave potential for the polarographic reduction of $2 \times 10^{-4}M$ sodium chromate at 25°C in $10^{-2}M$ solution of tetra-alkylammonium hydroxide in presence of $1M$ solution of the indicated sodium salts. The shift in half-wave potential is measured with respect to the wave in $10^{-2}M$ sodium hydroxide without additive. The abscissa scale is such as to linearize the results for tetraethylammonium ion. Same abbreviations as in Fig. 9-22 plus Ph (phenyl) [Gierst, Tondeur, Cornelissen, and Lamy (121)] (by permission of the authors).

b. Neutral Substances

The polarographic literature is rich in observations on the effect of adsorbed uncharged substances on the morphology of polarograms. Extensive reviews are available (123, 124). Early work was examined by Frumkin from the point of view of electrode kinetics (124a). Frumkin also reviewed recently these effects on hydrogen overvoltage for mercury (6). Much of the early work in polarography is qualitative because coverage variation resulting from slow adsorption with diffusion control, at low concentrations of adsorbate, was not realized until 1956 to 1957 (Sec. 5-8). Quantitative interpretation with varying coverage is not easy (Sec. 10c). Furthermore it is often not possible to avoid the mass-transfer problem by increasing the bulk concentration of adsorbate because coverage may then approach saturation.

It would seem easier to work with an electrode of constant area, for example, the hanging mercury drop, to allow adsorption equilibrium to be reached. Steady-state current measurements in stirred solution which might be considered are difficult with a liquid electrode. As an alternative we can avoid stirring and allow attainment of adsorption equilibrium at a potential at which the electrode reaction does not occur practically, for example, the equilibrium potential for a fast redox couple. Electrode kinetics can then be studied from the electrode response to some perturbation of potential or current. The coverage should not be changed appreciably by the variation of potential, and application of this procedure is limited to fast processes at low overvoltages (a few millivolts) or to measurements with excursion of potential in the rather flat top of the coverage-potential curve. These requirements preclude application of the foregoing method to many electrode processes. It would seem therefore that the study of adsorption of rather fast processes by relaxation or perturbation methods, with small excursion of potential, offers the simplest conditions for interpretation of double-layer effects with uncharged adsorbate. A few of these studies in which the coverage effect was primarily considered have been made. Aramata and Delahay (18) considered both coverage and variations of ϕ_2. Their work was continued by Torsi (128) in the writer's laboratory. This seems to be the first attempt at a quantitative interpretation aside from the work of the Prague group described in Sec. 9-10c. The latter involves mass-transfer considerations.

Aramata and Delahay (18) studied the effect of *n*-amyl alcohol adsorption on the discharge of zinc ion on zinc-amalgam with magnesium perchlorate as supporting electrolyte. Kinetic parameters were determined by a galvanostatic method with overvoltages not exceeding a few millivolts. It was first ascertained that the Frumkin double-layer correction holds in the absence of organic adsorbate (cf. Sec. 9-2 and Table 9-1). The validity of the Frumkin correction for a fixed concentration of adsorbate and a varying magnesium perchlorate concentration was then verified, the potential ϕ_2 being calculated by the method of Sec. 5-7. The apparent exchange current varied as expected from Eq. 5, the value of α ($= 0.30$) being the same as without adsorbate. Apparent exchange currents measured at constant magnesium perchlorate concentration for a varying alcohol concentration were corrected for the variation of ϕ_2, and the coverage effect was investigated. The apparent exchange current corrected for ϕ_2 (Fig. 9-24) seems to vary quite linearly with coverage at low coverages for n-amyl alcohol. This implies that the rate on the covered surface is quite negligible. The apparent exchange current at high coverages is much smaller than expected after correcting the effects of ϕ_2 and coverage. Aramata and Delahay pointed out that the calculation of ϕ_2 is quite tentative and that the definition of coverage near saturation involves experimental uncertainties as well as the difficulty arising from the change of the area per molecule with coverage (cf. Sec. 5-4). The structure of the double layer is completely altered near saturation and penetration of the discharged species may become determinative [cf. Frumkin (6) and Gierst (8)]. Further work toward quantitative evaluation of the coverage- and ϕ_2-effects seems highly desirable.

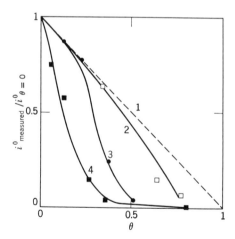

FIG. 9-24. Influence of coverage on the apparent exchange current for the discharge of $2 \times 10^{-3} M$ zinc ion in $0.125 M$ magnesium perchlorate on $0.046 M$ zinc-amalgam at $25°C$. The ratio $i^0_{\text{measured}}/i^0_{\theta=0}$ was computed for the potential ϕ_2 that prevailed for i^0_{measured}; $i^0_{\theta=0}$ was corrected accordingly. Linear ideal correction (line 1); n-amyl alcohol (curve 2); thymol (3); cyclohexanol (4) [Aramata and Delahay (18), Torsi (128)] (by permission of the American Chemical Society).

c. Influence of Mass Transfer

Detailed understanding of adsorption with mass-transfer control at the dropping mercury electrode is desirable because coverage during drop life must be known for the investigation of electrode kinetics with adsorbate. The coverage can be determined *approximately* by application of Eq. 5-14 (in the range of potentials in which the term $d\theta/dE$ can be neglected) from the variations of the differential capacity during drop life in the absence of the reacting species. Adsorption of the organic adsorbate should not be much affected by the addition of the reacting species, which therefore must not be specifically adsorbed to any significant extent. Only approximate coverages are obtained by this method because Eq. 5-14 is not rigorous. Correlation of the capacity data, measured in this fashion, with electro-capillary curves is not possible because the bulk concentration of adsorbate at the electrode is not known during drop life.

The problem can be attacked from the opposite point of view by calculation of the coverage as was done by the Prague polarographic group (129–133). Their results were recently summarized by Kůta and Weber (134). Theoretical analysis was progressively developed with increasing degree of agreement with experimental results. Values of ϕ_2 which give good agreement between experimental and theoretical current-time curves have not yet been calculated independently, and correlation of this work with that of Sec. 9-10b might be of interest.

9-11   Double-Layer Effects with Solid Electrodes in the Absence of Chemisorbed Film

Double-layer effects with solid electrodes in aqueous solution are generally complicated by formation of chemisorbed films of hydrogen or oxygen (cf. Chapter 10), but there are a few metals, such as cadmium, lead, thallium, and zinc, which are essentially free of adsorbed atomic hydrogen, even in the range of hydrogen evolution. Chemisorbed oxygen is not present either because potentials at which electrode kinetics can be studied with these metals are too cathodic. The behavior of these metals toward double-layer effects would be expected to be similar to that of mercury, as it is indeed the case, except for the interesting complication brought about in some cases by sluggishness of ion specific adsorption. Specific adsorption effects have been mostly studied for hydrogen evolution (6).

Effects of specific ionic adsorption on hydrogen ion discharge similar to those for mercury are observed with some of these metals. For instance, anion specific adsorption lowers the overvoltage on zinc, and cation

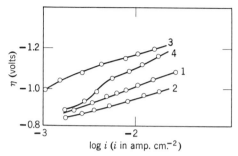

FIG. 9-25. Tafel plots for hydrogen evolution on monocrystalline zinc in $0.5M$ hydrochloric acid with the following additions: $0.5M$ potassium chloride (curve 1); $0.5M$ potassium iodide (2); $0.5M$ potassium chloride and $4 \times 10^{-4}M$ tetrabutylammonium ion (3); $0.5M$ potassium iodide and $4 \times 10^{-4}M$ tetrabutylammonium ion [Tsa-Chuang-Hshin and Iofa (135)] (by permission of Consultants Bureau Enterprises).

specific adsorption increases the overvoltage on this metal (Fig. 9-25; cf. with Fig. 6-5 for the influence of specific adsorption on differential capacity].

Pronounced hysteresis resulting from adsorption sluggishness is observed for some metals, for example, lead. The behavior of this metal and that of cadmium and thallium, which have somewhat similar features, was studied extensively by Kolotyrkin and co-workers (136–141) [cf. Frumkin (6) for review]. Two Tafel lines are observed depending on the conditions of measurement. "Rapid" (a few minutes) measurements with *decreasing* current yield the Tafel line AB of Fig. 9-26 at high current densitites. The

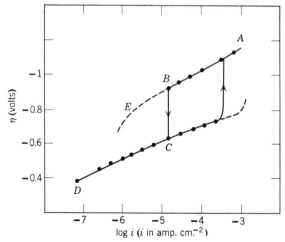

FIG. 9-26. Tafel plot for hydrogen evolution on lead in $0.5M$ sulfuric acid [Kolotyrkin (140)] (by permission of Butterworths).

overvoltage is not stable along this Tafel line at the lower currents and drifts toward the Tafel line DC. The latter can also be observed with *increasing* current up to a certain current at which the overvoltage drifts toward the higher overvoltage values along line AB. These observations can be explained qualitatively if we assume that sulfate adsorption and desorption are very slow. The line DC is in the range of positive potentials with respect to the point of zero charge. Hence specific adsorption of sulfate renders the potential ϕ_2 less positive and lowers the overvoltage. Sulfate is desorbed in the range of potentials corresponding to line AB, and the overvoltage increases accordingly. Sluggish ionic adsorption is commonly observed with solid electrodes, but it has not yet received a satisfactory explanation.

REFERENCES

1. A. N. Frumkin, *Z. physik. Chem.*, **164A**, 121 (1933).
2. P. Herasymenko and I. Šlendyk, *ibid.*, **149A**, 123 (1930).
3. T. A. Krjukova, *Doklady Akad. Nauk S.S.S.R.*, **65**, 517 (1949).
4. A. N. Frumkin, *Z. Elektrochem.*, **59**, 807 (1955).
5. A. N. Frumkin, *J. Electrochem. Soc.*, **107**, 461 (1960).
6. A. N. Frumkin *Advances in Electrochemistry and Electrochemical Engineering*, P. Delahay, editor, Interscience, New York, Vol. 1, 1961, pp. 65–122; Vol. 3, 1963, pp. 287–391.
7. R. Parsons, Ref. 6, Vol. 1, 1961, pp. 1–64.
8. L. Gierst, "Cinétique d'approche et réactions d'électrodes irréversibles," thèse d'agrégation, University of Bruxelles, 1958.
9. L. Gierst, *Transactions of the Symposium on Electrode Processes*, E. Yeager, editor, Wiley, New York, 1961, pp. 109–138.
10. M. Breiter, M. Kleinerman, and P. Delahay, *J. Am. Chem. Soc.*, **80**, 5111 (1958).
11. W. H. Reinmuth, L. B. Rogers, and L. E. I. Hummelstedt, *ibid.*, **81**, 2947 (1959).
12. K. M. Joshi, W. Mehl, and R. Parsons, Ref. 9, 249–263.
13. K. Asada, P. Delahay, and A. K. Sundaram, *J. Am. Chem. Soc.*, **83**, 3396 (1961).
14. O. A. Petrii and A. N. Frumkin, *Doklady Akad. Nauk S.S.S.R.*, **146**, 1121 (1962).
15. A. N. Frumkin, O. A. Petrii, and N. V. Nikolaeva-Fedorovich, *Electrochim. Acta*, **8**, 177 (1963).
16. J. J. Tondeur, A. Dombret, and L. Gierst, *J. Electroanal. Chem.*, **3**, 225 (1962).
17. A. N. Frumkin and O. A. Petrii, *Doklady Akad. Nauk S.S.S.R.*, **147**, 418 (1962).
18. A. Aramata and P. Delahay, *J. Phys. Chem.*, **68**, 880 (1964).
19. D. C. Grahame and B. Soderberg, *J. Chem. Phys.*, **22**, 449 (1954).
20. P. Delahay, *Progress in Polarography*, P. Zuman, editor, Interscience, New York, Vol. 1, 1962, pp. 65–80.
21. S. G. Mairanovskii, *J. Electroanal. Chem.*, **4**, 166 (1962).
22. L. Gierst and H. Hurwitz, *Z. Elektrochem.*, **64**, 36 (1960).
23. H. Matsuda, *J. Phys. Chem.*, **64**, 336 (1960).
24. H. Hurwitz, *Z. Elektrochem.*, **65**, 178 (1961).
25. V. G. Levich, *Doklady Akad. Nauk S.S.S.R.*, **67**, 309 (1949).
26. V. G. Levich, *ibid.*, **124**, 869 (1959).
27. M. J. Sparnaay, *Trans. Faraday Soc.*, **53**, 306 (1957).

28. M. J. Sparnaay, *Rec. trav. chim.*, **77**, 872 (1958).
29. H. Matsuda and P. Delahay, *J. Phys. Chem.*, **64**, 332 (1960).
30. H. Matsuda, *ibid.*, **64**, 339 (1960).
31. H. Matsuda and P. Delahay, Ref. 9, pp. 140–142.
32. M. Senda and P. Delahay, *J. Phys. Chem.*, **65**, 1580 (1961).
33. O. Dračka, *Collection Czechoslov. Chem. Commun.*, **26**, 1999 (1961).
34. S. K. Rangarajan, *J. Electroanal. Chem.*, **5**, 350 (1963).
35. A. N. Frumkin, *Acta Physicochim. U.R.S.S.*, **7**, 475 (1937).
36. S. Levina and M. Silberfarb, *ibid.*, **4**, 275 (1936).
37. S. Levina and V. Zarinskii, *ibid.*, **6**, 491 (1937).
38. V. S. Bagotskii, *Doklady Akad. Nauk S.S.S.R.*, **58**, 1387 (1947).
39. A. de Béthune, *J. Am. Chem. Soc.*, **71**, 1556 (1949).
40. J. O'M. Bockris and R. Parsons, *Trans. Faraday Soc.*, **45**, 916 (1949).
41. A. N. Frumkin, *Disc. Faraday Soc.*, **1**, 57 (1947).
42. A. N. Frumkin, *Zhur. Fiz. Khim.*, **24**, 244 (1950).
43. V. S. Bagotskii, *ibid.*, **22**, 1466 (1948).
44. V. S. Bagotskii and I. Yablokova, *ibid.*, **23**, 413 (1949).
45. S. Levina and V. Zarinskii, *Acta Physicochim. U.R.S.S.*, **7**, 485 (1937).
46. E. A. Maznichenko, B. B. Damaskin, and Z. A. Iofa, *Doklady Akad. Nauk S.S.S.R.*, **138**, 1377 (1961).
47. Z. A. Iofa, B. N. Kabanov, E. Kuchinsky, and F. Chistyakov, *Zhur. Phys. Khim.*, **13**, 1105 (1939).
48. Tsa Chuang-Hsin and Z. A. Iofa, *Doklady Akad. Nauk S.S.S.R.*, **126**, 1308 (1959).
49. R. Parsons, Ref. 9, pp. 14–15.
50. A. N. Frumkin, Ref. 9, p. 15.
51. N. Tanaka and R. Tamamushi, *Electrochim. Acta*, **9**, 963 (1964).
52. J. Koryta, *ibid.*, **6**, 67 (1962).
53. V. V. Losev and A. I. Molodov, *Doklady Akad. Nauk S.S.S.R.*, **130**, 111 (1960).
54. V. V. Losev and A. I. Molodov, *Zhur. Fiz. Khim.*, **35**, 11 (1961).
55. N. S. Hush and J. Blackledge, *J. Electroanal. Chem.*, **5**, 420 (1963).
56. J. Blackledge and N. S. Hush, *ibid.*, **5**, 435 (1963).
57. Kh. Z. Brainina, *Doklady Akad. Nauk S.S.S.R.*, **130**, 797 (1960).
58. A. G. Stromberg and Kh. Z. Brainina, *Zhur. Fiz. Khim.*, **35**, 2016 (1961).
59. L. Gierst and R. Cornelissen, *Coll. Czechoslov. Chem. Commun.*, **25**, 3004 (1960).
60. J. Dandoy and L. Gierst, *J. Electroanal. Chem.*, **2**, 116 (1960).
61. V. F. Ivanov and Z. A. Iofa, *Doklady Akad. Nauk S.S.S.R.*, **137**, 1149 (1961).
62. V. F. Ivanov and Z. A. Iofa, *Zhur. Fiz. Khim.*, **36**, 1080 (1962).
63. A. N. Frumkin and G. M. Florianovich, *Doklady Akad. Nauk S.S.S.R.*, **80**, 907 (1951).
64. N. V. Nikolaeva, N. S. Shapiro, and A. N. Frumkin, *ibid.*, **86**, 581 (1952).
65. T. V. Kalish and A. N. Frumkin, *Zhur. Fiz. Khim.*, **28**, 473 (1954).
66. T. V. Kalish and A. N. Frumkin, *ibid.*, **28**, 801 (1954).
67. N. V. Nikolaeva and A. A. Grosman, *Doklady Akad. Nauk S.S.S.R.*, **95**, 1013 (1954).
68. G. M. Florianovich and A. N. Frumkin, *Zhur. Fiz. Khim.*, **29**, 1827 (1955).
69. P. Kivalo and H. A. Laitinen, *J. Am. Chem. Soc.*, **77**, 5205 (1955).
70. A. N. Frumkin and N. V. Nikolaeva-Fedorovich, *J. Chem. Phys.*, **26**, 1552 (1957).
71. P. Kivalo, *J. Phys. Chem.*, **61**, 1126 (1957).
72. A. N. Frumkin and N. V. Nikolaeva-Fedorovich, *Vestnik Moskovskoga Universiteta Ser. Mat., Mekh. Astron., Fiz. i Khim.*, No. 4, 169 (1957); *Chem. Abstr.*, **52**, 11631 (1958).

73. A. N. Frumkin, *Nova Acta Leopoldina*, *N.F.*, **19**, 3 (1957).
74. A. N. Frumkin, *Surface Phenomena in Chemistry and Biology*, J. F. Danieli, K. G. A. Pankhurst, and A. C. Riddiford, editors, Pergamon, London, 1958, pp. 189–194.
75. N. V. Nikolaeva-Fedorovich and L. A. Fokina, *Doklady Akad. Nauk S.S.S.R.*, **118**, 987 (1958).
76. N. V. Nikolaeva-Fedorovich, L. A. Fokina, and O. A. Petrii, *ibid.*, **122**, 639 (1958).
77. A. N. Frumkin, O. A. Petrii, and N. V. Nikolaeva-Fedorovich, *ibid.*, **128**, 1006 (1959).
78. A. N. Frumkin, N. V. Nikolaeva-Fedorovich, and R. Ivanova, *Can. J. Chem.*, **37**, 253 (1959).
79. A. N. Frumkin, *Trans. Faraday Soc.*, **55**, 156 (1959).
80. O. A. Petrii and N. V. Nikolaeva-Fedorovich, *Zhur. Fiz. Khim.*, **35**, 1999 (1961).
81. S. Sat'yanarayan and N. V. Nikolaeva-Fedorovich, *Doklady Akad. Nauk S.S.S.R.*, **141**, 1139 (1961).
82. A. N. Frumkin, Ref. 9, pp. 1–12.
83. A. J. Gokhstein, paper presented at the Moscow C.I.T.C.E. meeting, 1963.
84. J. H. Green and A. Walkley, *Australian J. Chem.*, **8**, 51 (1955).
85. P. Delahay and A. Aramata, *J. Phys. Chem.*, **66**, 1194 (1962).
86. A. Aramata and P. Delahay, *ibid.*, **66**, 2710 (1962).
87. W. H. Reinmuth, Ref. 9, pp. 142–143.
88. R. A. Robinson and R. H. Stokes, *Electrolytic Solutions*, 2nd ed., Academic Press, New York, 1959, pp. 421–423.
89. L. Gierst, private communication.
90. P. Delahay, Ref. 9, pp. 138–140.
91. P. Delahay and M. Kleinerman, *J. Am. Chem. Soc.*, **82**, 4509 (1960).
92. V. I. Zykov and S. I. Zhdanov, *Zhur. Fiz. Khim.*, **32**, 644, 791 (1958).
93. V. I. Zykov, *ibid.*, **33**, 2156 (1959).
94. V. I. Zykov, *Doklady Akad. Nauk S.S.S.R.*, **129**, 376 (1959).
95. P. Delahay, Ref. 9, p. 12.
96. A. E. Alekperov and S. I. Zhadnov, *Zhur. Neorg.*, *Khim.*, **5**, 1743 (1960).
97. L. Gierst, Doctoral Dissertation, University of Brussels, 1952.
98. H. Gerischer, *Z. physik. Chem.* (*Frankfurt*), **2**, 79 (1954).
99. S. Siekierskii, *Roczniki Chem.*, **28**, 90 (1954).
100. S. Siekierskii, *ibid.*, **30**, 1083 (1956).
101. J. Koryta, *Z. Elektrochem.*, **61**, 423 (1957).
102. H. Gerischer, *ibid.*, **64**, 29 (1960).
103. M. Pérez-Férnandez and H. Gerischer, *ibid.*, **64**, 477 (1960).
104. V. S. Bagotskii and I. E. Yablokova, *Zhur. Fiz. Khim.*, **27**, 1663 (1953).
104a. J. Kůta and J. Koryta, paper presented at the Third International Congress of Polarography, Southampton, July, 1964.
105. I. M. Kolthoff and J. Jordan, *J. Am. Chem. Soc.*, **74**, 570 (1952).
106. R. Cornelissen and L. Gierst, *J. Electroanal. Chem.*, **3**, 219 (1962).
107. I. M. Kolthoff and K. Izutsu, *ibid.*, **7**, 85 (1964).
108. A. Martirosyan and A. Kryukova, *Zhur. Fiz. Khim.*, **27**, 851 (1953).
109. E. P. Andreeva, *ibid.*, **28**, 699 (1955).
110. A. A. Kryukova and M. A. Loshkarev, *ibid.*, **30**, 2236 (1956); **31**, 452 (1957).
110a. A. N. Frumkin, B. B. Damaskin, and N. Nikolaeva-Fedorovich, *Doklady Akad. Nauk S.S.S.R.*, **115**, 751 (1957).

111. Z. A. Iofa, A. N. Frumkin, and E. A. Maznichenko, *Zhur. Fiz. Khim.*, **31**, 2042 (1957).
112. Tsa Chuang-Hsin and Z. A. Iofa, *Doklady Akad. Nauk S.S.S.R.*, **125**, 1065 (1959).
113. A. N. Frumkin and B. B. Damaskin, *ibid.*, **129**, 862 (1959).
114. N. V. Nikolaeva-Fedorovich, B. B. Damaskin, and O. A. Petrii, *Coll. Czechoslov. Chem. Commun.*, **25**, 2982 (1960).
115. A. N. Frumkin. O. A. Petrii, and N. V. Nikolaeva-Fedorovich, *Doklady Akad. Nauk S.S.S.R.*, **136**, 1158 (1961).
116. P. Petrii and N. V. Nikolaeva-Fedorovich, *ibid.*, **141**, 1139 (1961).
117. V. I. Zykov, *Zhur. Fiz. Khim.*, **35**, 355 (1961).
118. B. B. Damaskin and N. V. Nikolaeva-Fedorovich, *ibid.*, **35**, 1279 (1961).
119. S. Sat'yanarajan and N. V. Nikolaeva-Fedorovich, *ibid.*, **35**, 1999 (1961).
120. M. A. V. Devanathan and M. J. Fernando, *Trans. Faraday Soc.*, **58**, 368 (1962).
121. L. Gierst, J. Tondeur, R. Cornelissen, and F. Lamy, paper presented at the Moscow C.I.T.C.E. meeting, 1963.
122. B. B. Damaskin, N. V. Nikolaeva-Fedorovich, and R. V. Ivanova, *Zhur. Fiz. Khim.*, **34**, 894 (1960).
123. C. N. Reilley and W. Stumm, *Progress in Polarography*, P. Zuman, editor, Interscience, New York, Vol. 1, 1962, pp. 81–121.
124. H. W. Nurnberg and M. von Stackelberg, *J. Electroanal. Chem.*, **4**, 1 (1962).
124a. A. N. Frumkin, *Doklady Akad. Nauk S.S.S.R.*, **85**, 373 (1952).
125. P. Delahay and I. Trachtenberg, *J. Am. Chem. Soc.*, **80**, 2094 (1958).
126. W. Lorenz and W. Müller, *Z. physik. Chem. (Frankfurt)*, **18**, 141 (1958).
127. W. Müller and W. Lorenz, *ibid.*, **27**, 23 (1961).
128. G. Torsi, unpublished work.
129. J. Weber, J. Koutecký, and J. Koryta, *Z. Elektrochem.*, **63**, 583 (1959).
130. J. Koutecký and J. Weber, *Coll. Czechoslov. Chem. Commun.*, **25**, 1423 (1960).
131. J. Kůta and I. Smoler, *Z. Elektrochem.*, **64**, 285 (1960).
132. J. Kůta, J. Weber, and J. Koutecký, *Coll. Czechoslov. Chem. Commun.*, **25**, 2376 (1960).
133. J. Kůta and I. Smoler, *ibid.*, **27**, 2349 (1962).
134. J. Kůta and J. Weber, *Electrochim. Acta.* **9**, 541 (1964).
135. Tsa-Chuang-Hsin and Z. A. Iofa, *Doklady Akad. Nauk S.S.S.R.*, **131**, 137 (1960).
136. J. M. Kolotyrkin and N. Ya. Bune, *Zhur. Fiz. Khim.*, **21**, 581 (1947); **29**, 435 (1955).
137. J. M. Kolotyrkin and L. A. Medvedeva, *ibid.*, **25**, 1355 (1951); **27**, 1344 (1953); **29**, 1477 (1955).
138. N. Ya. Bune and J. M. Kolotyrkin, *Doklady Akad. Nauk S.S.S.R.*, **100**, 295 (1955).
139. L. A. Medvedeva and J. Kolotyrkin, *Zhur. Fiz. Khim.*, **31**, 2668 (1957).
140. J. M. Kolotyrkin, *Proceedings of the International Committee on Electrochemical Thermodynamics and Kinetics, 9th Meeting*, Butterworths, London, 1959, pp. 406–419.
141. J. M. Kolotyrkin, *Trans. Faraday Soc.*, **55**, 455 (1959).

CHAPTER 10

Kinetics of Electrode Processes with Chemisorption of Reactants and/or Products

10-1 Classification of Electrode Processes with Adsorption

Electrode adsorption processes, just as metal-gas adsorption processes, can be divided into two groups according to the type of adsorption: physical adsorption and chemisorption. Physical adsorption does not involve the bonding on the electrode prevailing in chemisorption and requires the introduction of an electrical variable (potential or charge on the electrode) in description by an isotherm. Conversely, bonding of a chemisorbed species with the electrode may in limiting cases be so strong that an electrical variable often need not be introduced in the isotherm parameters. The intermediate situation of chemisorption with some influence of the electrical variable on the isotherm parameters may also prevail.

The distinction between the two types of adsorption carries over to analysis of current-overvoltage characteristics. One might think that processes with chemisorption would be easier to analyze than processes with physical adsorption because no electrical variable need be included in the isotherm for chemisorption. This simplification, however, is offset in practice because chemisorption is generally observed with solid electrodes with all the attendant difficulties resulting from rather poorly known surface properties. Furthermore, processes with chemisorption, for example, hydrogen and oxygen evolution, are often complex reactions. It is significant in this respect that full agreement is not yet reached on the mechanisms of hydrogen ion discharge on various metals after more than

240

half a century of intensive work. Further complication arises from specific ionic adsorption and, possibly, by unexpected participation of ions in electrode reactions [cf., for example, oxygen evolution in concentrated perchloric or sulfuric acid (Sec. 10-5a)].

Physical adsorption of reacting species is very common in organic electrode processes. Such processes have been studied extensively, in particular by the polarographic method, but many of these studies do not go beyond the determination of current-potential curves and more or less justified speculation about reaction mechanisms. Much valuable information (for example, correlation with structure, etc.) has been gathered in this way, but there is a need for a more fundamental approach. Derivation of current-potential characteristics is complicated by frequent simultaneous adsorption of reactant and product and by the frequent possibility of multiple reaction paths. The difficulty can be appreciated if it is recalled that physical adsorption on an ideal polarized electrode is still a topic of controversy (Chapter 5). Study with the mercury electrode offers the best chances for definitive results, but solid electrodes have the more immediate reward of practical application, for example, in fuel cells. Analysis of the anodic oxidation of organic substances on solid electrodes is still very tentative despite present vigorous efforts.

Processes with mixed adsorption must also be considered: chemisorption of one or several reacting species and physical adsorption of an additive or the opposite situation; and two chemisorption processes of which only one involves the reacting species.

We can distinguish the following three major types of electrode processes on the basis of the preceding discussion:

A. Processes without adsorption of reacting species.
B. Processes with chemisorption of reacting species.
C. Processes with potential dependent adsorption of reacting species.

For each of these types we consider the following cases:

1. No specific adsorption of supporting electrolyte.
2. Specific adsorption of supporting electrolyte or an additive.
   (*a*) Ionic specific adsorption.
   (*b*) Physical adsorption of an uncharged substance.
3. Chemisorption of a species not participating directly in the electrode process.

This classification corresponds somewhat to idealized conditions, but it has the merit of bringing some order to the variety of conditions under which electrode processes occur. We have already discussed type A-1 (Chapter 7), A-2*a* (Sec. 9-3), and A-2*b* (Sec. 9-10), and we shall examine types B-1, B-2, and B-3 in this chapter. Processes of type C will be discussed in Chapter 11.

10-2　Metal-Gas Chemisorption

a. Physical Adsorption versus Chemisorption

The subject will be introduced by some brief considerations on metal chemisorption (cf., for example, Refs. 1a and 1b) which are transposed to electrode chemisorption in Sec. 10-3. The difference between chemisorption and physical adsorption can be interpreted, according to Lennard-Jones (1932), from the potential energy diagram of Fig. 10-1 for the adsorption of a diatomic molecule A_2 on metal M_2. (Compare with Fig. 7-10.) The system can be described by the two curves for $M_2 + A_2$ (curve P) and $M_2 + 2A$ (curve C). Physical adsorption is caused by long range forces and does not involve dissociation of A_2. It is characterized by a heat of

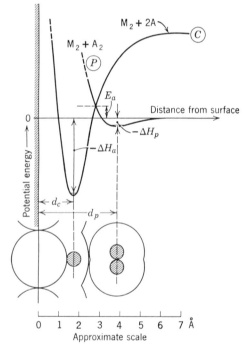

FIG. 10-1. Potential energy against distance from the surface (top) for physical adsorption and chemisorption of A_2 on metal M. Schematic representation of process (bottom). $-\Delta H_p$, heat of physical adsorption; $-\Delta H_a$, heat of chemisorption [Bond (1b)] (by permission of Academic Press).

adsorption $-\Delta H_p$ which is of the same order of magnitude as the heat of liquefaction of the gas A_2. Chemisorption involves short range forces and dissociation of A_2 over the energy barrier E_a whose height depends on the respective positions and slopes of the C- and P-curves. E_a, however, cannot exceed the dissociation energy of A_2. It follows from these simple considerations that physical adsorption at a gas-metal interface is extremely rapid, whereas chemisorption may be slow or rapid according to the magnitude of E_a.

The clear distinction between the two types of adsorption made on the basis of Fig. 10-1 is blurred in so-called weak and strong adsorption of some diatomic gases, for example, hydrogen. Weak adsorption prevails only at low temperature whereas strong adsorption is observed at much higher temperatures. Interpretation is debated but according to current views, summarized by Bond (1b), the distinction between strong and weak adsorption is now well established. It has been suggested that strong adsorption of hydrogen occurs only on permitted sites, whereas weak adsorption involves forbidden sites. Strongly adsorbed hydrogen atoms are presumably located on sites between the surface atoms. There is more than one such site per surface atom; for example, there are six sites per atom in an hexagonal array, of which only one-half are available for strong adsorption. The difference may be represented by the following diagrams where "*" represents a permitted site and "(*)" a forbidden one.

Strong adsorption

$$\begin{array}{cccccccc} \text{H—H} & & \text{H---H} & & \text{H} & & \text{H} \\ \rightarrow\!| & | & \rightarrow\!| & & | & & | \\ * & (*) & * & * & (*) & * & * & (*) & * \end{array}$$

Weak adsorption

$$\begin{array}{cccccc} \text{H—H} & \text{H} & \text{H---H} & \text{H} \\ | \rightarrow\!| & | & | \\ * & (*) & * & * & (*) & * \end{array}$$

Details cannot be given here, but the matter may deserve further study by the reader, for there is good evidence (Sec. 10-3) of weak and strong adsorption of hydrogen on several metal electrodes (for example, platinum).

b. Isotherms

The Langmuir and Temkin isotherms will be retained here among the various isotherms used in the description of metal-gas adsorption as they are most frequently applied to electrode chemisorption. Discussion of these isotherms has become classical (cf., for example, Refs. 1a and 1b), and the following treatment is limited to the writing of the isotherm equations [with Parsons' notation (82)] and the statement of the conditions for which these equations apply.

The Langmuir isotherm for chemisorption of a diatomic gas A_2 with dissociation into $2A$ is

$$\left(\frac{\theta_e}{1 - \theta_e}\right)^2 = p_{A_2} e^{-\Delta G^0/RT} \tag{1}$$

where θ_e is the coverage by atomic A, p_{A_2} the pressure of A_2, and ΔG^0 the standard free energy of adsorption. The subscript "e" is used, for the nonequilibrium coverage θ will be introduced in electrode kinetics (Sec. 10-4). Standard states correspond, for instance, to $p_{A_2} = 1$ atmosphere and $\theta_e = 0.5$. This isotherm presupposes immobile chemisorption of only one particle on each identical site without interaction between particles.

The logarithmic Temkin isotherm for the diatomic gas A_2 is

$$\theta_e = \frac{1}{s} \ln p_{A_2} - \frac{\Delta G^0}{sRT} + 0.5 \tag{2}$$

where s is a constant depending on the postulated linear variation of the heat of adsorption on coverage. We have for a constant entropy of adsorption

$$s = \frac{1}{RT} \frac{\partial \Delta G}{\partial \theta_e} = \frac{\partial \ln p_{A_2}}{\partial \theta_e} \tag{3}$$

Equation 2 is written for the standard state corresponding to $\theta_e = 0.5$, the choice of this value of θ_e being dictated by the validity of the isotherm at intermediate coverages (θ_e approximately from 0.2 to 0.8). At least three causes can be given for the decrease of the heat of adsorption with coverage: heterogeneity of the surface, particle-particle interaction, and variation of the metal work function with coverage. Details are given by Bond (1b), and it will suffice to note here that particle-particle interaction is probably the least important.

c. Heat of Adsorption

The *isosteric* heat of adsorption ΔH_i is defined at fixed coverage by

$$\left(\frac{d \ln p}{dT}\right)_{\theta_e} = -\frac{\Delta H_i}{RT^2} \tag{4}$$

Since ΔH_i varies with coverage it is convenient to quote its value at zero coverage (*initial heat of adsorption* ΔH_a). ΔH_i can be determined by several experimental methods (cf., for example, Refs. 1a and 1b) and can also be calculated from models for the chemisorption bond. The method of calculation will be briefly commented on because it is relevant to the kinetics of the hydrogen electrode (Sec. 10-4).

The initial heat of adsorption is computed, according to Eley (2a), from the metal-hydrogen bond energy (D_{MH}) and the hydrogen dissociation energy (D_{HH} = 103.2 kcal. mole^{-1}). Thus

$$-\Delta H_a = 2D_{MH} - D_{HH} \tag{5}$$

The covalent bond energy D_{MH} is calculated from the Pauling equation (2b)

$$D_{MH} = \tfrac{1}{2}(D_{MM} + D_{HH}) + 23.06(x_M - x_H)^2 \tag{6}$$

where the metal-metal bond energy D_{MM} can be equated, as a first approximation, to one-sixth of the heat of sublimation of the metal. The x's are the electronegativities of the metal and atomic hydrogen. Estimates of the last term in Eq. 6 vary somewhat according to the method [Bond (1b)]. Agreement with experimental initial heats (Table 10-1) is good for three metals (Fe, Ni, W), fair for a number of other metals (Co, Cu, Mo, Pd, Pt, Ta), and poor for some metals (Cr, Rh, Ru, Ir).

TABLE 10-1   Calculated and Experimental Values of ΔH_a and D_{MH} for Hydrogen Adsorption[a]

Metal	$-\Delta H_a$, kcal. mole^{-1}		D_{MH}, kcal. mole^{-1}	
	Experimental	Calculated	Experimental	Calculated
Cr	45	24	74.1	63.6
Fe	32 to 36	31.6	67.6 to 69.6	67.4
Co[b]	24	31.0	63.6	67.1
Ni	29 to 32	28.9	66.1 to 67.6	66.0
Cu[b]	28	25.6	65.6	64.4
Mo	40	42.9	71.6	73.0
Ru[b]	26	38.1	64.6	70.6
Rh	26	32.3	64.6	67.7
Pd	27	22.5	65.1	62.9
Ta	45	49.6	74.1	76.4
W	45 to 52	45.6	74.1 to 77.6	74.4
Ir[b]	26	38.1	64.6	70.6
Pt[b]	28	22.6	65.6	62.9

[a] From Bond (1b) who gives these calculated values from Stevenson (2c) as well as those from alternate methods.

[b] Experimental values determined with silica-supported metals; all other experimental values are for evaporated metal films.

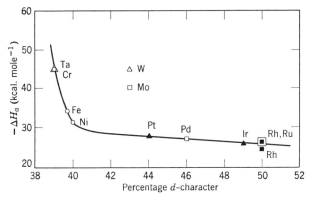

FIG. 10-2. Variation of the initial heat of adsorption of hydrogen as a function of percentage d-character of various metals. Open symbols, evaporated metal films; solid symbols, silica-supported metals [Bond (1b)] (by permission of Academic Press).

Attempts have been made to correlate heats of adsorption with parameters characterizing the nature of the metal, and a number of qualitative correlations have been established as plots of ΔH_a against parameters such as the periodic group number or the percentage of d-character of the transition metals [cf., for example, Bond (1b)]. Correlation with the latter parameter is fairly satisfactory with the exception of Group VIa elements (Figs. 10-2 and 10-3) and is useful in the interpretation of hydrogen overvoltage (Sec. 10-4).

10-3   Electrode Chemisorption

a. Hydrogen

Electrode chemisorption involves, in comparison with metal-gas chemisorption, the added complications caused by the presence of the

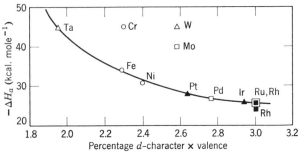

FIG. 10-3. Same plot as in Fig. 10-2 but against the product of percentage of d-character by valence [Bond (1b)] (by permission of Academic Press).

solvent and ionic specification adsorption. Ideas can be transposed from one field to the other, but techniques are generally quite different. Present knowledge of electrode chemisorption is relatively meager, as compared to chemisorption in general, and concerns mostly hydrogen and oxygen chemisorption on electrodes of the platinum group. [See Frumkin (3) and Breiter (4) for reviews on hydrogen.] Hydrogen absorption, for example, in palladium will not be discussed, for this topic is not essential to subsequent material. The subject, however, is of considerable importance both for the investigation of hydrogen overvoltage phenomena and it is possibly of practical application to hydrogen diffusion electrodes in fuel cells. Frumkin's detailed review (3) may be consulted. Methods for the determination of the amount of adsorbed hydrogen will be reviewed first.

Hydrogen chemisorption on electrodes of the platinum group metals has been studied by various techniques (3, 4): charging curves (5–25), impedance measurements (19, 26–31), and recording of current-potential curves with potentiostatic control of cyclic triangular potential-time variations (33–38). Pulse techniques and other methods applicable to metals other than those of the platinum group (39–41) and hydrogen permeation methods (3; also, for example, Ref. 42) also find application for the platinum-group metals. The charging curve and electrode impedance methods were developed by the Frumkin school, and the potentiostatic method was brought to a high state of development by Will and Knorr (32). [See Vielstich (38) for a review of the latter method.] Results from these three methods essentially agree.

Charging curves are recorded at constant current, and the amount of chemisorbed hydrogen is computed from the quantity of electricity consumed in the anodic oxidation of adsorbed hydrogen, due allowance being made for double-layer charging. Three regions can be distinguished that correspond to the regions mentioned in the discussion of Fig. 6-7 (Fig. 10-4). The amount of adsorbed hydrogen in electrode impedance measurements is determined by integration of the capacitive component of the electrode impedance after correction for the double-layer capacity (Fig. 10-5).

The amount of adsorbed hydrogen is deduced from current-potential curves, recorded at constant potential scanning rate, by integration of the current-time variations after correction for double-layer charging. The initial potential is adjusted to approximately 0.05 volt with respect to the equilibrium potential to minimize hydrogen evolution, and the scanning rate is between 0.01 and 10 volts per second. Anodic oxidation of hydrogen and oxygen adsorption occur in two well-distinguished ranges of potentials (Fig. 10-6) during the anodic sweep of potential at these rates of potential scanning. Overlapping during cathodic sweeps is observed in certain

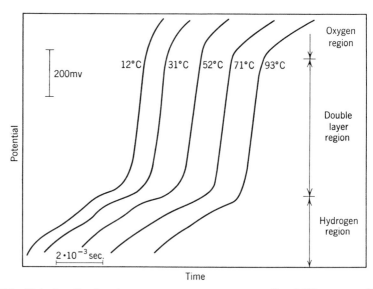

FIG. 10-4. Anodic charging curves at constant current ($i = 0.125$ amp. cm.$^{-2}$) for platinum in 20% sulfuric acid at different temperatures. The initial point of each curve corresponds to $\eta = 0$ [Breiter (31)] (by permission of John Wiley).

instances because of displacement of the reduction peak for adsorbed oxygen toward more cathodic potentials with respect to the peak for oxygen adsorption. Results for cathodic sweeps are not utilized for this reason. A stable current-potential pattern is observed with cyclic potential variation, and adsorbed impurities seem to be removed rapidly from the electrode because of the rather high anodic potentials that are reached. These impurities diffuse into the bulk of the solution, and are not markedly readsorbed because of their low bulk concentrations (Sec. 5-8). This simple way of minimizing the impurity problem and other features of the method accounts for its extensive current application. Results obtained by this method ought perhaps to be examined more cautiously than has generally been done since rapid scanning over a wide range of potentials may result in very complex phenomena when kinetics comes into play.

The "hydrogen region" is often characterized by two distinct peaks, although sometimes only one peak (Fig. 10-6, rhodium) or more than two peaks are observed. The "oxygen region" is discussed in Sec. 10-3b. A "double-layer" region between the hydrogen and oxygen regions which is characterized by a low current in the anodic sweep can often be distinguished (Fig. 6-7). Current in this region is primarily due to double-layer charging, although some caution must be exercised in its interpretation (Sec. 6-2).

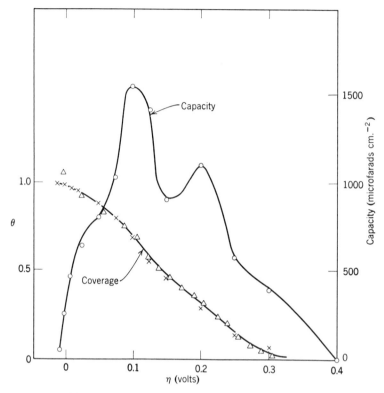

FIG. 10-5. Capacitive component, due to adsorbed hydrogen, of electrode impedance against overvoltage for platinum in 4M sulfuric acid, and coverage-overvoltage variations for the same system. Coverage calculated from the capacity-overvoltage variations ($\times$) and from charging curves ($\triangle$) [Breiter (31)] (by permission of John Wiley).

Isotherms for hydrogen adsorption are plotted in Fig. 10-7 for different temperatures according to Böld and Breiter (35). (See Ref. 35 for the isotherms for iridium and rhodium.) The saturation coverage, needed in the calculation of the coverage, is reached at zero overvoltage according to Breiter, Kammermaier, and Knorr (29) and corresponds to the ratio 1:1 of hydrogen to platinum. There is room for argument on this point (3), but a small error in coverage has no major consequence. The hydrogen pressure needed in the plotting of the isotherms is calculated on the assumption of electrode equilibrium, and consequently p_{H_2} is given directly by the Nernst equation. The exchange current for hydrogen ion discharge on the platinum metals is high, and application of the Nernst equation seems justified. The Temkin logarithmic isotherm (Eq. 2) holds quite well for intermediate coverages over a wide range of hydrogen

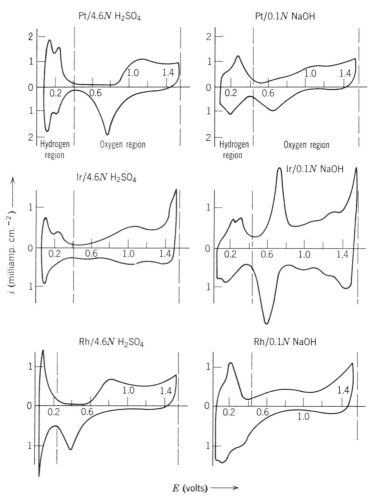

FIG. 10-6. Potentiostatic current-potential curves for platinum, iridium, and rhodium in 4.6N sulfuric acid and 0.1N sodium hydroxide at 25°C. Potential referred to hydrogen electrode at atmospheric pressure in solution being tested. Anodic sweep in the upper halves of diagrams; cathodic sweep in lower halves [Breiter (4)] (by permission of the New York Academy of Sciences).

pressures. This selection of isotherm is open to debate because results can also be interpreted by superposition of Langmuir isotherms with varying parameters for a heterogeneous surface [Eucken and Weblus (27)]. This point is discussed further by Breiter (4, 37) and Frumkin (3).

The differential isosteric heat of adsorption at constant coverage can be computed from plots of $\ln p_{H_2}$ against the reciprocal of the absolute

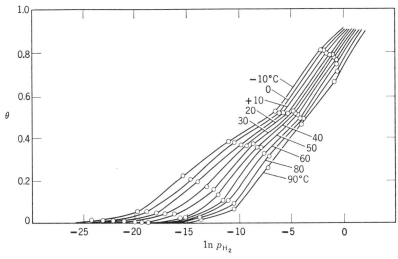

FIG. 10-7. Isotherms for adsorption of hydrogen on smooth platinum in 20% sulfuric acid at different temperatures [Böld and Breiter (35)] (by permission of the Bunsengesellschaft).

temperature by application of Eq. 4. The resulting ΔH_i's, which are practically independent of temperature, are plotted against coverage in Fig. 10-8. Two distinct branches are observed for platinum and iridium, whereas the break in the ΔH_i versus θ curve for rhodium is less apparent. ΔH_i is, as a first approximation, a linear function of coverage for each branch in Fig. 10-8, as would be expected for the Temkin isotherm. The break for platinum near $\theta = 0.5$ may be correlated with the transition from strong to weak adsorption (Sec. 10-2). Breiter (4) cites evidence for reversible adsorption for $\theta > 0.5$ and irreversible adsorption for $\theta < 0.5$ for platinum-hydrogen gas chemisorption. This rather striking correlation, however, may be quite fortuitous because of the profound difference between the two types of interfaces. There also seems to be a correlation between the breaks in the curves of Fig. 10-8 and the peaks in current-potential curves: platinum exhibits two peaks and a break in the ΔH_i versus θ plot, whereas rhodium has only one peak in Fig. 10-6 and hardly a break in Fig. 10-8. It must be noted (3), however, that the morphology of current-potential curves is markedly influenced by electrode pretreatment. These conclusions, although highly interesting, are therefore somewhat tentative.

At low coverages ($\theta < 0.1$), at which adsorption of strongly bonded hydrogen presumably prevails, Henry's law applies, and the coverage is proportional to $p_{H_2}^{1/2}$ (Fig. 10-9). Breiter (4, 37) calculated from Fig. 10-9

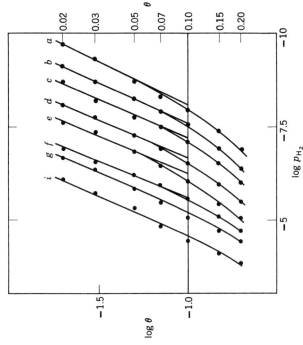

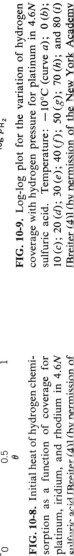

FIG. 10-9. Log-log plot for the variation of hydrogen coverage with hydrogen pressure for platinum in 4.6N sulfuric acid. Temperature: $-10°C$ (curve a); 0 (b); 10 (c); 20 (d); 30 (e); 40 (f); 50 (g); 70 (h); and 80 (i) [Breiter (4)] (by permission of the New York Academy

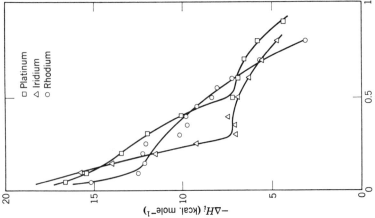

FIG. 10-8. Initial heat of hydrogen chemisorption as a function of coverage for platinum, iridium, and rhodium in 4.6N sulfuric acid [Breiter (4)] (by permission of

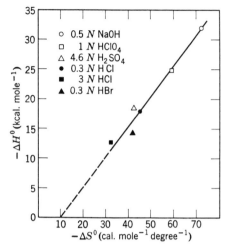

FIG. 10-10. Enthalpy change against entropy change at zero coverage for adsorption of hydrogen on platinum in different electrolytes [Breiter (4)] (by permission of the New York Academy of Sciences).

and similar diagrams for various electrolytes the initial ($\theta = 0$) standard free-energy change (ΔG^0), enthalpy change (ΔH^0), and entropy change (ΔS^0). Electrolyte composition has a very pronounced influence on these three data, but ΔH^0 varies linearly with ΔS^0 (Fig. 10-10). Hence a decrease in bond energy corresponds to increasing disorder of chemisorbed hydrogen.

The influence of anion specific adsorption (cf. Chapter 6) on hydrogen chemisorption has been studied in great detail by Frumkin and co-workers and was reviewed by this author (3). Figure 10-11 shows the effect of iodide adsorption on charging curves and indicates a marked decrease in the amount of chemisorbed hydrogen with increasing iodide concentration. The decrease in the heat of adsorption caused by anion specific adsorption can be interpreted by assuming that the platinum-hydrogen bond has the polarity Pt($+$) $-$ H($-$). Measurements of Volta potentials (1b, 3) lend support to this view. Conversely, specific cation adsorption increases the heat of adsorption. This is indeed true for $0.5M$ sodium hydroxide (Fig. 10-10) for which the equilibrium potential of the hydrogen electrode is sufficiently negative to allow cation adsorption. [See, however, Frumkin (3) for some objections.] Further details on the interplay of chemisorption and specific adsorption in kinetics are given in Sec. 10-5.

It is fair to conclude that, after thirty years of competent investigation, results on hydrogen adsorption on electrodes are still tentative. Henry's law applies at low coverages ($\theta < 0.1$), but this is not an unexpected result.

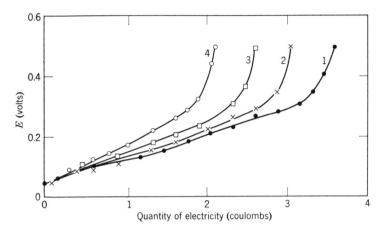

FIG. 10-11. Charging curve for platinized platinum in $0.5M$ sulfuric acid with the following concentrations of iodide: ○ (curve 1); 2×10^{-4} (2); 5×10^{-4} (3); and $10^{-3}M$ (4). Potential referred to hydrogen electrode at atmospheric pressure in solution being tested [Obrucheva (139); Frumkin (3)] (by permission of John Wiley).

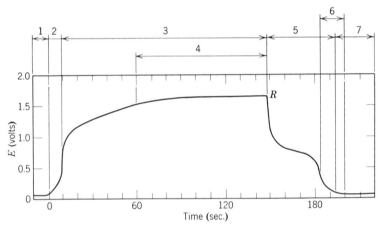

FIG. 10-12. Charging curve for platinum in $0.5M$ sulfuric acid at 25°C under nitrogen at 25 microamp. cm.$^{-2}$. Current switched from anodic to cathodic range at point R. Potential referred to hydrogen electrode at atmospheric pressure in solution being tested. The following regions can be distinguished according to Dietz and Göhr: (1) H_2 evolution; (2) Pt-H formation; (3) Pt-O formation; (4) O_2 evolution; (5) Pt-O removal; (6) Pt-H formation; and (7) H_2 evolution [Dietz and Göhr (70)] (by permission of Pergamon).

The logarithmic Temkin isotherm gives a fair approximation at intermediate coverages, but this conclusion is somewhat open to question (3). The role of ionic specific adsorption is understood qualitatively.

b. Oxygen

Present knowledge of oxygen chemisorption on electrodes of the platinum group is qualitative and still open to further argument. Vetter (43) reviewed the field to approximately 1959, but more recent intensive work (43a–81) has led to revision of interpretation. The methods used for hydrogen electrode adsorption are applicable to oxygen, and corroborating evidence is available from the study of rest potentials and the influence of adsorbed oxygen on the kinetics of electrode processes. The last topic is discussed in Sec. 11-4. Emphasis will be placed here on the platinum metals and gold. Essential facts will be summarized before interpretation is attempted.

The following facts emerge from the substantial body of experimental work. (a) Anodic film formation occurs at less anodic potentials than oxygen evolution, as is convincingly showed by charging curves (Fig. 10-12) and current-potential curves with cyclic scanning of potential (Fig. 10-6). (b) The anodic film is reduced at more cathodic potentials than those required for anodic film formation. The shift of potential varies somewhat from one metal to another; it is smaller for iridium than for platinum (Fig. 10-6) for instance. (c) The range of potentials for oxidation and reduction is pH-dependent, and current-potential curves shift approximately by 0.059 volt toward more cathodic values per unit pH increase (Fig. 10-13). The morphology of the current-potential curves is somewhat different in acid and alkaline solutions (Fig. 10-6). (d) Increase of temperature decreases somewhat the shift between the anodic and cathodic current-potential curves (Fig. 10-14). (e) Increase of scanning rate broadens somewhat the cathodic peak (Fig. 10-15). (f) The quantities of electricity for film formation (Q_a) and reduction (Q_c) indicate monolayer buildup for the platinum metals and gold. Multilayers are formed on metals such as iron, chromium, and nickel. Q_a and Q_c are essentially independent of pH. (g) The ratio Q_c/Q_a generally lies between 0.5 and 1, depending on experimental conditions.

Earlier interpretation [review in (43); also (47) and (70)] of the facts available to 1959 (mostly charging curves and measurements of Q_a and Q_c) postulated cathodic film reduction with intermediate hydrogen peroxide formation. Values of Q_c/Q_a smaller than unity at low current densities were explained by diffusion of hydrogen peroxide into the bulk of the solution, and values of Q_c/Q_a approaching unity at high current densities

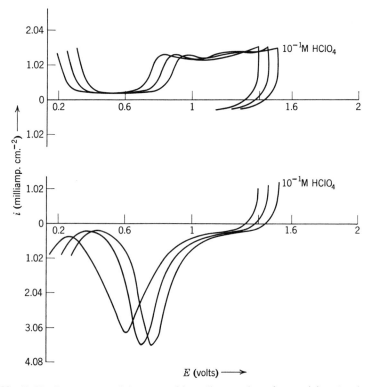

FIG. 10-13. Current-potential curves with cyclic scanning of potential at 1 volt sec^{-1} for platinum at 25°C in 5M sodium perchlorate + 10^{-3}, 10^{-2}, and 10^{-1}M perchloric acid. Anodic (top) and cathodic scanning (bottom). Potential referred to hydrogen electrode at atmospheric pressure in 5M sodium perchlorate + 0.1M perchloric acid [Böld and Breiter (56)] (by permission of Pergamon).

were accounted for by assuming that peroxide loss by diffusion is minimized by rapid scanning. Enhancement of the "activity" of platinum electrodes by anodic treatment and subsequent cathodic reduction was explained by formation of a loosely packed layer of platinum atoms which undergoes progressive rearrangement with a resulting decrease of activity (32). No detailed interpretation of irreversibility could be offered as of 1960.

More recently Böld and Breiter (56) assumed two consecutive slow reactions

$$Pt + H_2O = Pt\text{—}OH + H^+ + e$$
$$Pt - OH = Pt\text{—}O + H^+ + e$$

and developed rate equations, based on the logarithmic Temkin isotherm, which account for the flat top of the current-potential curve during

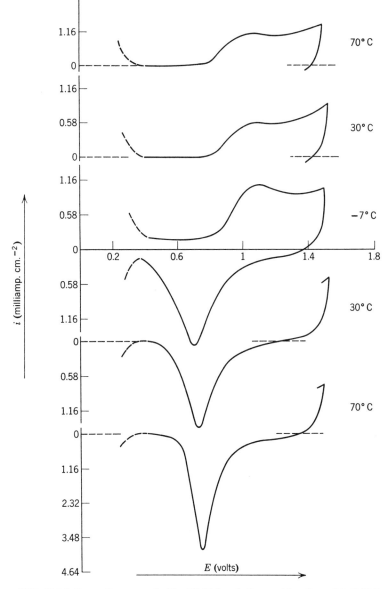

FIG. 10-14. Same diagram as in Fig. 10-13 for platinum at 1 volt sec^{-1} in 2.3M sulfuric acid at different temperatures. Potentials referred to hydrogen electrode at atmospheric pressure in solution being tested [Böld and Breiter (56)] (by permission of Pergamon).

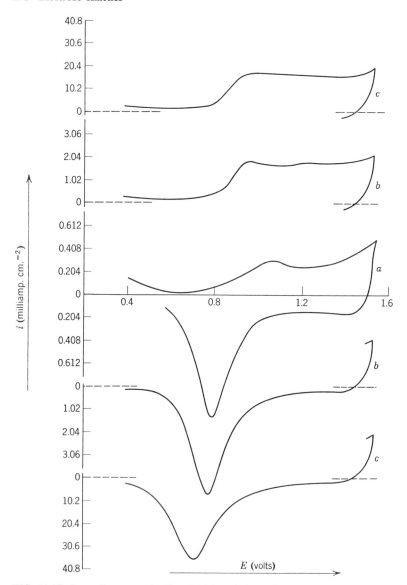

FIG. 10-15. Same diagram as in Fig. 10-13 for platinum in $1M$ perchloric acid at 25°C at the following scanning rates: 0.2 (curve a); 1 (b); and 10 volt sec^{-1} (c). Potential referred to hydrogen electrode at atmospheric pressure in solution being tested [Böld and Breiter (56)] (by permission of Pergamon).

anodic scanning and the shift of potential between the anodic and cathodic sweeps. This interpretation also accounts for the effect of pH, temperature, and rate of scanning. Splitting of the cathodic scanning curve into two peaks, previously reported by Will and Knorr (32), was attributed by Böld and Breiter (56) to an instrumental artefact.

Feldberg, Encke, and Bricker (72), using charging current and controlled potential electrolysis, modified the interpretation of Böld and Breiter and concluded that formation and reduction of Pt—OH is much slower than the reaction Pt—OH = Pt—O + H$^+$ + e. They found that constant current reduction may lead only to half-reduction of the film and that constant potential reduction may require hours to complete. Three states of platinum—reduced (Pt), half-reduced (Pt—OH), and oxidized (Pt—O) —are considered. Thus $Q_c/Q_a = 0.5$ for the Pt-electrode and $Q_c/Q_a = 1$ for the Pt—OH electrode. A simple kinetic treatment was derived by Feldberg et al. (72), but more detailed analysis of the type developed by Böld and Breiter (56) might prove of interest in the formulation of these ideas.

It is difficult to pass judgment on these different interpretations, for a definitive experiment, free of ambiguity in its analysis, has yet to be devised. The role of specific ionic adsorption should also not be overlooked (Sec. 10-5). Complications arising from *absorbed* oxygen, as detected by Schuldiner and Warner (204), may also have to be considered.

The influence of chemisorbed oxygen on the open circuit potential of the noble metals in presence of oxygen has been examined in detail by Hoare (61, 71, 77) and lately by Damjanovic, Rao, and Bockris (80). It has long been known that the equilibrium potential for the reaction

$$O_2 + 4H^+ + 4e = 2H_2O$$

($E^0 = 1.229$ volts versus N.H.E.) is seldom established in acid solution. The exchange current for this reaction is very low, and less positive potentials, which do not obey the Nernst equation, are observed. Hoare interprets them as mixed potentials resulting from the simultaneous occurrence of the preceding reaction and the reaction

$$PtO + 2H^+ + 2e = Pt + H_2O$$

The standard potential for the latter reaction, as calculated from thermodynamic data for bulk PtO, is 0.88 volt versus N.H.E. Other possible reactions must also be considered, for example,

$$O_2 + 2H^+ + 2e = H_2O_2 \quad (E^0 = 0.68 \text{ volt versus N.H.E.})$$
$$O_2 + H^+ + e = HO_2 \quad (E^0 = -0.13 \text{ volt versus N.H.E.})$$

Hoare favors, with reservations, the reaction involving PtO. He notes that, depending on the metal, the mixed potential is primarily determined by the reaction with $E^0 = 1.229$ volts or the reaction with $E^0 = 0.88$ volt. Irreproducibility of potential is attributed by him to traces of hydrogen peroxide and impurities. The equilibrium potential corresponding to E^0 equals 1.229 volts is obtained with platinum electrodes previously treated with concentrated nitric acid, possibly because the oxide-coated metal is free of a mixed potential mechanism and the oxide film has electronic conductivity. Hoare recently worked out (203) a quantitative treatment of the mixed potential which substantiates his previous conclusions. Mixed potentials were also invoked by Breiter and Weininger (62) to account for the dissolution of oxide on platinum in presence of chloride. (See also Refs. 43a and 65.)

This interpretation is questioned by Damjanovic et al. (80), who state in the extended abstract of an as yet unpublished investigation that a mixed potential mechanism does not account for the experimental facts. These authors suggest an explanation based on the surface potential produced by oxygen dipole adsorption. Assessment of the respective merits of the two conflicting interpretations must await the publication of Ref. 80 and possibly further work. See also the relevant detailed treatment by Macdonald and Barlow (202) of the change of work function caused by monolayer adsorption.

10-4 Electrode Processes with Chemisorption of a Reacting Species

a. Introduction

We shall treat electrode processes with chemisorption of a reacting species for the simplifying assumption of no adsorption of the supporting electrolyte. Conditions corresponding to this simplification seldom prevail, and the following analysis is only a first approximation. The effects of ionic adsorption are examined in the next section.

The derivation of the current-overvoltage characteristic in Sec. 7-2 can be transposed to processes with chemisorption of *one* reacting species. The writing of the activity of the chemisorbed species requires preliminary knowledge of the isotherm to be used. No definitive information on the latter point is available, and the problem is complicated further by heterogeneity of the electrode surface. Processes with more than one chemisorbed species are even more arduous to analyze because little is known about mixed chemisorption at electrodes. The following analysis must therefore be regarded as a first step, which nevertheless points toward some of the essential factors controlling kinetics.

Current-overvoltage characteristics will be derived for the particular case of hydrogen ion discharge because this is the outstanding process to which these equations can be applied. Mass transfer will not be considered unless specifically stated. The double-layer effect will be formally included in the exchange current. Quantitative treatment of the type developed in Chapter 9 is not justified for most solid electrodes because of the lack of detailed quantitative information about the double-layer structure.

It was pointed out in Sec. 8-2 that three reactions have to be considered in the hydrogen ion discharge:

$$H^+ + e = H \qquad (\textit{discharge reaction } I)$$
$$H^+ + H + e = H_2 \qquad (\textit{ion } + \textit{ atom reaction } II) \qquad (7)$$
$$H + H = H_2 \qquad (\textit{combination reaction } III)$$

This terminology was suggested by Parsons (82) to avoid the question of priority in the assignment of mechanisms. The following expressions derived from the name of the early investigators have been used frequently [for example, by Vetter (83)]: *Volmer reaction* for process I (84), *Heyrovsky reaction* for process II (85), and *Tafel reaction* for process III (86). The subsequent treatment follows Parsons (82) and represents a synthesis of earlier papers (26, 87–97), particularly by Frumkin and co-workers. Gerischer (98) independently reached conclusions similar to those of Parsons (82). The related papers of Krishtalik (100a) and Thomas (100b) may also be consulted. Detailed mathematical formulations are given by Castellan (99) and Vetter (100). The survey of hydrogen and oxygen overvoltage phenomena by Vetter (83) may be consulted.

Equations will be derived for reactions I, II, and III of Eq. 7 on the assumption that either the Langmuir or the logarithmic Temkin isotherm describes hydrogen chemisorption. Reactions I and II are typical of processes with charge-transfer control, whereas reaction III involves control by the kinetics of a surface reaction. Mixed control is discussed in Sec. 10-4d.

b. Current-Overvoltage Characteristics with Chemisorption Obeying the Langmuir or Logarithmic Temkin Isotherm

The derivation of Eq. 7-9 can be transposed to the kinetics of reactions I to III with chemisorption obeying the Langmuir isotherm. Results are summarized in Table 10-2, where θ represents the nonequilibrium coverage and other notations are similar to those in Eq. 7-9.

The overvoltage can be introduced, and the current-overvoltage characteristic can be written in terms of the apparent exchange current. We have, for instance, for reaction I

$$i_{\mathrm{I}} = i_{\mathrm{I}}^0 \left[\frac{1-\theta}{1-\theta_e} e^{-\alpha_{\mathrm{I}} f\eta} - \frac{\theta}{\theta_e} e^{(1-\alpha_{\mathrm{I}})f\eta} \right] \tag{8}$$

with

$$i_{\mathrm{I}}^0 = F \frac{kT}{h} a_{\mathrm{H}^+}^{1-\alpha_{\mathrm{I}}} (1-\theta_e)^{1-\alpha_{\mathrm{I}}} \theta_e^{\alpha_{\mathrm{I}}} \exp\left[-\frac{(1-\alpha_{\mathrm{I}})\overrightarrow{\Delta G_{\mathrm{I}}^0} + \alpha_{\mathrm{I}} \overleftarrow{\Delta G_{\mathrm{I}}^0}}{RT} \right] \tag{9}$$

The argument of the exponential in Eq. 9 is independent of potential and of the standard free energy of adsorption ΔG^0. The latter appears only through the equilibrium coverage θ_e. By eliminating θ_e between the Langmuir isotherm (Eq. 1) and Eq. 9 we obtain i_{I}^0 of Eq. c in Table 10-2. A similar procedure is applicable to the other cases.

TABLE 10-2   Kinetics of Reactions I to III with Hydrogen Chemisorption Obeying the Langmuir Isotherm [Parsons (82)]

Discharge Reaction I

$$\overrightarrow{v}_{\mathrm{I}} = (kT/h)a_{\mathrm{H}^+}(1-\theta)\exp[-(\overrightarrow{\Delta G_{\mathrm{I}}^0}/RT) - \alpha_{\mathrm{I}} f\phi_{\mathrm{M}}] \tag{a}$$

$$\overleftarrow{v}_{\mathrm{I}} = (kT/h)\theta \exp[-(\overleftarrow{\Delta G_{\mathrm{I}}^0}/RT) + (1-\alpha_{\mathrm{I}})f\phi_{\mathrm{M}}] \tag{b}$$

$$i_{\mathrm{I}}^0 = Q_{\mathrm{I}}\, a_{\mathrm{H}^+}^{1-\alpha}[p_{\mathrm{H}_2}^{1/2}\exp(-\Delta G^0/2RT)]^{\alpha_{\mathrm{I}}}[1 + p_{\mathrm{H}_2}^{1/2}\exp(-\Delta G^0/2RT)]^{-1} \tag{c}$$

$$Q_{\mathrm{I}} = F(kT/h)\exp\{-[(1-\alpha_{\mathrm{I}})\overrightarrow{\Delta G_{\mathrm{I}}^0} + \alpha_{\mathrm{I}}\overleftarrow{\Delta G_{\mathrm{I}}^0}]/RT\} \tag{d}$$

Ion + Atom Reaction II

$$\overrightarrow{v}_{\mathrm{II}} = (kT/h)a_{\mathrm{H}^+}\theta \exp[-(\overrightarrow{\Delta G_{\mathrm{II}}^0}/RT) - \alpha_{\mathrm{II}} f\phi_{\mathrm{M}}] \tag{e}$$

$$\overleftarrow{v}_{\mathrm{II}} = (kT/h)p_{\mathrm{H}_2}(1-\theta)\exp[-(\overleftarrow{\Delta G_{\mathrm{II}}^0}/RT) + (1-\alpha_{\mathrm{II}})f\phi_{\mathrm{M}}] \tag{f}$$

$$i_{\mathrm{II}}^0 = Q_{\mathrm{II}}\, a_{\mathrm{H}^+}^{1-\alpha_{\mathrm{II}}}[p_{\mathrm{H}_2}^{1/2}\exp(-\Delta G^0/2RT)]^{\alpha_{\mathrm{II}}}[1 + p_{\mathrm{H}_2}^{1/2}\exp(-\Delta G^0/2RT)]^{-1} \tag{g}$$

$$Q_{\mathrm{II}} = F(kT/h)\exp\{-[(1-\alpha_{\mathrm{II}})\overrightarrow{\Delta G_{\mathrm{II}}^0} + \alpha_{\mathrm{II}}\overleftarrow{\Delta G_{\mathrm{II}}^0}]/RT\} \tag{h}$$

Combination Reaction III[a]

$$\overrightarrow{v}_{\mathrm{III}} = (kT/h)\theta^2 \exp(-\overrightarrow{\Delta G_{\mathrm{III}}^0}/RT) \tag{i}$$

$$\overleftarrow{v}_{\mathrm{III}} = (kT/h)p_{\mathrm{H}_2}(1-\theta)^2 \exp(-\overleftarrow{\Delta G_{\mathrm{III}}^0}/RT) \tag{j}$$

$$i_{\mathrm{III}}^0 = Q_{\mathrm{III}}p_{\mathrm{H}_2}\exp[-(1-\alpha_{\mathrm{III}})\Delta G^0/RT][1 + p_{\mathrm{H}_2}^{1/2}\exp(-\Delta G^0/2RT)]^2 \tag{k}$$

$$Q_{\mathrm{III}} = 2F(kT/h)\exp(-\Delta G_{\mathrm{III}}^0/RT) \tag{l}$$

---

[a] $\Delta G_{\mathrm{III}}^0$ is the free energy of activation when the standard free energies of the initial and final states are equal. We set

$$\overrightarrow{\Delta G_{\mathrm{III}}^0} = \Delta G_{\mathrm{III}}^0 - \alpha_{\mathrm{III}}\Delta G^0, \quad \overleftarrow{\Delta G_{\mathrm{III}}^0} = \Delta G_{\mathrm{III}}^0 + (1-\alpha_{\mathrm{III}})\Delta G^0.$$

TABLE 10-3 Kinetics of Reactions I to III with Hydrogen Chemisorption Obeying the Logarithmic Temkin Isotherm [Parsons (82)]

Discharge Reaction I

$$\vec{v}_I = (kT/h)a_{H^+} \exp[-\alpha_I s(\theta - 0.5)/2] \exp[-(\overrightarrow{\Delta G_I^0}/RT) - \alpha_I f\phi_M] \qquad (a)$$

$$\overleftarrow{v}_{II} = (kT/h) \exp[(1 - \alpha_I)s(\theta - 0.5)/2] \exp[-(\overleftarrow{\Delta G_I^0}/RT) + (1 - \alpha_I)f\phi_M] \qquad (b)$$

$$i_I^0 = Q_I a_{H^+}^{1-\alpha_I} \qquad (c)$$

Ion + Atom Reaction II

$$\vec{v}_{II} = (kT/h)a_{H^+} \exp[\alpha_{II}s(\theta - 0.5)/2] \exp[-(\overrightarrow{\Delta G_{II}^0}/RT) - \alpha_{II}f\phi_M] \qquad (d)$$

$$\overleftarrow{v}_{II} = (kT/h)p_{H_2} \exp[-(1 - \alpha_{II})s(\theta - 0.5)/2] \exp[-(\overleftarrow{\Delta G_{II}^0}/RT) + (1 - \alpha_{II})f\phi_M] \qquad (e)$$

$$i_{II}^0 = Q_{II} a_{H^+}^{1-\alpha_{II}} \qquad (f)$$

Combination Reaction III

$$\vec{v}_{III} = (kT/h) \exp[\alpha_{III}s(\theta - 0.5)] \exp[-\overrightarrow{\Delta G_{III}^0}/RT] \qquad (g)$$

$$\overleftarrow{v}_{III} = (kT/h)p_{H_2} \exp[-(1 - \alpha_{III})s(\theta - 0.5)] \exp[-\overleftarrow{\Delta G_{III}^0}/RT] \qquad (h)$$

$$i_{III}^0 = Q_{III} p_{H_2}^{\alpha_{III}} \qquad (i)$$

Equation 8 reduces to the simpler Eq. 7-13 only when $\theta \approx \theta_e$ over the whole overvoltage range but, otherwise, the dependence of i on η is more involved because of the variation of θ with η. Representation of results by the Tafel equation takes then an operational character, and caution is necessary in the drawing of conclusions about mechanisms from Tafel plots. The same remark applies to the calculation of exchange currents by extrapolation of Tafel plots over several orders of magnitude of the current.

Equations for the kinetics of reactions I to III are listed in Table 10-3 when hydrogen chemisorption is described by the logarithmic Temkin isotherm (Eq. 2). It is noted that the apparent exchange current of Eqs. c, f, and i of Table 10-3 is independent of the standard free energy of adsorption.

c. Correlation between the Apparent Exchange Current and the Standard Free Energy of Adsorption

It follows from Eq. c, Table 10-2, that a plot of $\ln i_I^0$ against ΔG^0 is an inverted V-shaped curve with a maximum at $\Delta G^0 = 0$. Variations of $\ln i_I^0$ with ΔG^0 are linear for $\Delta G^0/2RT \gg 1$ (minor hydrogen adsorption) or $\Delta G^0/2RT \ll -1$ (major hydrogen adsorption). This conclusion holds

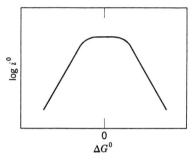

FIG. 10-16. Variations of the logarithm of the exchange current with the standard free-energy of adsorption of hydrogen. The horizontal segment corresponds to intermediate coverage and the logarithmic Temkin isotherm. The linear segments correspond to the Langmuir isotherm [Parsons (82)] (by permission of the Faraday Society).

for the discharge reaction but is also valid for the ion + atom reaction since Eq. *g* is identical in form to Eq. *c*. The same conclusion also applies to the combination reaction, but the slopes of the linear segments of the ln i^0 against ΔG^0 plot are twice the slopes for the other cases (cf. Eq. *k*, Table 10-2). Application of the logarithmic Temkin isotherm introduces a horizontal segment in the plot of ln i^0 against ΔG^0 (Fig. 10-16) because i^0 is independent of ΔG^0 for this isotherm (Eqs. *c, f, i*, Table 10-3). The horizontal segment is located on either side of $\Delta G^0 = 0$, for the isotherm applies to intermediate coverage and the standard state was taken at $\theta = 0.5$. Figure 10-16 should be valid *regardless of mechanism* (82).

A correlation similar to that of Fig. 10-16 also holds for catalytic processes, as pointed out by Balandin (206). The similarity between the catalytic and electrochemical cases was recently indicated by Parsons (207).

Experimental work related to these predictions of theory has been limited thus far to the dependence of the exchange current (or the overvoltage at fixed current) on the initial heat of adsorption. The entropy term in ΔG^0 is thus neglected. Even so, uncertainty in heats of adsorption and exchange currents blurs the correlation and so does the influence of the solvent and ionic adsorption. Exchange currents are somewhat uncertain because they are affected by an unknown double-layer correction, ionic adsorption, complications caused by variation of coverage with current, etc. Long range extrapolation of Tafel plots for the determination of low i^0's also adds to the uncertainty.

Bonhoeffer (101) had already noted in 1924 a correlation between hydrogen overvoltage and the heat for hydrogen adsorption, but it was only more recently that attempts at quantitative correlation were made. Rüetschi and Delahay (102) showed a definite correlation by using D_{MH} values for Eq. 6 but without attempting to make the electronegativity correction. This simplification was subsequently criticized by Temkin and

Frumkin (103) and by Conway and Bockris (104). [See also Rüetschi (105).] The latter authors made the electronegativity correction, but they expressed the view, at variance with Parsons' treatment (82), that a change in the heat of adsorption has opposite effects for the discharge and ion + atom reactions. [This would be the case, in Parsons' opinion, only for a discharge reaction with $\Delta G^0 > 0$ and an ion + atom reaction with $\Delta G^0 < 0$.] Uncertainty in data, as already indicated, does not allow the settlement of this question without recourse to theoretical argument. Aside from this disagreement, Parsons' essential prediction (82) of a maximum in the ln i^0 versus ΔG^0 plot seems to be confirmed. The following trend (82) probably holds and agrees qualitatively with Fig. 10-16. Metals such as Hg, Pb, Tl, Zn, Cd, and possibly Sn exhibit low hydrogen chemisorption ($\Delta G^0 > 0$) and have very low exchange currents; the metals of the platinum group adsorb hydrogen quite well and have high exchange currents; metals such as Mo, Ta, and W with strong hydrogen adsorption ($\Delta G^0 < 0$) have intermediate exchange currents (Fig. 10-17). (Uncertainty on the data plotted in Fig. 10-17, as already indicated, should be kept in mind!)

The terms in D_{MM} and x_M in Eq. 6 accounting for the variation of the heat of adsorption from one metal to another can be correlated to a number of properties of the metal. The exchange current can thus be correlated to these properties. A number of such correlations have been established: surface energy (107, 113), interatomic distance (108, 109, 114, 119), cohesion energy (110), compressibility (111), and melting point (114).

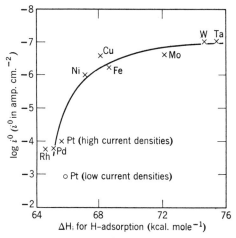

FIG. 10-17. Logarithm of apparent exchange current as a function of the initial experimental heat of adsorption of atomic hydrogen for different metals. See (104) for detailed references on hydrogen overvoltage data [Conway and Bockris (104)] (by permission of the American Institute of Physics).

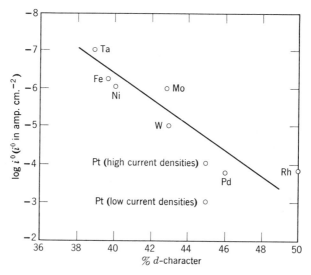

FIG. 10-18. Same plot as in Fig. 10-17 but against percentage d-character of metal [Conway and Bockris (104)] (by permission of the American Institute of Physics).

This type of correlation was interpreted by Rüetschi and Delahay (122) by examining the terms of Eq. 6 in the light of the electron theory of metals. They concluded that these various metal parameters provide a less direct correlation than the heat of adsorption.

Correlation with the work function, initially observed empirically by Bockris (106) was reexamined, together with the d-character of metals and alloys, by Bockris and Conway (104, 115–117, 120, 121). Since the heat of adsorption of hydrogen is a monotonic function of the d-character of the transition metals (with some exceptions) (Fig. 10-2), a similar dependence should hold for ln i^0 (Fig. 10-18). The same remark applies to the work function. Correlation with d-character has also been established for alloys (112, 118, 118a, 120a, 121).

d. Elucidation of Reaction Mechanisms

We consider separately reactions I to III of Eq. 7 and we now treat mixed mechanisms. Mathematical analysis [Vetter (100), Lukovtsev (123), Parsons (124)] is not difficult, although the algebra is quite heavy; it suffices to eliminate θ between pairs of rate equations for each step. [Compare with procedure in Sec. 8-1.] If adsorption equilibrium prevails, θ_e can be directly computed from the isotherms (Eqs. 1 or 2). Conclusions of this analysis (82) are given in Table 10-4. The parameter b (Eq. 7-18)

TABLE 10-4 Characteristics[a] of Mechanisms for Reactions I to III [Parsons (82)]

Mechanism	Rate-Determining Step	$\dfrac{b}{2.303}$	$-\dfrac{\partial \theta}{\partial \eta}$
$\Delta G^0 \gg 0 (\theta_e \to 0)$			
Discharge and	Discharge	$\dfrac{1}{\alpha_I f}$	0
ion + atom	Ion + atom	$\dfrac{1}{(1 + \alpha_{II})f}$	$f\theta$
Discharge and	Discharge	$\dfrac{1}{\alpha_I f}$	$\dfrac{\alpha_I f\theta}{2}$
combination	Combination	$\dfrac{1}{2f}$	$f\theta$
$\Delta G^0 \approx 0 \ (\theta_e \approx 0.5)$, following step in equilibrium			
Discharge and	Discharge	$\dfrac{1}{2\alpha_I f}$	$\dfrac{f}{s}$
ion + atom	Ion + atom	$\dfrac{1}{2\alpha_{II} f}$	$\dfrac{f}{s}$
Discharge and	Discharge	$\dfrac{1}{\alpha_I f}$	0
combination	Combination	$\dfrac{1}{2\alpha_{III} f}$	$\dfrac{f}{s}$
$\Delta G^0 \approx 0 \ (\theta_e \approx 0.5)$, following step not in equilibrium[b]			
Discharge and ion + atom	Discharge	$\dfrac{1}{f}\left[\dfrac{\alpha_I + \alpha_{II}}{\alpha_I \alpha_{II}}\right]$	$\dfrac{f}{s}\dfrac{\alpha_I - \alpha_{II}}{\alpha_I + \alpha_{II}}$
Discharge and Combination	Discharge	$\dfrac{1}{f}\dfrac{2\alpha_{III} + \alpha_I}{2\alpha_I \alpha_{III}}$	$\dfrac{f}{s}\dfrac{\alpha_I}{\alpha_I + \alpha_{III}}$

[a] For definition of the Tafel slope b see Eq. 7-18.
[b] Corrected from original paper (205).

TABLE 10-4 *Continued*

Mechanism	Rate-Determining Step	$\dfrac{b}{2.303}$	$-\dfrac{\partial\theta}{\partial\eta}$
		$\Delta G^0 \ll 0\ (\theta \to 1)$	
Discharge and	Discharge	$\dfrac{1}{\alpha_{\mathrm{I}} f}$	0
ion + atom	Ion + atom	$\dfrac{1}{\alpha_{\mathrm{II}} f}$	0
Discharge and	Discharge	$\dfrac{1}{\alpha_{\mathrm{I}} f}$	0
combination	Combination	∞	0

is $4.6\ RT/F$ with $\alpha = 0.5$ for several mechanisms, and this Tafel slope is indeed found for a number of metals. [See Tafel plots for numerous metals in (43, p. 432).]

This example shows that unambiguous elucidation of complex reaction mechanisms by an analysis purely based on current-overvoltage characteristics may not be feasible in some cases. It is, of course, essential to apply the methods of Chapter 8 and determine Tafel slopes, reaction orders, and stoichiometric numbers, but some other evidence is generally necessary. Moreover, complication by ionic adsorption may weaken arguments based purely on the morphology of current-overvoltage characteristics. Several methods involving transients, permeation studies (for hydrogen only), controlled mass transfer, isotopic methods, etc., have been developed and applied, in particular, to hydrogen evolution and oxidation, but even a cursory review of this extensive field is not within the scope of this monograph. A systematic and critical analysis of the potentialities and limitations of these various methods is very much needed. [See Frumkin (3) for some aspects.]

The cathodic evolution of hydrogen was selected as a typical example in the foregoing analysis because interpretation of this process has reached a more fundamental level than for most other processes involving a chemisorbed reacting species. Concepts and their mathematical formulation carry over to other processes although multiplicity of reaction paths may render such a task quite arduous and possibly futile. Attention is called in particular to the oxygen electrode which has been thoroughly reviewed by Vetter (125). [See also more recent papers (78, 126–138).]

10-5   Electrode Processes with Chemisorption of a Reacting Species and Specific Adsorption of the Electrolyte or an Additive

a. Ionic Specific Adsorption

The restriction made at the beginning of the previous section is now removed, and the effect of ionic adsorption is considered. This effect will be examined in relation to the hydrogen and oxygen electrodes since most available material deals with these electrodes. [See Frumkin (3) for a review on the hydrogen electrode.]

Anion specific adsorption has at least the following three effects on the kinetics of the hydrogen electrode: (*a*) variation of the potential ϕ_2 in the outer plane; (*b*) variation of the standard free energy for hydrogen adsorption (Fig. 10-10); (*c*) decrease of available area for hydrogen coverage. Each of these effects influences kinetics, but their relative importance varies from one metal to another and, for a given metal, with the current density. For instance, metals with low hydrogen coverage are influenced primarily by the change of ϕ_2, just as for the simpler case of mercury (Sec. 9-6a). Each metal must be examined individually over a wide range of current densities, and a substantial body of information has been gathered toward this end, mostly by the Frumkin school (3).

Direct participation of anions may occur at the highly positive potentials in oxygen evolution at high current density. Work on this effect (143–149) is summarized by Frumkin (140, 141) and by Breiter (128). Sulfuric acid was used in early work, but interpretation is complicated by formation of peroxydisulfuric acid and the Caro acid H_2SO_5. (See Ref. 142 for review.) This complication is avoided with perchloric acid. The Tafel plot for oxygen evolution on platinum in perchloric acid (also sulfuric acid) exhibits a rapid transition toward higher overvoltages at high current density (Fig. 10-19) with pronounced hysteresis (Fig. 10-20). Isotopic experiments with oxygen-18 labeled perchloric acid show significant evolution of oxygen-18 in the upper segment of the Tafel plot but not in the lower one (Fig. 10-21). Exchange of oxygen between water and perchloric acid in solution is negligible, and a mechanism involving formation of ClO_4 radical with subsequent decomposition into ClO_2 and O_2 does not account for experimental facts (140). Perchlorate ion must therefore be involved in some way in the electrode reaction, possibly by exchange of oxygen between perchlorate and the oxide film. The electrode capacity, determined from potential decay curves by the interrupter method, is abnormally high (up to 90 microfarads cm^{-2}) in the lower segment of the Tafel plot of Fig. 10-19, but is much smaller (20 microfarads cm^{-2}) in

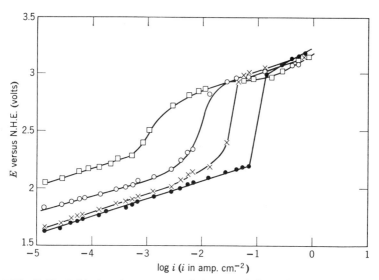

FIG. 10-19. Tafel plots for oxygen evolution on platinum in perchloric acid at the following concentrations: ● 1.34M; × 2.9M; ○ 5M; □ 9.8M [Frumkin (141)] (by permission of Pergamon).

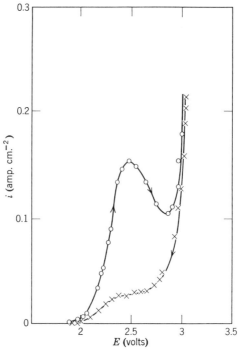

FIG. 10-20. Current-potential curve for platinum in 2.6M perchloric acid with continuous variation of potential at 8 millivolt sec^{-1}. Arrows indicate direction of scanning. Potential referred to hydrogen electrode at atmospheric pressure in solution being studied [Frumkin (140)] (by permission of Butterworths).

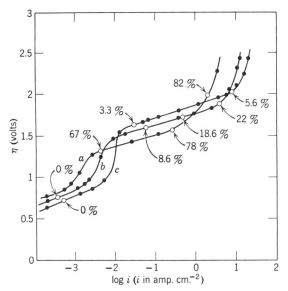

FIG. 10-21. Tafel plot for oxygen evolution on platinum in O^{18}-labeled perchloric acid of the following concentrations: $5.8M$ (curve a); $7.6M$ (b); and $10M$ (c). Number for each point is the percentage of oxygen-18 in evolved oxygen [Frumkin (140)] (by permission of Butterworths).

the upper segment. Finally, ozone is evolved in the upper segment of the Tafel plot.

These facts can be *tentatively* explained (141) by assuming that sites with a high energy for oxygen adsorption are progressively covered with formation of a multilayer film as the current density is increased. The film may have semiconductor properties at high anodic currents, and this may account for the low capacities observed in the upper Tafel range. Ozone would be produced by decomposition of the film at the electrode. This explanation is in agreement with earlier work of Rüetschi and Delahay (150), who calculated M—OH bond energies and found a monotonic increase of oxygen overvoltage with decrease of this bond energy. These authors also explained the switch from one Tafel line to another one at high overvoltages, which is observed with certain metals (for example, palladium and gold) by a decrease in the M—OH bond energy.

Further information on oxygen evolution at highly anodic potentials is obtained from the influence of cations on Tafel plots. Erdey-Gruz and Shafarik (151) were the first to point out that the increase of oxygen overvoltage caused by the presence of alkali cations follows the same sequence as the tendency of these cations toward adsorption. This rather surprising effect of cations at very anodic potentials was further studied in

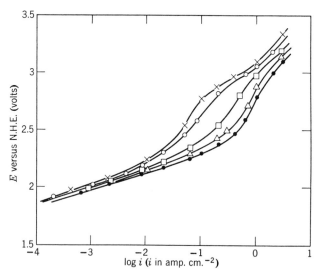

FIG. 10-22. Tafel plot for oxygen evolution on platinum in $3M$ sulfuric acid (●) and in the same solution plus $0.5M$ sulfate of lithium (△), sodium (□), potassium (○), and cesium (×) [Frumkin, Kaganovich, Yakovleva, and Sobol' (152); Frumkin (141)] (by permission of Pergamon).

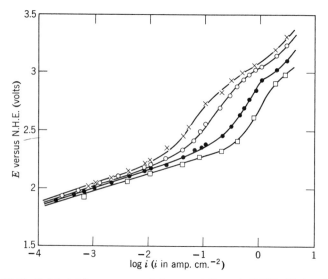

FIG. 10-23. Tafel plot for oxygen evolution on platinum in $2.5M$ sulfuric acid (□) and in the same solution plus $5 \times 10^{-3}M$ (●), 5×10^{-2} (○), and $5 \times 10^{-1}M$ (×) cesium sulfate [Frumkin, Kaganovich, Yakovleva, and Sobol' (152); Frumkin (141)] (by permission of Pergamon).

Frumkin's laboratory (141, 152). The overvoltage increases from lithium to cesium and, for a given alkali cation, increases with cation concentration. Results are given in Figs. 10-22 and 10-23 for sulfuric acid, but a similar effect is observed in perchloric acid. Limited solubility of some of the alkali perchlorates, however, hampers exploration over a wide range of concentrations. The overvoltage increase is quite minor in the lower segment of the Tafel plot and is most pronounced in the transition from one Tafel curve to the other.

The cation effect can be interpreted (141) by noting that chemisorption of oxygen causes a positive difference of potential between metal and solution. Local cation adsorption is thus possible and is presumably more pronounced for alkali cations than for hydrogen ions despite the overwhelming excess of the latter. Cation adsorption increases the adsorption energy of specifically adsorbed anions much in the same way as cesium ion adsorption on mercury enhances iodide adsorption. Increase in stability of the adsorbed layer hinders oxygen evolution (150) and the overvoltage increases accordingly. This effect should be most pronounced when the electrode is nearly completely covered, and the cation effect is enhanced in the transition from the lower Tafel curve to the upper one. Moreover, complete electrode coverage by oxide should favor cation adsorption and results in overvoltage increase in the transition region. Further increase of potential beyond the transition range hinders cation adsorption whose influence therefore diminishes. The cation effect in the lower Tafel branch is rather minor because anion specific adsorption is less pronounced than at more positive potentials. This interpretation, as Frumkin notes (141), is only preliminary, but it fits the facts. Similar ideas have been applied to cation effects in the oxygen evolution on other metals and in the Kolbe reaction (141).

Ionic specific adsorption should also influence other processes than oxygen evolution whenever there is a chemisorbed film, but data are lacking. The halogen electrodes, whose mechanisms have been investigated in recent years, would deserve further examination from this point of view. [See review in (153); more recent paper in (154–157).]

b. Uncharged Substances

The action of a variety of organic substances, which primarily undergo physical adsorption, has been studied (107, 158–163) for hydrogen evolution on solid electrodes. Inhibition is observed, probably because of the combined effect of electrode coverage and variation of ϕ_2. Penetration of the adsorbed film may also have to be considered (Sec. 9-10). Quantitative separation of these factors has not been attempted and would be difficult. These studies do not add much to the understanding of electrode kinetics, but they are very valuable in the interpretation of corrosion inhibition by organic additives. The substantial literature on the latter subject may be consulted for practical details.

The action of inorganic substances which are chemisorbed is discussed in Section 10-6. Catalytic action of certain organic substances on hydrogen evolution is covered in Sec. 11-2 and 11-3.

10-6   Inhibition of Electrode Processes by a Chemisorbed Film

a. Inhibition of the Hydrogen Electrode Reaction

Inhibition by a chemisorbed film is observed for electrode processes occurring without or with formation of a chemisorbed film involving a reacting species. The latter film may be identical to or different from the inhibiting film. Interaction and competition between the chemisorbed film and specifically adsorbed ions may also have to be considered. Therefore the unraveling of experimental facts may prove a very difficult task. We shall examine: (*a*) inhibition of the hydrogen electrode by various chemisorbed films, and principally chemisorbed oxygen; (*b*) inhibition of the anodic oxidation of organic substances by chemisorbed oxygen.

Inhibition of hydrogen evolution by inorganic additives such as mercury and arsenic (9, 15, 89, 164–171) as well as carbon disulfide (16) and carbon monoxide (170) has been studied quite extensively. (For recent studies of carbon monoxide adsorption on platinum; cf. Refs. 172, 173, and 178.) These substances are probably chemisorbed or form a superficial alloy (for example, mercury) and influence hydrogen chemisorption. The action varies somewhat from one substance to another: mercury, for instance, prevents adsorption of hydrogen on platinum, whereas arsenic does not but increases the electrode hydrogen bonding energy. Pronounced effects are observed even at very low additive coverage, much in the same way as in inhibition by chemisorbed oxygen. Implications of this type of electrode "poisoning" were recently examined by Shlygin (174). He concluded from a series of examples that reduction proceeding via formation of adsorbed hydrogen might be strongly inhibited by poisoning, whereas reduction via the formation of a radical by electron addition is not markedly inhibited. Mixed mechanisms were also examined by Shlygin.

Inhibition of electrode processes by chemisorbed oxygen was recognized by Nernst (1905) and received renewed attention with recent investigations of hydrogen anodic oxidation. [See earlier references in Breiter (59).] Inhibition of a few other reactions which do not involve chemisorbed

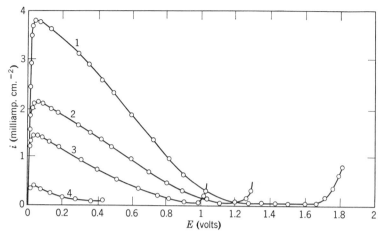

FIG. 10-24. Current potential curves for anodic oxidation of hydrogen on a platinum rotating-disk electrode. Curve 1, $0.5M$ sulfuric acid at $20,000$ r.p.m.; curve 2, $1M$ hydrochloric acid at $7,000$ r.p.m.; curve 3, $1M$ hydrobromic acid at $7,000$ r.p.m.; curve 4, $0.1M$ hydrochloric acid $+ 1M$ potassium iodide at $2,000$ r.p.m. Potential referred to hydrogen electrode at atmospheric pressure in solution being tested [Frumkin and Aikasjan (177); Frumkin (3)] (by permission of John Wiley).

reacting species has been investigated: reduction of oxygen (for example, 38, 78), vanadium(V) (68), iodate (68), oxidation of ferrocyanide (57), and iron(II) (175). Feldberg et al. (72) reported acceleration in the reduction of vanadium(V) and iodate on what they call half-reduced platinum electrodes (possibly Pt-OH) (Sec. 10-3b).

This discussion is limited to hydrogen anodic oxidation. The kinetics of this reaction is reviewed by Vetter (176) and by Frumkin (3) and will not be discussed in detail here, for we are primarily interested in inhibition by chemisorbed oxygen. Mass transfer of the slightly soluble hydrogen must be controlled and corrected for. Current-potential curves obtained with the rotating-disk electrode (177) exhibit a maximum and a subsequent decrease of current at more anodic potentials (Fig. 10-24). The decrease in current is initially caused by specific anion adsorption and, at more anodic potentials, by chemisorbed oxygen. Very strong inhibition then prevails. The latter was studied in detail by Breiter (59), who found hysteresis in current-potential curves with continuous scanning of potential. Little hysteresis is observed when the direction of scanning is reversed before marked oxygen chemisorption occurs, whereas pronounced hysteresis prevails under the opposite conditions. Hysteresis and lowering of the anodic current for hydrogen oxidation are clearly related to oxygen coverage (Fig. 10-25). The current for hydrogen oxidation, after correction for mass transfer, decreases rapidly with coverage (Fig. 10-26). Breiter

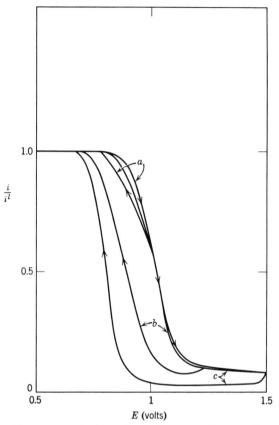

FIG. 10-25. Current-potential curves for hydrogen anodic oxidation on platinum with vigorous stirring in $1M$ perchloric acid (left) with continuous scanning of potential at 39 millivolts sec^{-1} at 30°C; plot of oxygen coverage against potential for the conditions prevailing in the recording of current-potential curves (right). Arrows indicate direction of scanning. Potential referred to hydrogen electrode at atmospheric pressure in $1M$ perchloric acid. Direction of scanning was reversed at 1, 1.25, and 1.5 volts, respectively, for curves a, b, c. Curve d in diagram on the right was recorded under argon stirring [Breiter (59)] (by permission of Pergamon).

concludes that hydrogen oxidation occurs primarily on active sites covering an area of less than 10% of the total electrode area.

b. Inhibition of the Oxidation of Certain Organic Substances by Chemisorbed Oxygen

Inhibition of the anodic oxidation of simple organic substances is discussed here, and not in Chapter 11, because these substances probably

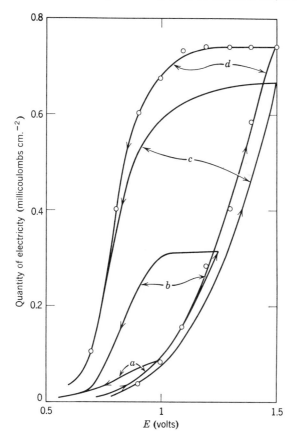

undergo dissociative chemisorption at solid electrodes, as we shall see later. The literature on this type of anodic processes is rapidly growing because of current interest in fuel cells. Much work on the electrochemical oxidation of the lower aliphatic hydrocarbons probably remains unpublished because of potential (perhaps long-range!) technological applications. Recent publications centered on a few substances; methanol (180, 182–184, 186, 189, 191, 192), ethanol (179, 190, 194), formic acid (183, 185, 187, 192, 195, 196), oxalic acid (55, 69, 193), formaldehyde (183), ethylene (188), and miscellaneous organic substances (181). Current views on mechanisms of inhibition by chemisorbed films were surveyed by Bagotskii and Vasilyev (197) and poisoning effects were discussed by Shlygin (174). Related work on anodic oxidation of a few inorganic substances, aside from hydrogen, can also be cited: carbon monoxide (191), carbon dioxide (200), ammonia (201), and hydrazine (198, 199).

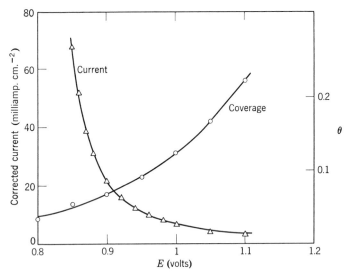

FIG. 10-26. Current (corrected for mass transfer) for hydrogen anodic oxidation and oxygen coverage against potential. Same scale of potentials as in Fig. 10-25 [Breiter (59)] (by permission of Pergamon).

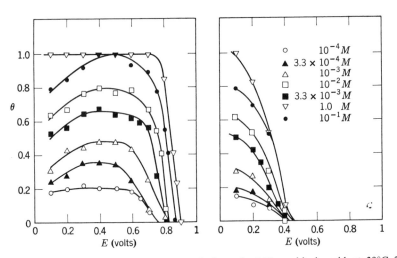

FIG. 10-27. Formic acid coverage on platinum in $1M$ perchloric acid at 30°C for anodic (left) and cathodic (right) scanning of potential at 30 millivolts sec^{-1} for different concentrations. Potential referred to hydrogen electrode at atmospheric pressure in solution being studied [Breiter (185)] (by permission of Pergamon).

Adsorption of uncharged substances on solid electrodes was discussed in Sec. 6-2d. Some additional results whose discussion requires preliminary study of electrode chemisorption will now be reviewed. The subject has been studied, or at least referred to, by most authors already cited and especially by Breiter. His earlier paper on n-amyl alcohol adsorption on platinum (181) is only preliminary, but he subsequently reported data on methanol (180, 184, 189) and formic acid (185). Two conclusions about adsorption emerge from his and other studies: (*a*) chemisorbed oxygen displaces the organic adsorbate, and the amount of chemisorbed oxygen is hardly dependent on the bulk concentration of the organic substance; (*b*) sluggish reduction of chemisorbed oxygen causes pronounced hysteresis in the variations of coverage by the organic adsorbate with potential [Figs. 10-27 and 10-28; see the original paper (185) for experimental details and methods of calculation]. Bagotskii and Vasilyev (197) state that adsorption on platinum is described by the Temkin isotherm, as might be expected for a heterogeneous surface (Sec. 10-2).

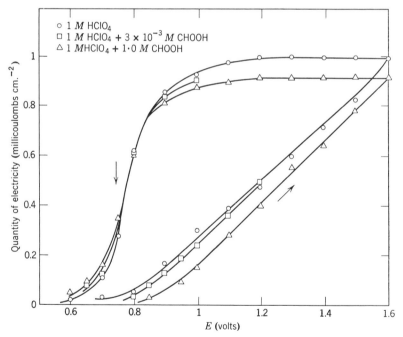

FIG. 10-28. Amount of chemisorbed oxygen against potential during anodic (arrow pointing to the right) and cathodic scanning of potential. Chemisorbed oxygen determined from cathodic charging curves at 91 milliamp. cm.$^{-2}$. Same conditions as for Fig. 10-27 [Breiter (185)] (by permission of Pergamon).

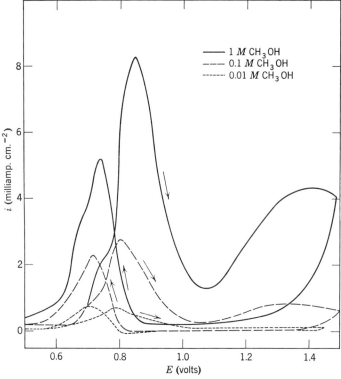

FIG. 10-29. Current-potential curves with potentiostatic control of potential at a scanning rate of 30 millivolts sec^{-1} for platinum in $1M$ perchloric acid and different concentrations of methanol. Potential referred to hydrogen electrode at atmospheric pressure in solution being studied [Breiter (180)] (by permission of Pergamon).

Current-potential curves exhibit marked hysteresis when recorded with periodic slow scanning of potential (Fig. 10-29). The morphology of these curves depends somewhat on experimental conditions but, according to Bagotskii and Vasilyev (197), there is a striking similitude between such curves for a variety of substances (Fig. 10-30). They consider that most of the curves they obtained (and those of other investigators) by scanning toward increasingly anodic potentials exhibit three more or less well-defined minima in the following ranges of potential: 0.55 to 0.8, 0.9 to 1.1 1.3 to 1.6 volts versus a hydrogen electrode in the solution being studied (0.5M sulfuric acid). These minima result from inhibition of anodic oxidation of the organic adsorbate by chemisorbed oxygen. Oxygen coverage increases as a monotonic function of potential [Breiter (185) (Fig. 10-28), Wroblowa, Piersma, and Bockris (188)], and the minima in Fig. 10-30 cannot be ascribed to maxima of oxygen adsorption. They may be

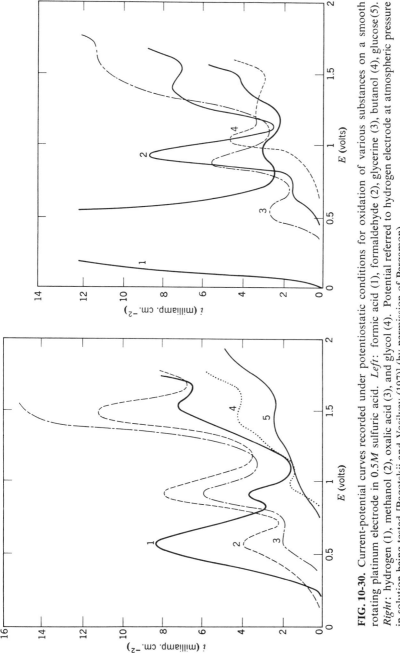

FIG. 10-30. Current-potential curves recorded under potentiostatic conditions for oxidation of various substances on a smooth rotating platinum electrode in $0.5M$ sulfuric acid. *Left*: formic acid (1), formaldehyde (2), glycerine (3), butanol (4), glucose (5). *Right*: hydrogen (1), methanol (2), oxalic acid (3), and glycol (4). Potential referred to hydrogen electrode at atmospheric pressure in solution being tested [Bagotskii and Vasilyev (197)] (by permission of Pergamon).

explained (197) by assuming that three types of oxygen are chemisorbed with different binding energies. The current rises beyond a minimum because of the normal acceleration of oxidation with an increasingly anodic potential. The main peak undoubtedly results from inhibition by oxygen coverage, but the other two peaks may possibly be due to complications arising from continuous scanning of potential. This point ought to be clarified.

Current-potential curves which are recorded during the return scanning toward increasingly cathodic potentials exhibit only a single peak in the range of 0.6 to 0.8 volt versus the hydrogen electrode in the solution being studied. The difference between the curves obtained by anodic or cathodic scanning is ascribed by Bagotskii and Vasilyev (197), in agreement with other authors, to hysteresis in the reduction of chemisorbed oxygen.

Bagotskii and Vasilyev (197) found that the current in the descending branches of current-potential curves is essentially an exponential function of potential. Since oxygen coverage varies quite linearly with potential, the preceding relationship implies that current inhibition increases, as a first approximation, according to an exponential function of oxygen coverage.

Since adsorption of the organic substance is described by the Temkin isotherm, we would expect from Eq. a, Table 3, that the current be an exponential function of the organic adsorbate coverage. This is indeed the case for methanol oxidation (Fig. 10-31) as Bagotskii and Vasilyev (197) showed by using Breiter's data (180, 184, 189). The latter author

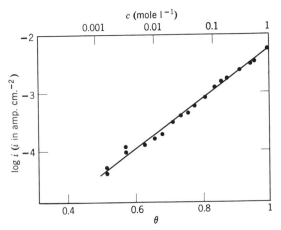

Fig. 10-31. Logarithm of rate of methanol oxidation on platinum in $1M$ perchloric acid at 0.92 volt against equilibrium methanol coverage. Potential referred to hydrogen electrode at atmospheric pressure in solution being tested. Methanol concentration plotted along upper abscissa scale. [Bagotskii (197a)] (by permission of the author).

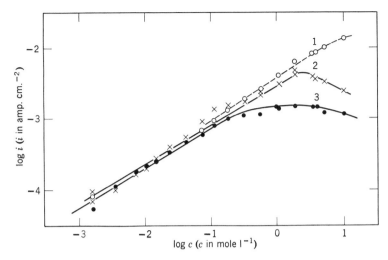

FIG. 10-32. Log-log plot of current against concentration for methanol oxidation on platinum at 1.35 (curve 1); 0.85 (curve 2); and 0.65 (curve 3) volt. Potential referred to hydrogen electrode at atmospheric pressure in solution being tested [Bagotskii and Vasilyev (197)] (by permission of Pergamon).

thought that the relationship between current and coverage is linear, but the plots he reported fit poorly such a linear relationship. The exponential dependence of the current on θ in Fig. 10-31 up to $\theta = 1$ is surprising since the logarithmic Temkin isotherm holds only for intermediate coverages $(0.2 < \theta < 0.8)$. An error in the saturation coverage might be the explanation for the abnormally good fit at high coverages.

Further information on anodic oxidation can be gathered from the dependence of the anodic current, at constant potential, on the bulk concentration of adsorbate. Log-log plots of current against concentration are linear at highly anodic potentials but exhibit a maximum at less positive potentials (Fig. 10-32). This departure from linearity probably results from saturation coverage by the organic adsorbate at the lesser anodic potentials. Verification of this point from Breiter's coverage determination for methanol (180) is not possible since this author did not explore the 1 to $10M$ concentration range for which the leveling off and drop in current is most pronounced. The slope of the linear segments in Fig. 10-32 is about 0.5 for methanol. This value holds approximately for other organic substances (197).

From these and other observations on the effect of pH and addition of foreign electrolyte Bagotskii and Vasilyev conclude, following the suggestion of Frumkin and Podlovchenko (190), that the most likely mechanism is the dissociative chemisorption of the organic substance according to, for example, for methanol

$$CH_3OH \rightarrow CH_2OH + H$$

At more anodic potential direct oxidation by chemisorbed oxygen may prevail, for example,

$$CH_3OH + \text{adsorbed oxygen} \rightarrow CH_2OH + H_2O$$

All species in these equations are adsorbed. Hydrogen ionization and formation of OH radicals may occur at the more anodic potentials. The mechanism involving one-electron transfer followed by deprotonation seems to be ruled out because of the lack of any significant dependence of the anodic current on supporting electrolyte concentration. A double-layer effect would indeed be expected, especially for oxidation of organic anions. Transitory formation of an anion with a double negative charge also appears unlikely.

In conclusion, inhibition of anodic processes by chemisorbed oxygen is beginning to be understood. Analysis of reaction mechanisms is certainly not definitive, but an interpretation which seems to fit presently available facts can at least be advanced.

REFERENCES

1a. D. O. Hayward and B. M. W. Trapnell, *Chemisorption*, 2nd edition, Butterworths, London, 1964.

1b. G. C. Bond, *Catalysis by Metals*, Academic Press, New York, 1962.

2a. D. D. Eley, *Disc. Faraday Soc.*, **8**, 34 (1950); *J. Phys. Colloid Chem.*, **55**, 1017 (1951).

2b. L. Pauling, *Nature of the Chemical Bond*, Cornell University Press, Ithaca, 1939, p. 60.

2c. D. P. Stevenson, *J. Chem. Phys.*, **23**, 203 (1955).

3. A. N. Frumkin, *Advances in Electrochemistry and Electrochemical Engineering*, Vol. 3, P. Delahay, editor, Interscience, New York, 1963, pp. 287–391.

4. M. W. Breiter, *Ann. New York Acad. Sci.*, **101**, 709 (1963).

5. F. B. Bowden, *Proc. Roy. Soc.*, **125A**, 446 (1929).

6. J. A. V. Butler and G. Armstrong, *ibid.*, **137A**, 604 (1932).

7. G. Armstrong, F. R. Himsworthand, and J. A. V. Butler, *ibid.*, **143A**, 89 (1933).

8. A. N. Frumkin and A. I. Shlygin, *Doklady Akad. Nauk S.S.S.R.*, **2**, 173 (1934).

9. A. I. Shlygin and A. N. Frumkin, *Acta Physicochim. U.R.S.S.*, **3**, 791 (1935).

10. A. I. Shlygin, A. N. Frumkin, and V. Medvedovsky, *ibid.*, **4**, 911 (1936).

11. A. N. Frumkin and A. I. Shlygin, *ibid.*, **5**, 819 (1936).

12. B. V. Ershler, *ibid.*, **7**, 327 (1937).

13. B. V. Ershler, G. Deborin, and A. N. Frumkin, *ibid.*, **8**, 565 (1938).

14. J. D. Pearson and J. A. V. Butler, *Trans. Faraday Soc.*, **34**, 1163 (1938).

15. B. V. Ershler and A. N. Frumkin, *ibid.*, **35**, 464 (1939).

16. A. Hickling, *ibid.*, **41**, 333 (1945).

17. A. Obrucheva and I. L. Rubinstein, *Doklady Akad. Nauk S.S.S.R.*, **63**, 403 (1948).

18. T. I. Zalkind and B. V. Ershler, *Zhur. Fiz. Khim.*, **25**, 565 (1951).

19. M. Breiter, C. A. Knorr, and W. Völkl, *Z. Elektrochem.*, **59**, 681 (1955).
20. Yu. A. Podvyaskin and A. I. Shlygin, *Zhur. Fiz. Khim.*, **31**, 1305 (1957).
21. Yu. M. Tyurin and A. I. Shlygin, *ibid.*, **32**, 2487 (1958).
22. J. Giner, *Z. Elektrochem.*, **63**, 386 (1959).
23. Yu. M. Tyurin, *Doklady Akad. Nauk S.S.S.R.*, **126**, 827 (1959).
24. C. H. Presbrey and S. Schuldiner, *J. Electrochem Soc.*, **108**, 985 (1961).
25. A. Obrucheva, *Doklady Akad. Nauk S.S.S.R.*, **142**, 859 (1962).
26. P. Dolin and B. V. Ershler, *Acta Physicochim.*, *U.R.S.S.*, **13**, 747 (1940).
27.' A. Eucken and B. Weblus, *Z. Elektrochem.*, **55**, 114 (1951).
28. E. Wicke and B. Weblus, *ibid.*, **56**, 169 (1952).
29. M. Breiter, H. Kammermaier, and C. A. Knorr, *ibid.*, **60**, 37, 119 (1956).
30. T. P. Birintseva and B. N. Kabanov, *Zhur. Fiz. Khim.*, **33**, 844 (1959).
31. M. Breiter, *Transactions of the Symposium on Electrode Processes*, E. Yeager, editor, Wiley, New York, 1961, pp. 307–321.
32. F. G. Will and C. A. Knorr, *Z. Elektrochem.*, **64**, 258, 270 (1960).
33. T. C. Franklin and S. L. Cooke, *J. Electrochem. Soc.*, **107**, 556 (1960).
34. J. M. Kolotyrkin and A. N. Chemodanov, *Doklady Akad. Nauk S.S.S.R.*, **134**, 128 (1960).
35. W. Böld and M. Breiter, *Z. Elektrochem.*, **64**, 897 (1960).
36. M. Breiter and B. Kennel, *ibid.*, **64**, 1180 (1960).
37. M. Breiter, *Electrochim. Acta*, **7**, 25 (1962).
38. W. Vielstich, *Z. Instrumentenkunde*, **71**, 29 (1963).
39. M. A. V. Devanathan, J. O'M. Bockris, and W. Mehl, *J. Electroanal. Chem.*, **1**, 143 (1959–60).
40. J. O'M. Bockris and R. Thacker, *The Determination of the Coverage of Corrodable Metals with Hydrogen during Electrolytic Evolution*, Technical Report No. 3 to the Office of Naval Research, contract Nonr 551(22), NR 036–028, December 1959.
41. J. O'M. Bockris and M. A. V. Devanathan, *The Determination of the Coverage on Nickel and Steel during Electrolytic Hydrogen Evolution*, Technical Report No. 4 to the Office of Naval Research, Contract Nonr 551(22), NR 036–028, February 1961.
42. I. A. Bagotskaia, *J. chim. phys.*, **54**, 269 (1957).
43. K. J. Vetter, *Elektrochemische Kinetik*, Springer, Berlin, 1961, pp. 500–506.
43a. F. C. Anson and J. J. Lingane, *J. Am. Chem. Soc.*, **79**, 4901 (1957).
44. G. Rädlein, *Z. Elektrochem.*, **61**, 727 (1957).
45. M. Breiter, K. Hoffman, and C. A. Knorr, *ibid.*, **61**, 1168 (1957).
46. F. C. Anson, *J. Am. Chem. Soc.*, **81**, 1554 (1959).
47. H. A. Laitinen and C. G. Encke, *J. Electrochem., Soc.*, **107**, 773 (1960).
48. J. J. Lingane, *J. Electroanal. Chem.*, **1**, 379 (1960).
49. J. Giner, *Z. Elektrochem.*, **64**, 386, 491 (1960).
50. H. A. Laitinen and M. S. Chao, *J. Electrochem. Soc.*, **108**, 726 (1961).
51. F. C. Anson, *Anal. Chem.*, **33**, 934 (1961).
52. A. Hickling and G. G. Brjosek, *Trans Faraday Soc.*, **57**, 123 (1961).
53. M. Mochizuki, *J. Electrochem. Soc., Japan*, **28**, E 232 (1961).
54. K. Nagel and H. Dietz, *Electrochim. Acta*, **4**, 1 (1961).
55. J. Giner, *ibid.*, **4**, 42 (1961).
56. W. Böld and M. Breiter, *ibid.*, **5**, 145, 169 (1961).
57. O. L. Kabanova, *Zhur. Analit. Khim.*, **16**, 135 (1961).
58. E. Lewartowicz, *Compt. rend.*, **253**, 1260 (1961).
59. M. Breiter, *Electrochim. Acta*, **7**, 601 (1962).
60. M. Breiter, *J. Electrochem. Soc.*, **109**, 425 (1962).

61. J. P. Hoare, *ibid.*, **109**, 858 (1962).
62. M. Breiter and J. L. Weininger, *ibid.*, **109**, 1135 (1962).
63. J. J. MacDonald and B. E. Conway, *Proc. Roy. Soc.*, **269A**, 419 (1962).
64. M. Czuha, K. W. Gardiner, and D. T. Sawyer, *J. Electroanal. Chem.*, **4**, 51 (1962).
65. D. G. Peters and J. J. Lingane, *ibid.*, **4**, 193 (1962).
66. A. Kozawa, *Bull. Chem. Soc. Japan*, **35**, 1051 (1962).
67. D. M. Mohilner, W. J. Argersinger, and R. N. Adams, *Anal. Chim. Acta*, **27**, 194 (1962).
68. F. C. Anson and D. M. King, *Anal. Chem.*, **34**, 362 (1962).
69. F. C. Anson and F. A. Schultz, *ibid.*, **35**, 1114 (1963).
70. H. Dietz and H. Göhr, *Electrochim. Acta.*, **8**, 343 (1963).
71. J. P. Hoare, *J. Electrochem. Soc.*, **110**, 245, 1019 (1963).
72. S. W. Feldberg, C. G. Encke, and C. E. Bricker, *ibid.*, **110**, 826 (1963).
73. R. A. Osteryoung, G. Lauer, and F. C. Anson, *ibid.*, **110**, 926 (1963).
74. S. Schuldiner and R. M. Roe, **110**, 1142 (1963).
75. E. Lewartowicz, *J. Electroanal. Chem.*, **6**, 11 (1963).
76. D. H. Evans and J. J. Lingane, *ibid.*, **6**, 283 (1963).
77. J. P. Hoare, *J. Electrochem. Soc.*, **111**, 232, 610 (1964).
78. M. Breiter, *Electrochim. Acta*, **9**, 441 (1964).
79. N. Watanabe and M. A. V. Devanathan, *J. Electrochem. Soc.*, **111**, 615 (1964).
80. A. Damjanovic, M. L. B. Rao, and J. O'M. Bockris, paper presented at the Toronto Meeting of the Electrochemical Society, 1964, abstract No. 205.
81. S. B. Brummer, M. J. MacLaren, and A. C. Makrides, *ibid.*, abstract No. 210.
82. R. Parsons, *Trans. Faraday Soc.*, **54**, 1053 (1958).
83. K. J. Vetter, *Angew. Chem.*, **73**, 277 (1961).
84. T. Erdey-Gruz and M. Volmer, *Z. physik. Chem.*, **150A**, 203 (1930).
85. J. Heyrovsky, *Rec. trav. chim.*, **46**, 582 (1927).
86. J. Tafel, *Z. physik. Chem.*, **50**, 641 (1905).
87. L. P. Hammett, *Trans. Faraday Soc.*, **29**, 770 (1933).
88. A. N. Frumkin, *Acta Physicochim., U.R.S.S.*, **7**, 475 (1937).
89. P. Dolin, B. V. Ershler, and A. N. Frumkin, *ibid.*, **13**, 779 (1940).
90. M. I. Temkin, *Zhur. Fiz. Khim.*, **15**, 296 (1941); **21**, 517 (1947).
91. A. N. Frumkin and N. Aledzhalova, *Acta Physicochim. U.R.S.S.*, **19**, 1 (1944).
92. J. O'M. Bockris and E. C. Potter, *J. Electrochem. Soc.*, **99**, 169 (1952).
93. H. Gerischer and W. Mehl, *Z. Elektrochem.*, **59**, 1049 (1955).
94. J. O'M. Bockris, *Modern Aspects of Electrochemistry*, J. O'M. Bockris, editor, Butterworths, London, Vol. 1, 1954, pp. 198–213.
95. M. Breiter and R. Clamroth, *Z. Elektrochem.*, **58**, 493 (1954).
96. K. J. Vetter, *ibid.*, **59**, 435 (1955).
97. K. J. Vetter and D. Otto, *ibid.*, **60**, 1072 (1956).
98. H. Gerischer, *Bull. Soc. Chim. Belg.*, **67**, 506 (1958).
99. G. W. Castellan, *J. Electrochem. Soc.*, **108**, 277, 283, 686 (1961).
100. K. J. Vetter, Ref. 43, pp. 412–430.
100a. L. I. Krishtalik, *Zhur. Fiz. Khim.*, **33**, 1715 (1959); **34**, 117 (1960).
100b. J. G. N. Thomas, *Trans. Faraday Soc.*, **57**, 1603 (1961).
101. K. F. Bonhoeffer, *Z. physik. Chem.*, **113A**, 199 (1924).
102. P. Rüetschi and P. Delahay, *J. Chem. Phys.*, **23**, 195 (1955).
103. M. I. Temkin and A. N. Frumkin, *Zhur. Fiz. Khim.*, **29**, 1513 (1955); **30**, 1162 (1956).
104. B. E. Conway and J. O'M. Bockris, *J. Chem. Phys.*, **26**, 532 (1957).
105. P. Rüetschi, *J. Electrochem. Soc.*, **106**, 819 (1959).

106. J. O'M. Bockris, *Trans. Faraday Soc.*, **43**, 417 (1947).
107. H. Fischer, *Z. Elektrochem.*, **52**, 111 (1948).
108. H. Leidheiser, *J. Am. Chem. Soc.*, **71**, 3634 (1949).
109. E. N. Khomatov, *Zhur. Fiz. Khim.*, **24**, 1201 (1950).
110. N. I. Kobozev, *ibid.*, **26**, 112 (1952).
111. A. K. Lorents, *ibid.*, **27**, 317 (1953).
112. M. J. Brabers, *Electronic Structure of Metals and Overvoltage*, doctoral dissertation, Technical University, Delft, 1954.
113. G. I. Volkov, *Zhur. Fiz. Khim.*, **29**, 390 (1955).
114. N. Chtani, *Sci. Repts. Research Inst. Tokoku Univ.*, **A8**, 399 (1956).
115. B. E. Conway and J. O'M. Bockris, *Nature*, **178**, 488 (1956).
116. B. E. Conway and J. O'M. Bockris, *Naturwissensch.* **43**, 446 (1956).
117. B. E. Conway and J. O'M. Bockris, *Can. J. Chem.*, **35**, 1124 (1957).
118. S. Schuldiner and J. P. Hoare, *J. Phys. Chem.*, **61**, 705 (1957).
118a. J. P. Hoare and S. Schuldiner, *ibid.*, **62**, 229 (1958).
119. S. G. Christov and N. A. Pangarov, *Z. Elektrochem.*, **61**, 113 (1957).
120. B. E. Conway, *Trans. Roy. Soc. Can.*, **54**, 19 (1960).
120a. J. P. Hoare, *J. Electrochem. Soc.*, **107**, 820 (1960).
121. B. E. Conway, E. M. Beatty, and P. A. D. DeMaine, *Electrochim. Acta*, **7**, 39 (1962).
122. P. Rüetschi and P. Delahay, *J. Chem. Phys.*, **23**, 1167 (1955).
123. P. D. Lukovtsev, *Zhur. Fiz. Khim.*, **21**, 589 (1947).
124. R. Parsons, *J. chim. phys.*, **49**, C 82 (1952).
125. K. J. Vetter, Ref. 43, pp. 497–525.
126. A. U. Akopyan, *Zhur. Fiz. Khim.*, **33**, 1625 (1959).
127. T. Erdey-Grúz and I. Vajasdy, *Acta Chim. Acad. Sci. Hung.*, **29**, 47 (1961).
128. M. Breiter, *Advances in Electrochemistry and Electrochemical Engineering*, Vol. 1, P. Delahay, editor, Interscience, New York, 1961, pp. 123–138.
129. J. J. Lingane, *J. Electroanal Chem.*, **2**, 296 (1961).
130. A. C. Riddiford, *Electrochim. Acta*, **4**, 170 (1961).
131. G. Bianchi, G. Caprioglio, F. Mazza, and T. Mussini, *ibid.*, **4**, 232 (1961).
132. G. Bianchi, F. Mazza, and T. Mussini, *ibid.*, **7**, 457 (1962).
133. D. T. Sawyer and R. J. Day, *ibid.*, **8**, 589 (1963).
134. V. A. Zakharov and O. A. Songina, *Zhur. Fiz. Khim.*, **37**, 1450 (1963).
135. S. Palous and R. Buvet, *Bull. Soc. Chim. France*, 2490 (1963).
136. T. R. Blackburn and J. J. Lingane, *J. Electroanal. Chem.*, **5**, 216 (1963).
137. L. N. Nekrasov and L. Myuller, *Doklady Akad. Nauk S.S.S.R.*, **149**, 1107 (1963).
138. L. Myuller and L. N. Nekrasov, paper presented at the Moscow C.I.T.C.E. meeting, 1963.
139. A. Obrucheva, cited in Ref. 3, p. 332.
140. A. N. Frumkin, *Proceedings of the International Committee on Electrochemical Thermodynamics and Kinetics, 9th meeting*, Butterworths, London, 1959, pp. 396–403.
141. A. N. Frumkin, *Electrochim. Acta*, **5**, 265 (1961).
142. M. Breiter, *Chem. Ing. Technik*, **35**, 376 (1963).
143. R. I. Kaganovich, M. A. Gerovich and E. K. Enikeev, *Doklady Akad. Nauk S.S.S.R.*, **108**, 107 (1956).
144. K. I. Rozental' and V. I. Veselovskii, *ibid.*, **111**, 637 (1956).
145. M. A. Gerovich, R. I. Kaganovich, V. M. Vergelesov, and L. N. Gorokhov, *ibid.*, **114**, 1049 (1957).
146. R. I. Kaganovich and M. A. Gerovich, *Zhur. Fiz. Khim.*, **32**, 957 (1958).

147. A. A. Rakov, V. I. Veselovskii, K. I. Nosova, E. V. Kasatkin, and T. I. Borisova, *ibid.*, **32**, 2702 (1958).
148. K. I. Rozental' and V. I. Veselovskii, *ibid.*, **35**, 2670 (1961).
149. M. A. Gerovich, R. I. Kaganovich, Yu. A. Mazitov, and L. N. Gorokov, *Doklady Akad. Nauk S.S.S.R.*, **137**, 634 (1961).
150. P. Rüetschi and P. Delahay, *J. Chem. Phys.*, **23**, 556 (1955).
151. T. Erdey-Grúz and I. Shafarik, *Proceedings of the Fourth Soviet Conference on Electrochemistry, Moscow, 1956,* Academy of Sciences, Moscow, 1959, pp. 263–271 (not in the English translation by Consultants Bureau, New York, 1958).
152. A. N. Frumkin, R. I. Kaganovich, E. V. Yakovleva, and V. V. Sobol', *Doklady Akad. Nauk S.S.S.R.*, **141**, 1416 (1961).
153. K. J. Vetter, Ref., 43, pp. 367–376.
154. J. D. Newson and A. C. Riddiford, *J. Electrochem. Soc.*, **108**, 699 (1961).
154a. J. Jordan and R. A. Javick, *Electrochim. Acta*, **6**, 23 (1962).
155. J. Llopis and M. Vàzquez, *ibid.*, **6**, 167, (1962); **8**, 163 (1963).
156. S. Schuldiner and C. H. Presbrey, *J. Electrochem. Soc.*, **111**, 457 (1964).
157. R. A. Osteryoung and F. C. Anson, *Anal. Chem.*, **36**, 975 (1964).
158. L. Wanyukowa and B. N. Kabanov, *Zhur. Fiz. Khim.*, **14**, 1620 (1940).
159. H. Fischer, *Z. Elektrochem.*, **55**, 92 (1951).
160. J. O'M. Bockris and B. E. Conway, *J. Phys. Colloid Chem.*, **53**, 527 (1949).
161. H. Fischer and H. Heiling, *Z. Elektrochem.*, **54**, 184 (1950).
162. J. Elze and H. Fischer, *Metalloberfl.*, **6**, A 177 (1952).
163. P. J. Hillson, *Trans. Faraday Soc.*, **48**, 462 (1952).
164. N. Kobosev and N. J. Nekrassov, *Z. Elektrochem.*, **36**, 529 (1930).
165. M. Volmer and H. Wick, *Z. physik. Chem.*, **172A**, 429 (1935).
166. A. I. Shlygin, E. Rasumovskaja, and K. I. Rozental', *Zhur. Fiz. Khim.*, **13**, 1079 (1939).
167. B. V. Ershler, *ibid.*, **13**, 1092 (1939).
168. A. I. Shlygin and B. V. Ershler, *Acta Physicochim. U.R.S.S.*, **11**, 45 (1939).
169. A. Hickling and F. W. Salt, *Trans. Faraday Soc.*, **37**, 333 (1941).
170. J. O'M. Bockris and B. E. Conway, *Trans. Faraday Soc.*, **45**, 989 (1949).
170a. S. Schuldiner and J. P. Hoare, *J. Chem. Phys.*, **26**, 1771 (1957).
171. A. V. Shashkina and I. I. Kulakova, *Zhur. Fiz. Khim.*, **37**, 1966 (1963).
172. R. A. Munson, *J. Electroanal. Chem.*, **5**, 292 (1963).
173. T. B. Warner and S. Schuldiner, *J. Electrochem. Soc.*, **111**, 992 (1964).
174. A. I. Shlygin, paper presented at the Moscow C.I.T.C.E. meeting, 1963.
175. O. L. Kabanova, *Zhur. Fiz. Khim.*, **35**, 2465 (1961).
176. K. J. Vetter, Ref., 43, pp. 441–446.
177. A. N. Frumkin and E. A. Aikasjan, *Doklady Akad. Nauk S.S.S.R.*, **100**, 315 (1955).
178. S. Gilman, *J. Phys. Chem.*, **66**, 2657 (1962); **67**, 78 (1963).
179. G. A. Bogdanovskii and A. I. Shlygin, *Zhur. Fiz. Khim.*, **34**, 57 (1960).
180. M. Breiter, *Electrochem. Acta*, **7**, 533 (1962).
181. M. Breiter, *J. Electrochem. Soc.*, **109**, 42 (1962).
182. M. Breiter and S. Gilman, *ibid.*, **109**, 622 (1962).
183. R. P. Buck and L. R. Griffith, *ibid.*, **109**, 1005 (1962).
184. S. Gilman and M. Breiter, *ibid.*, **109**, 1099 (1962).
185. M. Breiter, *Electrochim. Acta*, **447**, 457 (1963).
186. M. Breiter, *ibid.*, **8**, 973 (1963).
187. A. Kutschker and W. Vielstich, *ibid.*, **8**, 985 (1963).
188. H. Wroblowa, B. J. Piersma, and J. O'M. Bockris, *J. Electroanal. Chem.*, **6**, 401 (1963).

189. M. Breiter, *J. Electrochem. Soc.*, **110**, 449 (1963).
190. A. N. Frumkin and B. I. Podlovchenko, *Doklady Akad. Nauk S.S.S.R.*, **150**, 349 (1963).
191. S. Gilman, *J. Phys. Chem.*, **67**, 1898 (1963).
192. J. Giner, *Electrochim. Acta*, **9**, 63 (1964).
193. J. W. Johnson, H. Wroblowa, and J. O'M. Bockris, *ibid.*, **9**, 639 (1964).
194. R. A. Rightmire, R. L. Rolwand, D. L. Boos, and D. L. Beals, *J. Electrochem. Soc.*, **111**, 242 (1964).
195. M. H. Gottlieb, *ibid.*, **111**, 465 (1964).
196. C. W. Fleischmann, G. K. Johnson, and A. T. Kuhn, *ibid.*, **111**, 602 (1964).
197. V. S. Bagotskii and Yu. B. Vasilyev, *Electrochim. Acta*, **9**, 869 (1964).
197a. V. S. Bagotskii, paper presented at the Moscow C.I.T.C.E. meeting, 1963.
198. S. Karp and L. Meites, *J. Am. Chem. Soc.*, **84**, 906 (1962).
199. A. J. Bard, *Anal. Chem.*, **35**, 1602 (1963).
200. J. Giner, *Electrochim. Acta*, **8**, 857 (1963).
201. H. G. Oswin and M. Salomon, *Canad. J. Chem.*, **41**, 1686 (1963).
202. J. R. Macdonald and C. A. Barlow, *J. Chem. Phys.*, **39**, 412 (1963).
203. J. P. Hoare, *J. Electrochem. Soc.*, in press.
204. S. Schuldiner and T. B. Warner, Naval Research Laboratory Report, NRL 6136, September 1964.
205. R. Parsons, private communication.
206. A. A. Balandin, *Problems of Chemical Kinetics, Catalysis and Reactivity*, Academy of Sciences, Moscow, 1955, p. 462.
207. R. Parsons, *Solid Surfaces*, H. G. Gatos, editor, North-Holland Publishing Company, Amsterdam, 1964, p. 418.

CHAPTER 11

Kinetics of Electrode Processes with Potential-Dependent Adsorption of Reactants and/or Products

11-1   Current-Potential Characteristic

This chapter covers electrode processes with reactants and/or products undergoing potential-dependent adsorption of the type described in Chapter 5. The reacting species are either specifically adsorbed ions, such as Tl(I), or organic substances. Theoretical analysis is still quite rudimentary, although it does not require the introduction of any concept not already discussed in preceding chapters. Some guiding principles have emerged in the analysis of the reduction of organic substances as is apparent from the recent reviews of Frumkin (1) and Mairanovskii (2, 3). The simpler case of discharge of a specifically adsorbed ion has hardly been examined from a fundamental point of view, although it has been studied in some detail in papers primarily concerned with methodology (faradaic impedance, faradaic rectification, etc.).

Consider the electrode reaction

$$O + ne = R \tag{1}$$

and assume that substance O is adsorbed and R is not. The treatment of Sec. 7-2 can be transposed to this case provided we take into account the adsorbed state between the states corresponding to the outer plane and the activated complex. The writing of the standard free energy for the adsorbed species requires selection of an iostherm and knowledge of the potential ϕ in the adsorbed state. To simplify matters, it can often be assumed (Secs. 5-8) that adsorption equilibrium is established. One of the isotherms of Chapter 5 may be selected and the dependence of the standard free energy of adsorption on the electrical variable—potential or charge on the electrode—can be written in an explicit form with some confidence (linear dependence for ions, quadratic dependence for uncharged species). The selection of the potential ϕ in the adsorbed state raises a difficulty but, as a first approximation, we can equate this potential to ϕ_1 in the inner plane. Evaluation of ϕ_1 by the methods of Sec. 4-4b is feasible for specifically adsorbed ions and could be attempted for neutral substances. Derivation of the current-potential characteristic along the lines of Sec. 7-2 should not involve any further difficulty once these two questions have been settled. Only two attempts have been made [Ershler, Tedoradze, and Mairanovskii (4) and Mohilner and Delahay (5)].

Three possible complications in the treatment just outlined must be recognized, simultaneous adsorption of species O and R of Eq. 1 and occurrence of consecutive charge-transfer reactions and/or coupled chemical reactions. The consequences of simultaneous adsorption are minimized at low coverage when adsorption is described by Henry's law, but the complexity of reaction mechanisms is a major stumbling block. Detailed mathematical treatment of current-potential curves of complex processes may not prove useful, for the inverse process of analysis of experimental data would seldom yield unambiguous answers. Indications about mechanisms, however, may be obtained from double-layer effects (Sec. 11-3) and by application of the methods of Chapter 8.

We shall now examine the treatment of Ershler, Tedoradze, and Mairanovskii (4), who assumed that adsorption equilibrium is established and is described by Henry's law (Table 5-1), that is,

$$\theta = \beta a \tag{2}$$

with (Eq. 5-1)

$$\beta = e^{-\Delta G^0/RT} \tag{3}$$

The standard free energy of adsorption ΔG^0 in Eq. 3 is a function of the electrical variable (potential or charge). For uncharged substances, Eq. 3 may be written as

$$\beta = \beta_{max} e^{-(s/2)(E - E_{max})^2} \tag{4}$$

where s is defined by Eq. 5-24 and E_{max} is the potential for maximum adsorption. The current for the forward reaction of Eq. 1 can now be derived by assuming that it is proportional to θ and to the usual exponential function of potential E. The current i is then proportional to

$$\exp\left[-\frac{s}{2}(E - E_{max})^2 - \alpha n f E\right]$$

The argument of this exponential goes through a maximum as E varies and the current i does likewise. This maximum is simply explained by two competitive effects resulting from the variation of E toward increasingly more cathodic values: increase of the rate of reduction and decrease of coverage. These two effects were previously taken into account by Mairanovskii to explain certain catalytic hydrogen waves (Sec. 11-2) and by Antropov (6) in a discussion of electro-organic processes. Koryta also briefly referred to this point (22).

Frumkin (1) estimates for the usual order of magnitude of the parameters s, E_{max}, and α that the maximum should be observed at about -1.85 volts versus N.C.E. for $n = 1$. A maximum in current-potential curves, which can probably be explained by these considerations, is indeed observed in certain cases (1, 7) (Fig. 11-1).

The foregoing treatment is definitely interesting, but it must be regarded as a first approximation for the following reasons. (*a*) It is based on Henry's law and this is applicable only at sufficiently low concentrations. (*b*) It neglects, in the form given, parallel charge transfer by reduction of the unadsorbed species. Ershler et al. (4) did consider this point and gave equations for kinetics of reduction with two parallel paths, The question as to whether adsorption must precede charge transfer is not fully settled. (*c*) No correction similar to the term $E - \phi_2$ made for the double-layer effects in the absence of specific adsorption is introduced here by subtracting the potential ϕ for the adsorbed state from E (in $\alpha n f E$). (*d*) Adsorption of reaction products, which is justifiably neglected because of low coverage, should be considered at higher coverages. (*e*) Finally, it must be recognized that many current-potential curves do not exhibit a maximum even at very cathodic potentials.

The ideas expressed by Ershler et al. (4) were independently couched in a

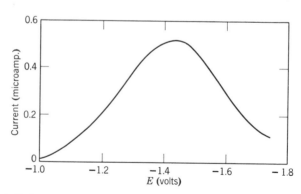

FIG. 11-1. Polarogram for the reduction of $9 \times 10^{-4}M$ benzyl chloride in $0.5M$ sodium acetate in presence of 60% ethyl alcohol [Frumkin (1)] (by permission of Pergamon).

different way by Mohilner and Delahay (5). These authors assumed that the species being discharged obeys the logarithmic Temkin isotherm. As Frumkin noted (1), this isotherm implies particle-particle repulsion on a homogeneous surface and should be applicable to small, highly polar molecules and to aromatic substances with π-electron interaction. Application to ionic specific adsorption might also be considered (Sec. 4-2). The current-overvoltage characteristic derived in (5) is identical to Eq. 7-9 except for an additional term which is analogous to the double-layer term but concerns specific adsorption. This term is expressed as a function of the difference between the charge-dependent part of the standard free energies of adsorption at the potential E and E^e, respectively. No experimental results have yet been examined in the light of this treatment.

11-2   Processes with Coupled Chemical Reactions

Discussion will be limited to two important cases in which charge transfer is preceded by a chemical reaction, namely catalytic hydrogen waves in the presence of certain organic bases and reduction of organic substances with preprotonation. The former type of reaction was thoroughly reviewed by Mairanovskii (3) and only some recent references which are relevant to this discussion can be cited here (8–19).

Polarographic catalytic hydrogen currents are observed with a number of organic substances existing in the acid form BH^+ and its conjugated (Brönsted) base B. Proton addition is related to the presence of an unshared pair of electrons on such atoms as nitrogen, sulfur, oxygen, etc. Thus

$$B + DH^+ = BH^+ + D \tag{5}$$

where DH^+ is a proton donor and D its conjugated base. The protonated form of the catalyst, BH^+, is reduced with the formation of an unstable radical, BH, which regenerates B with formation of $\frac{1}{2}H_2$ on decomposition:

$$BH^+ + e = BH$$
$$BH \rightarrow B + \tfrac{1}{2}H_2 \tag{6}$$

Catalytic hydrogen currents can be divided into two extreme cases (2, 9, 11): *surface* catalytic currents when reaction 5 occurs mostly on the electrode surface; *bulk* catalytic currents when the equilibrium for reaction 5 is disrupted up to some distance from the electrode. A somewhat similar classification was made in the discussion of double-layer effects in processes with a coupled chemical reaction in Sec. 9-4. Mairanovskii (2) pointed out that physical adsorption of catalyst B strongly enhances surface catalytic currents even when the coverage is smaller than 1%. Coverage by B

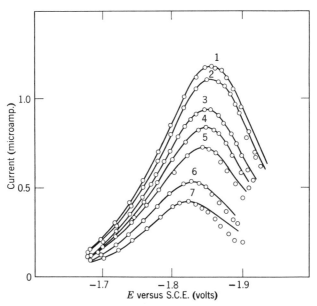

FIG. 11-2. Catalytic polarographic wave of $3 \times 10^{-6}M$ quinine in borate buffer of pH 9.5 with varying concentration of sodium chloride. Sodium chloride concentration: 0.04 (curve 1); 0.045 (2); 0.050 (3); 0.055 (4); 0.06 (5); 0.07 (6); and 0.08M (7). Experimental points and calculated curves [Mairanovskii, Klynkina, and Frumkin (10); Mairanovskii (3)] (by permission of Elsevier).

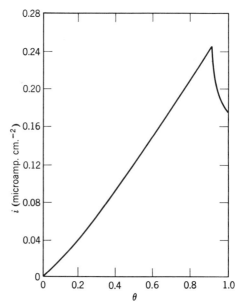

FIG. 11-3. Catalytic current for hydrogen evolution on mercury at −0.8 volt versus N.C.E. from 0.2M hydrochloric acid in presence of diphenylamine as a function of catalyst coverage [Frumkin, Dzhaparidze, and Tedoradze (19); Frumkin (1)] (by permission of Pergamon).

294

exhibits a maximum, and we might expect catalytic currents to exhibit a maximum much in the same way as in Sec. 11-1 (Fig. 11-2). A complication arises at high coverages of catalyst because of blocking action by the adsorbed catalyst, as was recently found by Frumkin, Dzhaparidze, and Tedoradze (1, 16, 17, 19). Blocking probably becomes predominant in Fig. 11-3 near saturation coverage.

Similar considerations apply to the reduction of organic substances in which protonation precedes charge transfer (2). Even minor adsorption of the organic substance gives a "surface" character to the protonation reaction. Double-layer effects must also be considered because the concentration of hydrogen ions in the outer plane is higher than the bulk concentration when ϕ_2 is negative (20, 21). Examples and mechanisms are reviewed in detail by Mairanovskii (2). One infers from Fig. 11-4 that desorption of the organic substance with increasingly negative potentials causes a maximum to appear in the current-potential curve.

Variation of the coverage of the substance being reduced with potential may distort plots of half-wave potential against pH. This effect can be

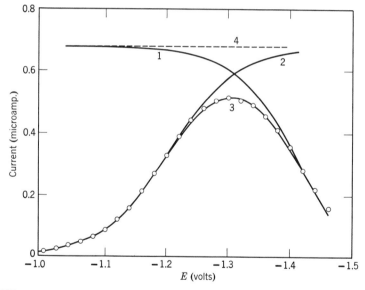

FIG. 11-4. First polarographic reduction wave of 5-brom-2-acetylthiophene in $0.1M$ potassium chloride + $0.1M$ potassium hydroxide. Curve 1 was calculated for control by the kinetics of protonation and diffusion; curve 2 was calculated for a constant adsorbed amount; curve 3 was calculated for control by the kinetics of protonation for a varying coverage, due allowance being made for diffusion; curve 4 is the calculated diffusion current [Mairanovskii as given by Frumkin (1)] (by permission of Pergamon).

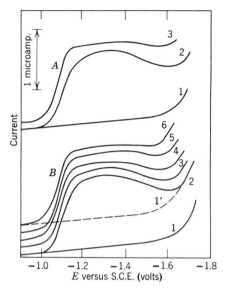

FIG. 11-5. Polarograms for the reduction of $4 \times 10^{-4} M$ 2-acetylthiophene semi-carbazone in acetate buffer of pH 6.75. Diagram A: ionic strength adjusted at 0.5 with potassium chloride; $0.1 M$ (curve 2), and $0.4 M$ (3) acetic acid. Diagram B: $0.1 M$ acetic acid; ionic strength adjusted with potassium chloride at 1.6 (curve 2); 0.8 (3); 0.4 (4); 0.2 (5); and $0.1 M$ (6). Curves 1 and 1′ are for the supporting electrolyte at the ionic strength of 1.6 and 0.1, respectively [Mairanovskii (2)] (by permission of Elsevier).

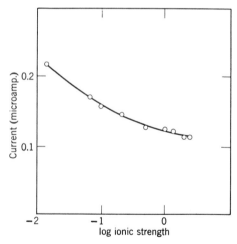

FIG. 11-6. Height of the catalytic hydrogen wave against logarithm of ionic strength for 0.11 mM pyridine in borate buffer of pH 8 at constant buffer capacity. Ionic strength varied by addition of potassium chloride [Mairanovskii (2)] (by permission of Elsevier).

combined with a shift of mechanism from reduction with preprotonation in acid medium to direct reduction in neutral or alkaline media. The polarographic reduction of nitromethane can probably be accounted for by these various factors according to Mairanovskii (2).

11-3   Double-Layer Effects

The double-layer structure affects adsorption of the uncharged reacting species and, more significantly, the concentration of hydrogen ions in the plane of closest approach. The latter factor can be predominant in catalytic surface waves (3, 10, 12, 13) and reduction with surface preprotonation (2, 20, 21). Quite obviously, processes which are reversible under polarographic conditions are not significantly affected by changes in the double-layer structure because electrode kinetics need not be considered.

As a *first approximation*, the change of overvoltage $\Delta\eta$ resulting from a variation $\Delta\phi_2$ is equal to $\Delta\phi_2$ for a neutral substance (Eq. 9-2) provided no ion is involved in the electrode process (2). Processes involving hydrogen ion, such as catalytic hydrogen waves and charge transfer with pre-protonation, are also influenced by the variation of the hydrogen ion concentration (Fig. 11-2). It is helpful in such cases to study separately variations of the preprotonation rate and the influence of the double-layer structure. The preprotonation rate changes with the buffer capacity, but the double-layer structure is not altered provided the total ionic strength is kept constant. Double-layer effects are studied at constant buffer capacity and varying ionic strength (2). This approach is illustrated in Fig. 11-5 in which the drop in current at the more negative potentials is caused by desorption of the substance being reduced. This drop is less pronounced when the protonation becomes faster either (*a*) by increase of the buffer capacity (curves *A*) at constant ionic strength or (*b*) by decrease of ionic strength at constant buffer capacity (curves *B*).

When the chemical reaction occurs in a thicker layer than the diffuse double layer, the double-layer effect is minimized (cf. Sec. 9-4). This is the case for bulk catalytic currents for which the decrease in current with increasing ionic strength indeed is much less rapid than for surface waves (Figs. 11-2 and 11-6). The attraction of hydrogen ions in the diffuse double layer is secondary for these processes because the reaction zone extends beyond the diffuse double layer.

Addition of a tetra-alkylammonium salt, which is specifically adsorbed, renders ϕ_2 less negative and thus decreases the concentration of hydrogen ions in the outer plane. This results in a marked lowering of rate for catalytic surface waves and processes with preprotonation. Competitive adsorption between the organic reactant and tetra-alkylammonium cations may have to be considered. These inferences are borne out by several examples cited by Mairanovskii (2, 3).

It is only possible here to state these essential points, but their consideration leaves little doubt about the essential role of double-layer studies in the elucidation of polarographic reduction of organic substances. Just as for inorganic reactants (Chapter 9), application need not await the settlement of the finer points in the quantitative treatment of adsorption and of the double layer. Semiquantitative or even purely qualitative analyses may prove most illuminating. Much order can be put in the prolific polarographic literature on organic processes by simple experiments designed to test mechanisms by the systematic application of double-layer effects, as is amply demonstrated in Mairanovskii's reviews (2, 3).

REFERENCES

1. A. N. Frumkin, *Electrochim. Acta*, **9**, 465 (1964).
2. S. G. Mairanovskii, *J. Electroanal. Chem.*, **4**, 166 (1962).
3. S. G. Mairanovskii, *ibid.*, **6**, 77 (1963).
4. A. B. Ershler, G. A. Tedoradze, and S. G. Mairanovskii, *Doklady Akad. Nauk S.S.S.R.*, **145**, 1324 (1962).
5. D. M. Mohilner and P. Delahay, *J. Phys. Chem.*, **67**, 588 (1963).
6. L. I. Antropov, *Zhur. Fiz. Khim.*, **24**, 1428 (1950).
7. W. Kemula and A. Cisak, *Roczniki Chem.*, **31**, 337 (1957).
8. J. Koutecký, V. Hanuš, and S. G. Mairanovskii, *Zhur. Fiz. Khim.*, **34**, 651 (1960).
9. S. G. Mairanovskii, *Doklady Akad. Nauk S.S.S.R.*, **132**, 1352 (1960); **133**, 162 (1960).
10. S. G. Mairanovskii, L. D. Klynkina, and A. N. Frumkin, *ibid.*, **141**, 147 (1961).
11. S. G. Mairanovskii, *ibid.*, **142**, 1327 (1962).
12. V. G. Levich, B. I. Khaikin, and S. G. Mairanovskii, *ibid.*, **145**, 605 (1962).
13. V. G. Levich and B. I. Khaikin, *ibid.*, **147**, 146 (1962).
14. S. G. Mairanovskii, J. Koutecký, and V. Hanuš, *Zhur. Fiz. Khim.*, **36**, 2621 (1962).
15. S. G. Mairanovskii and N. V. Barashkova, *Izvest. Akad. Nauk S.S.S.R., Otdel. Khim. Nauk*, 186 (1962).
16. D. I. Dzhaparidze and G. A. Tedoradze, *ibid.*, 1718 (1962).
17. G. A. Tedoradze and D. I. Dzhaparidze, *ibid.*, 402 (1963).
18. S. G. Mairanovskii, J. Koutecký, and V. Hanuš, *Zhur. Fiz. Khim.*, **37**, 18 (1963).
19. A. N. Frumkin, D. I. Dzhaparidze, and G. A. Tedoradze, *Doklady Akad. Nauk S.S.S.R.*, **152**, 163 (1963).
20. S. G. Mairanovskii and J. P. Stradins, *Izvest. Akad. Nauk S.S.S.R., Otdel. Khim. Nauk*, 2239 (1961).
21. S. G. Mairanovskii, *Doklady Akad. Nauk S.S.S.R.*, **142**, 1120 (1962).
22. J. Koryta, *Z. Elektrochem.*, **64**, 23 (1960).

APPENDIX

List of Most Important Symbols

The location of each definition is given whenever necessary.

a activity of solute (also used as coefficient in the Tafel relationship)

a^s bulk activity outside the diffuse double layer and, as the case may be, outside the diffusion layer

A quantity defined by the Eq. 3-11

b coefficient in Tafel relationship (Eq. 7-18)

c concentration

c^s bulk concentration outside the diffuse double layer and, as the case may be, outside the diffusion layer

C differential capacity of double layer per unit area (Eq. 2-20)

C^i integral capacity of double layer per unit area (Eq. 2-19)

$C_{\pm}$ differential capacity components per unit area corresponding to the surface excess of cations (C_+) or anions (C_-) in the double layer (Eq. 2-23)

C_{M-2} differential capacity of the compact double layer per unit area (Eq. 3-13)

C_{2-s} differential capacity of the diffuse double layer per unit area (Eq. 3-13)

E electrode potential

$E_{\pm}$ electrode potential against a reference electrode which is reversible to a particular cation (E_+) or anion (E_-) in a cell without liquid junction

E_z potential at zero charge (Sec. 2-2)

E^e equilibrium potential

E^0	standard potential
f	quantity defined by $f = F/RT$ (Eq. 3-3)
F	faraday
g	interaction parameter in isotherms (Table 5-1)
G^0	free energy per mole
ΔG^0	standard free energy per mole
h	Planck constant
ΔH_i	initial heat of adsorption per mole (Eq. 10-4)
i	current density (Eq. 7-10)
$\vec{i}$	current density for the forward electrode reaction (Eq. 7-9)
$\overleftarrow{i}$	current density for the backward electrode reaction (Eq. 7-9)
i^l	limiting current density (Eq. 7-34)
i_a^l or i_c^l	anodic or cathodic limiting current density (Eq. 7-34)
i^0	apparent exchange current density (Eq. 7-12)
i_t^0	true exchange current density (Eq. 7-11)
k^0	apparent standard rate constant (Eq. 7-27)
k_t^0	true standard rate constant (Eq. 7-26)
n	number of electrons involved in electrode reaction
p	pressure
P	surface pressure (Eq. 5-3)
q	charge on the electrode per unit area
$q_\pm$	charge in the double layer per unit area for cations (q_+) or anions (q_-) (Eq. 4-1)
$q_\pm^1$	charge of specifically adsorbed cations (q_+^1) or anions (q_-^1) per unit area
$q_\pm^{2-s}$	component of the charge in the diffuse double layer per unit area for cations (q_+^{2-s}) or anions (q_-^{2-s})
R	gas constant
t	time
T	absolute temperature
$\vec{v}$	rate of the forward electrode reaction per unit area (Table 10-2)
$\overleftarrow{v}$	rate of the backward electrode reaction per unit area (Table 10-2)
x	distance from the electrode
x_1	distance from the electrode to the inner plane of closest approach
x_2	distance from the electrode to the outer plane of closest approach
z	ionic valence with sign
α	transfer coefficient (Eq. 7-3)
β	quantity defined by Eq. 5-1
γ	interfacial tension
Γ	surface excess (Eq. 2-1) or surface concentration (Sec. 5-1)
Γ_s	saturation surface concentration (Table 5-1)

$\Gamma_{\pm}$ surface excess, relative to solvent, of cations (Γ_+) or anions (Γ_-) (Eq. 2-10)

ϵ dielectric constant

η overvoltage

θ coverage

θ_e equilibrium coverage, whenever it must be distinguished from nonequilibrium coverage

κ reciprocal Debye length defined by Eq. 3-16

μ chemical potential per mole (Sec. 1-3)

$\bar{\mu}$ electrochemical potential per mole (Sec. 1-3)

μ^s chemical potential per mole in bulk of solution outside the diffuse double layer

μ^0 standard chemical potential per mole

ν stoichiometric number (Sec. 8-2)

ξ quantity defined by $\xi = \gamma + qE$ (Sec. 5-1)

ϕ inner potential (Sec. 1-3)

ϕ_M inner potential of electrode

ϕ_1 potential in inner plane of closest approach referred to the potential in the bulk of the solution outside the double layer

ϕ_2 potential in outer plane of closest approach referred to the potential in the bulk of the solution outside the double layer

χ surface potential (Sec. 1-3)

ψ outer potential (Sec. 1-3)

Author Index

303

Subject Index